Social Approaches to Mental Patient Care

Social Approaches
to Mental Patient Care

by
Morris S. Schwartz
Charlotte Green Schwartz

and

MARK G. FIELD   ELLIOT G. MISHLER

SIMON OLSHANSKY   JESSE R. PITTS

RHONA RAPOPORT   WARREN T. VAUGHAN, JR.

Columbia University Press
New York and London 1964

Professor Morris S. Schwartz is chairman of the Department of Sociology at Brandeis University. He was director of the Task Force on Patterns of Patient Care which was established by the Joint Commission on Mental Illness and Health to make this study. Charlotte Green Schwartz, who was associate director of the Task Force, is Research Associate in the Department of Sociology at Brandeis University.

Preface

We undertook to study the problems in caring adequately for mental patients on the assumption that social science can make a valuable contribution to their solution. This, of course, is not to imply that the neurological, biochemical, or psychological points of view are less useful or appropriate, and we hope that similar analyses will come from them so that problems we have raised and issues we have neglected might be discussed from other perspectives.

This book is written for practitioners who are trying to help emotionally disturbed persons and is focused on a range of programs that are currently in use. We analyze their assumptions and their methods in the hope of providing new insights into their procedures and into the ways in which their institutional contexts are organized. In addition, we explore the issues with which innovators are grappling and their implications for the future, all with the objective of facilitating the development of more effective ways of caring for mental patients.

The work of the group that prepared this report proceeded in three stages. In the first year, three teams carried out the field work: Mark G. Field and Warren T. Vaughan, Jr., in the out-patient section; Elliot G. Mishler and Jesse R. Pitts in the in-patient section; Charlotte Green Schwartz and Simon Olshansky in the section on ex-patients; Rhona Rapoport in both in-patient and ex-patient sections. Each section member wrote reports on programs he visited, identified significant problems and issues connected with innovations there, and covered the relevant literature. Morris S. Schwartz and Charlotte Green Schwartz were together responsible for the project as a whole.

In addition, Henry Wechsler did a special study on ex-patient

clubs, and Anton Weiner gathered materials on the relation between psychiatry and law. R. W. Boyd, Lida Carmen, Rose Coser,
Ann Davis, Natalie Goethals, Jay Greenfield, and Carl Seltzer
served as readers and reviewed the literature in related fields.

In the second year, we continued our analysis of the field data
and developed a framework for the report. Working papers for
each part of the book were written by various staff members. A
single individual was made responsible for a given chapter, but
each draft was circulated to all members of the group and revised
in light of their comments. Thus, the initial conceptualization,
organization, and writing of the book was a collective product.
We wish to acknowledge the special contribution of Elliot G.
Mishler and Rhona Rapoport who worked most closely with the
senior authors during this phase of the developing of the report
and helped them with problems that arose in the course of the
writing.

The project officially terminated at the end of the second year.
At that time there were draft chapters or working papers for most
of the substantive chapters but not for the concluding chapters of
each section (Chapters 7, 12, and 17) nor for the last chapter.

During the third stage—a two-year period—the senior authors
gave the book its final form. The present version contains seven
chapters that are substantially the original drafts, seven that are
markedly revised, and four original chapters (7, 12, 17, and 18)
written by the senior authors following the termination of the
project. Since they were not written in collaboration with the
co-authors, these four chapters do not necessarily represent their
point of view.

The book was originally to be published as one of a series of
volumes sponsored by the Joint Commission on Mental Illness
and Health, but it was completed too late for inclusion. However,
a draft of the volume was available to the Joint Commission for
their use in the preparation of their final report, *Action for Mental Health.*

It is not possible to mention by name the many persons in the
field of mental health and illness who gave us freely of their time

and thought and who opened up their institutions and programs to us. We can only thank them collectively.

In its final version, our manuscript was read by Richard Fisch, M.D., Vera Fryling, M.D., David Hamburg, M.D., and Edmund H. Volkart, PH.D. We are grateful to them for their comments and criticisms. We also wish to thank Joan Kaufman, Alice Mills, and Ruth Zolot for their diligent secretarial services. Finally, we would like to thank Helen MacGill Hughes for her considerable editorial help and Brandeis University for its financial assistance.

MORRIS S. SCHWARTZ
CHARLOTTE GREEN SCHWARTZ

September, 1963

Contents

Contents

Part V. Conclusion

Part I

Introduction

Chapter 1

The Context of the Study

The Project

This is the final report of the Project on Patterns of Patient Care, one of ten study groups established by the Joint Commission on Mental Illness and Health whose mandate was stated in a resolution of the United States Congress in 1955.[1] The Commission's Committee on Objectives and Methods further defined the Congressional mandate as follows:

It [the Joint Commission] should act on a conviction that the solution of the problem is far more important than any tradition, institution, procedure, alignment, or professional responsibility, or set of theoretical assumptions. . . . It will be in no position to reject without examination any proposed solution to the problem . . . and should boldly seek out such divergent viewpoints as from biologists, public administrators, anthropologists, etc. The Commission should be ready to recommend a radical reconstruction of the present system if such is indicated rather than advocating a patching up of our present system.

In general the goal will be the development of new approaches by the use of present knowledge in new constellations or in different perspectives rather than the development of new basic facts.

Out of such an examination of the formal and informal resources might hopefully come a radical reconceptualization of the problem and possibly a reconstruction of the institutions so that resource use might be more economical and mental health better served.[2]

The project on Patterns of Patient Care was charged specifically with preparing a report on the *major developments, problems, and issues regarding the care of mental patients*. While it was expected that we would review the literature, consult with experts, and observe selected programs, clearly we were expected neither to engage in original empirical research nor simply to collate information on existing programs. We were asked to produce a report that was interpretive and analytic. Our primary job was to take a fresh and comprehensive look at the problems of patient care, to attend especially to new perspectives and new developments, and to search out promising and workable alternatives to conventional arrangements.

In this monograph we examine the social aspects of the care and treatment of the mentally ill or emotionally disturbed in our society: the professions and institutions whose specific and primary responsibility is to help them. In this connection we consider some prevalent trends and prominent issues both in practice and thought. Our efforts to gather, organize, and interpret relevant information aim at increasing the therapeutic effectiveness of our resources.

The care of mental patients has called into being three major systems [3] each of which is responsible for a particular group of patients: out-patients, in-patients, and ex-patients. The in-patients are the hospitalized mentally ill, out-patients are those who receive psychiatric treatment while continuing to reside in the community, and ex-patients are those with a history of previous hospitalization. As here defined, mental patients include all three categories, and these categories shaped the major division of labor in the project staff and is followed in the organization of this report.

There are several broad, pervasive issues and problems regarding mental illness and the care of mental patients in our society. These and the extent of the problem, the societal context of therapy, and conceptions of mental illness and its treatment are the subject of this introductory chapter.

The Extent of the Problem

How many mental patients are there? Have there been changes in the proportions of patients treated in the various types of facility? Has the increase in the numbers of mental patients been disproportionately high in comparison with the growth of the general population?

None of these questions can be answered unequivocally. Estimates in the technical and popular literature of the numbers of persons under treatment for mental disorder vary by tens and even hundreds of thousands, reflecting the lack of a unified and standardized system for reporting information on mental patients.[4] Often basic data are simply not available and assumptions about practice have to be made in order to arrive at estimates of, for example, the number of patients being treated by psychiatrists in private practice. Moreover, certain categories of patients are excluded from the tabulations, for example, the thousands of patients in institutions for epileptics and the mentally retarded. In the absence of uniform and reliable data, any over-all estimate of the magnitude of the problem must rest on inferences and arbitrary decisions about certain categories of patients and facilities. One quickly learns to scrutinize footnotes and the small print on the bottom of tables in order to understand the significance of the figures and the range of their legitimate extrapolation.[5]

To the population of individuals who are receiving a recognized treatment for a mental disorder under psychiatric auspices must be added large numbers suffering from mental or emotional illness not being treated in any of the formal systems of psychiatric care. Some are receiving explicit but nonmedical help for a psychological or emotional disturbance in counseling or therapy by ministers, psychologists, or social workers. Others are being treated for physical illness by internists or general practitioners who take into account in their treatment the fact that psychological disturbances may be a major or important secondary component of the pathology. Another group of large but undetermined size is those who appear to be mentally ill (including ex-patients with recurrent or continuing impairment in functioning) but who at the moment are not receiving any form of professional help.

The mental patient, that is, the individual being treated for a mental illness in a formal system, is the central concern of this report. However, he, his problems, and the systems of care must be viewed against the background of this larger population of persons who, presumably, also need help. Certainly estimates of future needs and proposals for long-term developments have to take the total group into account. But it is extremely difficult to compute the size of this population in need: a number of complex and unresolved problems enter into the matter of defining an individual as mentally ill if he is not in treatment. By any definition there is no clearly distinguishable line between the mentally ill and those who seem to be disturbed but are not mentally ill. How does one determine, for example, whether certain reactions to life crises are normal or pathological, or when an individual's level of functioning calls for psychiatric intervention?

Studies in the epidemiology of mental disorders might provide a basis for estimates. The early studies used standard psychiatric nomenclatures developed in clinical practice; recent research has more flexible and less uniform criteria and diagnostic categories. In general, the trend has been toward broadening the conception of mental illness so as to include many more types of personal difficulty and social impairment than was so in earlier years; [6] hence, estimates derived from the early studies and now considered conservative are that between 4 and 10 percent of the population suffer from mental illness that is disabling to some degree.[7]

Estimates from more recent epidemiological studies are much higher. For example, the Stirling County Study gives a figure of 37 percent of the population as showing "symptoms that were almost certainly indicative of psychiatric disorder"; and the Midtown Study reports 23 percent of its sample with psychiatric symptoms and at least a marked impairment in social role and daily life functioning.[8] In view of changes in definition and the tendency noted above to stretch the meaning of the term "mental illness," the early and recent studies cannot be directly compared with each other; they refer to overlapping groups with psychological problems. However—and this is far more important—whether we use the earlier or the later figures, it is clear that a great gap exists between needs and resources.

The Social Context of Help

Help for mental illness is sought or provided in our society within a context of certain limiting and facilitating conditions: the socially patterned values and norms and the common attitudes to mental illness, the provisions for care and treatment, and the contingencies affecting those seeking and getting it.

VALUES AND NORMS

Our society has developed at least two ways of dealing with the deviant—the violator of norms and values—when his behavior is sufficiently extreme to arouse concern and a self-protective response. One is to classify the grossly deviant as wayward or criminal and incarcerate him or otherwise punish him. But society also recognizes that mental illness is a legitimate alternative explanation of deviant behavior and its treatment a legitimate endeavor and, consequently, that the mentally ill person has the right to ask for treatment and become a patient. The role of mental patient is legitimated by (a) the recognition of the patient's need of help or protection and his right to them; (b) the prediction that, through help, he may recover his independence and productivity and begin again to make his "normal" contribution to society; and, finally, (c) society's obligation to protect its members from him, by setting him apart, when necessary, and by giving him treatment with the object of bringing his deviant behavior to an end.

It offends our conception of human dignity and individual worth to put up with preventable damage to mind or emotion. Our citizens must be free men in full possession of their senses, for the ability to think freely and independently is prerequisite to the survival of democratic society. We cannot, therefore, from a long range point of view, afford to have citizens who continue to be mentally ill or emotionally disturbed, for in our highly complex technological society we are all interdependent and must rely upon each other in the necessary complex cooperative transactions. And we are not only concerned about physical safety, but we must also protect ourselves against violations of norms and values and the failure of ordinary expectations to be fulfilled. Thus, helping the mentally ill is a way of defending our society and its accepted conventions.

Other values enter in. Help given mental patients must always be provided with a concern for the individual's civil rights. We cannot, for example, set up a system of identifying the mentally ill that invades the privacy of the home; nor can we order treatment unless the patient is a clear danger to himself or others. Even though a professional recognizes that a child is being psychologically damaged, he can neither compel the parents or the child to undertake treatment nor take the child from his home without the parent's consent, willingly and freely given. Thus, what may be good for mental health may conflict with other values apparently more important.

In our society the pursuit of ends other than mental health involves competition among them for scarce resources, funds, and skills. Gross inadequacies in the treatment of mental patients indicate that it does not rank high in our hierarchy of values. The state mental hospitals, for example, operate on budgets too small to permit them to establish and maintain environments suitable for treatment, to provide the amenities of life to their patients in the form of pleasant activities and surroundings, or to offer salaries attractive to personnel of high caliber. Economic and administrative considerations often outweigh the therapeutic decisions made about patients and their treatment in the hospitals, the out-patient clinics, and aftercare facilities.

ATTITUDES

All mental illness is characterized by some disruption of normal social and interpersonal relationships. The mentally ill person, because of his inappropriate and maladaptive behavior, requires adaptive responses from others at various points from onset to recovery. Moreover, the responses set off in others by the mentally ill are often unsympathetic, varying from impatience or mere annoyance to severe anxiety, disgust, and condemnation, and these, altogether and in all their forms, are sometimes referred to as "stigma." Especially significant is the fact that by contrast the social attitudes and responses elicited by other forms of illness are usually sympathetic.

At best, the public view might be described as intensely ambivalent. Concern and sympathy for mental patients is tempered by a tendency to devalue them as nonproductive, dependent, and weak, and, although the belief that mental illness is a punishment for sin does not seem current now, popular sentiment persists in being moral and condemnatory. Only in recent times are certain forms of deviant behavior assessed as signs of emotional or psychological disturbance requiring psychological treatment and not as signs of criminal intent requiring legal punishment. The distinction is not yet accepted completely throughout our society, and the mental patient is often the butt of responses and attitudes more appropriate to antisocial deviants and criminals.[9]

All in all, this complex of negative attitudes is associated with a belittling of the mental patient and rejection of his role. All this affects the quantity and quality of available facilities, their organization, the help they offer, and what is expected of treatment on the part of both patient and staff.

CONTINGENCIES IN SEEKING AND GETTING HELP

Many contingencies [10] determine whether and how a person will enter a treatment system, yet they may have little to do with the specific characteristics of his illness. Thus, rejection of the role of mental patient and resistance to entering treatment may lead to the neglect of early manifestations of illness and, in the end, delay help. Or the norms and values of his own group may encourage or discourage a disturbed person from seeking treatment. It appears, for example, more difficult for men than women in our society to recognize problems in themselves for which they may need outside help. For this reason, men are less likely than women to enter treatment systems. (Gurin, *et al.*, 1960.) Another circumstance not directly related to the illness is the availability of help in or near the person's place of residence. For certain psychoses there may be higher incidences of hospitalization if a state mental hospital is located within twenty miles of the community than if it is farther away.[11] Other conditions, such as the individual's financial resources, his education, his social status, and his access to various media of information, affect both his awareness and his utilization of available facilities.

Thus, the objective features of mental illness are only some among the many involved in whether a disturbed person receives treatment and these contingencies are not accidental but are patterned in meaningful ways.

PROVISION FOR CARE AND TREATMENT

Provision for the care and treatment of the mental patient includes the forms of intervention, the practicing professionals, and the settings. Each of the systems of care—out-patient, in-patient and ex-patient—works with only a certain group of patients. They differ among themselves in historical development, in orientation, in their mode of intervention, and in the dominant professional groups involved.

Of considerable importance in the functioning of a system of care is the heterogeneity of patients in terms of the severity, history, and current status of the patients' illness. While there is some specialization of function, by and large most facilities for in-patients are designed to handle everything and anything. This means that variation in goals and in treatment processes exists not only among different treatment institutions but within them as well. Out-patient and aftercare facilities, however, tend to specialize in certain types of patient or service, and here there are problems of coverage and coordination.

Psychiatrists, social workers, clinical psychologists, nurses, occupational and recreational therapists, and ward attendants are the most prominent, although not the only professional groups involved. Depending in part on their professional competence and in part on what they actually do, their intervention may be called therapy, counseling, rehabilitation, training, or re-education. The medical profession as represented by the psychiatrist plays the dominant role in the treatment of mental patients. Even where physicians are not themselves participants in the therapeutic process, treatment is likely to proceed according to medical ideals and values. For example, the mental patient is conceded as having a "right" to receive help regardless of his ethnic background, social position, or other social characteristics. On the other hand, this help cannot be forced upon him—a man has a right to remain unhappy, anxious, or impotent, and, according to the current ethic of practice, treatment should be offered, wherever possible, as a private contract between patient and practitioner. These and other aspects of private medical practice tend to color the orientation toward the treatment of the mentally ill, even when practice itself proceeds along quite different lines, as in the state mental hospital.

How the facilities for therapy are organized, their policies, assumptions, and requirements will in part be determined by the nature, monetary and otherwise, of the participation, if any, of the local, state, and federal government. And the ways in which private and governmental activities combine in the facilities will also determine the patterns of usage and the forms they take.

Conceptions of Mental Illness and Its Treatment

Help and treatment will proceed according to the current conceptions of the causes of mental illness and the current theories about what kind of intervention will alleviate, improve, or cure emotional and mental disorder.[12] Thus the achievements, developments, limitations, and inadequacies in theory and knowledge at the time will be reflected in the practitioners' effectiveness in providing successful care and treatment.

The mental illnesses manifest themselves at all levels of the human personality—somatic, psychological, and social. They involve disturbances in many spheres of life affecting the individual's feelings about himself, his relations with others, and his ability to work productively. There is also a variety of ways in which people get into trouble and come to be looked upon as emotionally or mentally disturbed and a variety of conditions that are defined as mental illness. Similarly, professionals entertain different assumptions and interpretations. They differ on what persons "are" when they are emotionally disturbed or mentally ill, on how they got that way, on what is wrong with them, or who should be placed in the category, on why they stay that way, and on what should be done. The source of variation lies in the diversity of the professionals' social background, technical training, theoretical commitments, and general philosophy.

It is not our task to explore the problems and issues in conceptualizing mental illness and its treatment in any detail. We will, however, discuss a few areas briefly in order to present the conceptual context and dilemmas within which help and treatment proceed.

CONCEPTIONS OF MENTAL ILLNESS
AND EMOTIONAL DISTURBANCE

Although psychiatrists are called upon daily to state whether or not a person is mentally ill or emotionally disturbed, there is nevertheless a great deal of difficulty in defining "mental illness." On the one hand, professionals may use the term as if it were unitary, but, on the other hand, they speak as if there were many quite distinct mental illnesses. When the term is used by professionals to emphasize shared or similar aspects of all mental illnesses, it is not clear if these are seen to reside in the common underlying organic defect, in the common psychic conflicts, in the deviant behavior, in the fact that these persons have been injured in some psychic-social-emotional way, or in their classification in the category "mentally ill," thus indicating that they share a common fate. If the difference between mental illnesses is the focus, then the question arises: What distinguishes one type of mental illness from another? To identify the critical differences between one illness and another appears to be simple for some organic pathologies and a very difficult problem for most other psychopathologies.

Whatever are conceived as the common or differentiating characteristics, how does one determine if it is the similarities, the differences, or both that are primarily relevant for the treatment of different types of patient?

In order to determine who needs treatment and what is the magnitude of the problem of mental illness, it is important to differentiate between mental illness and nonmental illness. Here, again, there are divergent points of view and unresolved issues. Is it important to distinguish among those not mentally ill those who are mentally *healthy* from those who are just not mentally *ill?* If such a distinction is made, are the mentally ill, the nonmentally ill, and the mentally healthy on the same continuum? Many professionals hold that there is no clear and unmistakable line of demarcation between the mentally ill and the others, and they disagree on the criteria to be used for placing a person in one category or another. That all persons may become disturbed at times in the course of their lives seems to be universally accepted: difficulties lie in distinguishing between normal and pathological suffering, between normal and pathological reactions to crises, between normal and pathological anxiety, between odd, unconventional, idiosyncratic, or creative behavior and sick behavior. Even if a person's reactions are considered by the professional to be those of one who is emotionally disturbed, how "sick" must he be before he is considered in need of treatment?

There is even a difference of opinion about the advisability of offering treatment to some who are emotionally disturbed. Although many practitioners assume that individuals manifesting emotional disturbance should have some form of treatment, others maintain that some are best left alone to work out their own problems. The circumstances under which a therapist would treat or not treat a patient are not always clear; neither are the criteria of choice.

The problem of differentiating the mentally ill from others is further complicated by a considerable body of opinion that holds, as observed above, that all persons are capable of becoming mentally ill, given sufficient stress. Since stress is a fairly pervasive aspect of modern life, it is important to be able to identify when and what types of stress exceed a particular person's tolerance and the processes of transition as he passes from potential to actual mental illness. Such knowledge seems at present to be only rudimentary.

Since mental illness is not "an illness" that pervades the total personality, how much of it must one "have," or how much of one's personality has to be affected, to be categorized as mentally ill or emotionally disturbed and in need of treatment? Since mental illness is not a constant (a person is not continuously mentally ill), how much of the time must he be ill to be diagnosed as such? Psychiatrists differ on their criteria and on the importance they attribute to the frequency and severity of the disturbance, and on whom to include or exclude from the category. Differences of opinion will, of course, be more evident about persons who are mildly disturbed or hovering on the brink than about the severely psychotic. But some professionals take the position that we are all more or less emotionally disturbed or neurotic and that, if it were practicable, we should all have treatment. This point of view eliminates the problem of identifying the mentally ill, but it then makes it impossible to cope with the patient population.

In differentiating the mentally ill from the nonmentally ill and the mentally healthy, the question arises: Are these differences of degree or of kind? The professional's assumptions will influence significantly his attitudes toward patients and their treatment and what he expects to achieve with them. Some see psychoses, neuroses, and mental health all as being but differences of degree; others see them all as differences of kind. An in-between view singles out psychoses as different in kind from neuroses and mental health.

The relationship between physical illness and mental illness has been a controversial question for some time. Where there is a clear organic pathology, it is relatively easy to see the connection. Where, however, the illness appears to be functional, there are differences of opinion about the similarities and dissimilarities between physical and mental illness. Concerning an illness such as schizophrenia, there is much unresolved disagreement about "what" should be treated. The major division in psychiatry at the present time seems to be between those who emphasize an organic view of mental illness and focus on a somatic treatment and those who emphasize a psychodynamic view and focus on psychological or interpersonal measures.

The issue between the "organicists" and the "psychodynami- cists" is in the conception of the locus: to the former, the locus is a diseased part, the "trouble" residing in the brain or body; to the latter, there is no tangible or specific physical pathology, but, instead, a disturbance within the psychological "self," or in inter- personal relations. The more sociologically oriented group projects the locus beyond the individual, upon the family, the community, or the society.

There is as much controversy over the etiology of most mental disorders as there is over their "location": they are attributed to somatic, genetic, or developmental defects, or to deprivation, psychic trauma, insufficient love or other stressful social situations, or to inadequate socialization. All these explanations may be offered for the same type of mental illness as well as for different types. It is clear that no one cause is sufficient to explain the various kinds of mental illness.

Related is a problem of specifying what a patient needs to "get well." Mental illness is seen as a disequilibrium in one or more areas of functioning—biological, psychological, or social. Thus, professionals differ as to their interpretations of patients' needs: which are most important and which need or combination of needs is salient for treatment; for their interpretations are, of course, associated with their various conceptions of how to change the disequilibrium—biological, psychological or social—so that the patient will no longer be defined as mentally ill.

In addition to the above problems, the classifying and differentiating of different types of mental illness are far from satisfactory. According to Reid (1957) the function of nosological categories is to enable one: (a) to communicate clearly about patients; (b) to label the disorder unambiguously; (c) to investigate the causes of illness; (d) to make inferences as to prognosis; and, (e) to decide what is the best form of therapy. Psychiatric classification has not as yet achieved these objectives. The deficiency in sorting out and labeling is a major deterrent in developing the form of treatment and system of care appropriate to each category of patient. In addition, there is disagreement about the usefulness of the present diagnostic categories, about the dimensions and orientation of a new diagnostic system, and even about the desirability and usefulness of having any diagnostic categories at all.

The identifying and describing of the characteristics of mentally ill or emotionally disturbed persons is also fraught with controversy. Although there is general agreement that there is "some-

thing wrong," there is none on what the abnormality consists
of and how it should be referred to. Some practitioners think of
the individual's disturbances as a mental disease: adopting a phys-
ical-medical point of view, they consider crucial the "illness" aspect of the patient. Others describe the disturbed person as emo-
tionally-psychologically disturbed, as maladjusted, as incompetent
or inadequate, as suffering from psychic conflicts or anxiety, or as
having distortions of perception or inappropriate affect: theirs is
psychodynamic or psychological perspective. Closely allied is the
interpersonal frame of reference: the individual is said to be having difficulties in living and in relating to himself and others.
Finally, a sociological frame of reference presents him as a deviant, deficient in role performance, inadequately socialized, or
unable to meet certain expectations. These points of view overlap; there are variations and many sub-views within each; there
are attempts to use more than one frame of reference, and there
are varying emphases for different kinds of patient. But there is
no agreement as to which frame of reference is most appropriate
to characterize each type of illness—except, of course, for some
clear-cut organic mental illnesses. These disparities are most evident in reference to the schizophrenic patient.

The view that the disturbance in mental illness is a function
of a combination of the organic, the psychodynamic, and social
systems of action implies that a description using any one of these
alone has its limitations. When a mental illness is described from
a single point of view, it seems insufficient to explain its range
and variation. In addition, those committed to one interpretation
often have difficulty in communicating with those committed to
another, and it is not easy to integrate various interpretations
into a coherent and usable frame of reference.

The current explanations for the continuation of a mental illness show the same variations in orientation. Some psychiatrists
see it as persistent somatic defect or deterioration; others as unresolved psychic conflicts; still others as being perpetuated by the
patient's social environment and paucity of opportunities for
learning.

CONCEPTIONS OF HELP AND TREATMENT

There are at present unresolved issues in the philosophy of treatment and practice, and practitioners disagree on the value and efficacy of various modalities of treatment and on the answers to the questions: What is wrong with the patient? What does he need? What should be changed? When he eventually selects a certain treatment as the most efficacious, a practitioner reveals incidentally what he considers to be the appropriate unit of treatment. The trend in defining the unit of treatment seems to be moving in two directions: some professionals define the unit of treatment as a specific organic area, but an increasing number see it as encompassing a wide range of processes and procedures, for example, the community. The dilemma in delineating the unit of treatment is serious. On the one hand, it must be sufficiently circumscribed to be manageable; but this may leave significant and relevant aspects unfocused on or untreated. On the other hand, the conception of the unit must be broad enough to include significant and relevant factors, for example, sociocultural factors. But, so broadened, the unit of treatment may turn out to be an entity unmanageable for therapeutic purposes—how does one, and can one, "treat" a community? Thus, the problem is: Can the unit of treatment be circumscribed so that its limits are clear and manageable and, at the same time, include significant and relevant variables? In other words, can the strategic and salient factors in different kinds of mental illnesses be specified and managed so as to bring about regular improvement?

Isolating the appropriate unit of treatment involves some further unresolved questions. Under what circumstances and with what kinds of patient is one or another unit of treatment most appropriate? Leaving aside the clear organic cases, such as acute toxic states, general paresis, and cerebral arteriosclerosis, the question implies that no one unit of treatment should be identified as appropriate at all times to all types of mental illness. Other questions follow from this. May different units of treatment be selected for the same illness or for the same person under differing social circumstances? Upon what bases or criteria should one unit of treatment be preferred over another?

Once the unit of treatment has been identified, the question arises: What can be done to, for, with, or about it, to help the patient? The forms or modes of treatment advocated vary: injection, incision, convulsion, tranquilization, advice, support, psychotherapy, psychoanalysis, group therapy, family therapy, and milieu or environmental therapy. Again, different modes of treatment will be used for different patients, and more than one mode of treatment will be advocated for the same patient.

Whatever mode of treatment is advocated or used, there are many unanswered questions—how change comes about, the circumstances and the types of patient with which a particular treatment will succeed or fail, and why. Many therapies proceed without a conceptual or theoretical rationale or even any attempt to develop one; many practitioners are primarily interested in the results and not in their implications. A puzzling problem is that advocates of various modalities of treatment can and do claim the same degree of success with their particular mode. It seems that each modality has success with some type of patient. By selecting that part of the patient population to which a particular mode of treatment seems most applicable, most, if not all, treatment procedures can be used with some success; it is rare for anyone to claim complete success. Yet the same treatment may fail consistently with another kind of patient.

Because adequate procedures for evaluation have not been developed and because evaluation studies, especially comparative ones, are too rarely made, and because, in general, evaluation is complex and difficult, competing therapeutic modes can persist without being subjected to a definitive test. Unfortunately, there is a tendency on the part of some practitioners to generalize from success with selected patients to all types. The evidence now available is that no one mode of treatment is effective for all types of mental patients and for all kinds of persons who become patients. The tendency toward specialization along particular therapeutic lines is associated with different ideologies and points of view rather than with scientifically established knowledge.

There are a number of other issues in treatment. Practitioners vary in their goals for patients and their expectations of what they will be able to achieve, ranging from the one extreme, that of curing the patient, to the other, that of making him more comfortable or relieving his symptoms. In between there are goals such as preventing further deterioration, correcting a defect, increasing insight, resolving psychic conflicts, reducing tension, helping personal adjustment, and restoring the patient to normal social functioning. The evaluation of success or failure will, of course, depend, in part, upon the goals the practitioners select. Since they do not generally agree on their goals, either for all patients or for types of patient, the criteria of success or failure of modes of treatment fluctuate. The continuation of partisan claims and the skepticism about the usefulness of an opposing group's therapeutic techniques is to be accounted for, in part, by the variation in practitioners' goals.

The unresolved problems of treatment can be summarized as those of isolating and classifying different kinds of mental illness, identifying appropriate units of treatment, and differentiating modalities of treatment in order to fit the treatment process to the patient—to the nature of his illness or disturbance and to him as a person and a social being.

Although there is much to be desired in conceptualizing and treating mental illness, this is not the "fault" of any particular discipline. It is rather in the nature of our present human situation where our understanding of man and his functioning and our knowledge about human relationships falls so far short of our urgent needs.

We have tried in this chapter to convey something of the background of this study of the care of the mental patient by describing the social and conceptual contexts and associated problems and issues. In the following chapter we shall describe the specific procedure and point of view of our study.

Chapter 2

Development of the Study

Procedures

The eight persons who constituted the professional staff of the Project on Patterns of Patient Care all had had previous experience in research either in hospitals or in the general field of social psychiatry.[1] One was a psychiatrist experienced in community organization and the administration of mental health programs; another was an expert in rehabilitation previously trained in economics; the remaining six were social scientists with backgrounds in sociology and social psychology.

They divided the field work in three sections, each one primarily focused on a major system of care. Members of the staff, usually in teams of two for from one to three days each, visited 121 facilities providing care to mental patients: 30 out-patient, 32 in-patient, and 59 ex-patient facilities. In each place they observed aspects of the programs and interviewed individuals responsible for specific activities and for over-all operations.

Among the provisions for out-patient service examined in our survey were: court and mental health clinics, guidance centers, mental health associations, as well as private practitioners [2] and public health programs in psychiatry, and projects in emergency and home care. We visited both large and medium-sized state mental hospitals, Veterans Administration mental hospitals, small private institutions, the psychiatric sections of general hospitals, and research and training institutes. A variety of aftercare organizations and services were included: rehabilitation centers, sheltered workshops, half-way houses, clinics, and a number of agencies dealing with public welfare assistance, public health nursing, social work, and vocational rehabilitation.

Although our sample includes examples of almost every type

of facility for patient care, it is not a representative sample in a statistical sense of all facilities in the United States. Each institution in our sample was selected deliberately according to the criterion set forth in our mandate, namely, that it be a place where promising, novel, or unconventional programs were in progress or process of development. We aimed at heterogeneity in such things as institutional auspices, size, and geographical region. Thus, our sample was designed to provide coverage of new trends and developments.

In our observation and interviews we were concerned particularly with the beliefs and assumptions that underlie the introduction of new programs, the background of problems and issues that led to their development, objectives of the programs, and their functions and results. In addition, we tried to determine the nature of the problems that emerged when such programs were introduced into traditional institutions and systems of patient care. Interviews were conducted with administrative and operating personnel at various levels, and, wherever posssible, the program was observed in operation.

In addition to field visits to treatment installations and interviews with personnel attached to them, we interviewed a total of 179 other experts in the mental health field: 52 were concerned primarily with out-patient care, 48 with ex-patient care, and 79 took a more general interest in the field. Some of the interviews lasted for three and four hours, the average running to about two hours.

Our experts were drawn from many different mental health professions and included nurses, psychiatrists, psychologists, sociologists, anthropologists, social workers, and various other specialists. Some were administrators or directors of publicly supported departments or institutions; others were private practitioners. Some of our respondents were concerned primarily with theoretical issues and with research, while, to others, problems of practice and public education were basic.

All of our interviews were relatively unstructured. They varied in substance depending on the respondent's background and position, the program, and the facility. On the whole, we asked those interviewed to share their ideas with us about the most important problems and issues in patient care, to describe what they believed to be the most promising lines of development in their own institution and the field in general, and the directions they thought should be taken in the future.

After a visit to a treatment facility, each member of the observation team prepared independently a summary of his impressions. Primarily, it was an interpretive and analytic report focused on the general and potential significance of the programs for the care of patients. As our inquiry proceeded and our objectives became more sharply defined, the memoranda also changed; the topics were those discussed in the following chapters. Reports of interviews with expert respondents also stressed general principles and broad issues more than concrete details of specific programs. These memoranda were the most important material drawn upon for this monograph.

Point of View

Probably the most important assumption in our analysis is, briefly, that the viewpoint of social science may be profitably adopted in studying mental illness. Specifically, we assume that social and interpersonal relationships—the forms they manifest, the values they embody, the patterns of their development—are variables equal in importance to those in biological and psychological realms for more fully understanding mental illness and more adequately dealing with patients. This conviction is evinced in two ways here.

First, to a large extent, we shall concentrate upon problems of social structure, cultural values, and the social organization of treatment systems, and upon social factors in the introduction and maintenance of certain forms and agents of treatment. In other words, our way of looking at events as social scientists lends importance to certain problems and issues that would not receive the same amount of attention were we oriented primarily toward, for example, the biological components of mental illness. Second, we shall be interested in the therapeutic or antitherapeutic signif-

icance of certain social processes themselves. Many new developments in the treatment of patients utilize properties of the social
milieu or emphasize the benefits of patient participation in the
institutional community along with his involvement in traditionally defined therapies. We shall pay particular attention to a number of programs that attempt to make explicit therapeutic use of
social processes.

Thus, we are interested in social variables both as contexts
within which various forms of help are offered and as specific
forms of therapy in and of themselves.

Method of Analysis

In three separate sections we shall examine, successively, provisions for the care and treatment of out-patients, in-patients, and
ex-patients. Each section is introduced by an overview of the particular system's background and history and a brief description
of the major facilities. Within the sections we have arranged descriptions and interpretations around issues or themes of general
concern to students and practitioners.

Each of the analytic subsections, that is, the chapters, dealing
with particular themes within each of the major divisions, starts
with a discussion of the theme of concern as it is reported by practitioners. Relevant programs are then described. Finally, we comment on the implications of each program for the treatment of
mental patients and for the social organization of treatment facilities and discuss the issues involved. A chapter at the end of each
section treats general implications and problems of the relations
among the different themes and general issues in the care of patients. A final chapter incorporates our recommendations and conclusions.

Three themes selected for discussion in each section reflect
trends in the many specific recent programs for improving patient
care. These themes of concern are:

For out-patients: providing immediate help; extending out-
patient services in the community; and broadening the conceptions
of help.

For in-patients: individualizing care and treatment; breaking down the barriers between hospital and community; and developing a therapeutic milieu.

For ex-patients: tailoring aftercare; grading stress; and providing continuity of care.

One or another of these themes represents the original or the leading impetus in new and significant developments. Many of the activities we shall describe are relevant to a number of themes, and, when that is so, we discuss the programs within the context that professionals see as particularly relevant, if certain critical questions of psychiatric practice may be illuminated thereby. For example, the establishing in general hospitals of psychiatric sections for in-patients, which could be discussed from various angles, is generally seen as part of the trend to break down barriers between hospital and community and, in particular, to combat the stigma attached to mental illness and to facilitate admission to treatment.

We have focused on new possibilities in the care and treatment of patients and have explored problems created by the introduction of new programs into traditional systems and facilities. It is true, for example, that a detailed inventory of current practices reporting the numbers of institutions that have introduced therapeutic milieus might be useful for some purposes; however, we believe that it is more important to approach the problem qualitatively and to analyze the various assumptions and implications contained in the major forms of therapeutic milieu. Throughout we have tried to keep the impact of the system of care on the patient as our central focus.

No panaceas are offered. We hope that when the reader finishes the book he will have become less certain of his beliefs about the most effective ways of helping mental patients but more committed to the search for better ones.

Part II

The Out-patient System

Chapter 3

Characteristics of the Out-patient System

In this chapter we describe the out-patient system of care for emotionally disturbed persons, beginning with a general description and an historical synopsis to provide a background for the discussion of new developments and trends.

An Overview

Although it is difficult to estimate the need for out-patient services in any particular community, that they are insufficient to meet the actual and the potential demand is demonstrated by the fact that as soon as a clinic opens it is overwhelmed with applications and within a short time has to establish a waiting list.[1] Moreover, it is well known that many private practitioners have to turn patients away. Generally throughout the country, a shortage of facilities and professional workers is made worse by the ever-increasing demand for their services.

Because the pressures are so great, most professionals spend their time in giving direct treatment to patients. Many psychiatrists, however, carry on "mixed activity"—teaching, training, and consultation in addition to treatment. This state of affairs is occasioned by the increase in requests for consultation by nonpsychiatric health and welfare agencies, by the increasing importance of the teaching of psychiatry in medical schools, and by requests for consultation by physicians, judges, clergymen and others.

The services to out-patients rendered by public and private clinics and by private practitioners in psychiatry and psychotherapy have grown rapidly, resulting in a diversified system of care. For example, there are clinics conducted under the auspices of the federal government, state governments, and local governments, and there are private agencies, some supported by the community chest; there are clinics attached to courts, schools, industrial plants, medical schools, private mental hospitals, and the psychiatric sections of general hospitals.

Help is supplied not only by psychiatrists but also to an increasing degree, and often despite the opposition of psychiatrists, by nonmedical therapists, such as clinical psychologists and psychiatric social workers, who vary widely in background, orientation, and ideas of treatment. Individuals suffering from psychoses, neuroses, or alcoholism or who manifest criminal or suicidal behavior or who struggle with problems in school or in marriage may be treated by psychoanalysis, drugs, group therapy, or electric shock. Each practitioner tends to specialize in one type of therapy and holds out different goals for his patients.

Although the idea of "going to a head-shrinker" is still ridiculed, the public is more and more willing to accept psychiatric treatment, though it often entertains unrealistic expectations of quick and easy cures. When miracles are not performed, the patient or his relatives may grow skeptical of the psychiatrist's ability. Some physicians still misunderstand and reject psychiatry and psychiatrists, although many argue that closer cooperation and the acceptance of psychiatry as a respectable branch of medicine is not only desirable but inevitable.

Clinics and private practitioners tend to function in isolation from each other and maintain little formal connection with in-patient or ex-patient facilities. Because of the pressure of demand, many agencies devote themselves exclusively to the immediate problems of their patients. However, under the influence of new programs such as emergency psychiatric services and day-and-night hospitals, isolation breaks down. Moreover, the present tendency to see the unit of treatment as including more than a particular patient is forcing practitioners to pay greater attention to the community and the social environment. For example, the treatment of children in recent years has come increasingly to include treating the child's family.

Each mental hygiene clinic establishes its own criteria for admission, selecting the type of patients who fit in and rejecting those who do not. Thus, patients may be accepted or rejected on the basis of such considerations as age, diagnosis or type of problem, education, or "readiness" for treatment. Clinics also vary according to the type of treatment they emphasize, its frequency and intensity, and the social class of the patients.

Clinics are ordinarily under medical direction, responsibility resting with a psychiatrist. However, psychiatrists are frequently only part-time employees whereas the bulk of the work is carried on, under their general direction and supervision, by social workers. Of late, psychologists have taken a more active role in clinics, and the clinical team includes the psychiatrist, psychologist, and social worker, integrating the skills of each and maximizing their help to the patient. While mental health clinics have proliferated and expanded in our cities, so, too, the private practice of psychiatry, psychotherapy, and especially of psychoanalysis has developed rapidly since World War II. The private practice of psychiatry tends to be polarized around either psychotherapy or somatic treatment. Somatic out-patient treatment consists primarily of chemical and electric shock therapy. Among the various kinds of psychotherapy, the psychoanalytically oriented is a dominant mode. Fees are too high for those of low income to seek it out or to enjoy continuing treatment as private patients, and the private practitioners on the whole serve the middle and upper class while the others depend on the community clinic or state mental hospital. But even those able to pay high fees frequently experience difficulty getting the help of private practitioners when they want it because they are so much in demand.

Historical Survey

Help for emotional disturbance given while the patient is not institutionalized is at once old and new.[2] Before the advent of institutions for the specific treatment or custody of the mentally ill in the late eighteenth and early nineteenth century in this country, most sufferers remained in the community. If they were fortunate, they received some help or were left alone. A less fortunate minority were imprisoned. The individual who lived with his family was "managed" within the framework of a society largely rural: the availability of simple tasks, the close integration of the family, and often its isolation made it possible to keep him in his natural setting. As the industrial Northeast developed and migration to the West broke up many homesteads, the housing of mentally disturbed persons became for the first time an acute problem, whose solution was often to place them in workhouses, poorhouses, and jails.

The humanitarian appeals of Dorothea Dix inspired the development of the mental hospital as the appropriate place for the cure and treatment of mental patients. Beginning in the mid-1800s, the focus of psychiatric activities shifted to the large public mental hospital. As these grew larger and more preoccupied with their own inner life, they grew isolated from and neglected by the communities which they served and whose support they needed. Not until the 1900s was there a widespread movement to return psychiatric activities to the community. It was stimulated by progress in scientific medicine, the development of psychotherapeutic methods, and the expanding mental hygiene movement, which, it was hoped would do for psychic illness what public health was beginning to do for communicable diseases.

Although physicians in their day-to-day private practice have treated mentally disturbed persons for centuries, the treatment of mental patients living in the community is at most seventy to eighty years old. It seems to be associated with a broadened conception of what is susceptible to psychiatric treatment and with the abandonment of the idea that patients suffering from the severer pathologies must be completely separated from their families. At present many practitioners maintain that the treatment of the patient in his natural surroundings often will be of greater benefit than hospitalization and that hospitalization, when needed, is but one phase of a program of treatment.

When Hammond in 1879 maintained that mental patients might fare better outside mental hospitals, he expressed a growing body of medical opinion. Thus, several decades before the turn of the century psychiatrists began to develop clinical services in the community. A little later the Michigan Neuropsychiatric

Institute at Ann Arbor (1906), the Boston Psychopathic Hospital (1912), and the Henry Phipps Clinic of the Johns Hopkins University (1913) were founded with fully developed psychiatric out-patient services.

CLINICS

Although so-called "Nerve Clinics" had been established in Philadelphia in 1867 and in Boston in 1873, the first real out-patient psychiatric clinic in this country was opened in 1885 in Philadelphia when the managers of the Pennsylvania Hospital for the Insane extended the operations of the out-patient department of the Pine Street Hospital to provide a dispensary for those suffering from incipient mental disease.[3] The service, considered experimental, was undertaken with the "conviction that in a city of one million inhabitants, a large number were suffering from premonitory symptoms of insanity such as nervous prostration and depression, who might receive timely advice and treatment and that a further development of mental disorder might thus be arrested" (Hurd, et al., 1916, pp. 415–16). A few months later, the trustees of the State Hospital for the Insane at Warren, Pennsylvania, started an out-patient service (Deutsch, 1949, p. 296). In 1891 Dr. Walter E. Fernald began consultations at the Massachusetts State School (Fernald, 1920), and in 1913 there were clinics for mental defectives in several other states. In New York City Cornell Medical School developed a mental clinic in 1904 headed by Dr. Adolf Meyer and the staff members of the State Pathological Institute (Cheney, 1923, p. 234).

Traveling clinics were first established in New York State in 1909 and in Massachusetts the following year. Most were diagnostic and operated by the state hospitals using state hospital personnel. They were an outgrowth of an effort to make hospital clinics an integral part of the community (Barhash, et al., 1952, p. 7).

Although the first clinics started under hospital auspices and primarily served adults and the severely disturbed, the growth of clinics throughout the country owes much of its impetus to the development of the child guidance movement. The first community services for children grew out of the interests of progressive juvenile court judges and interested physicians. In 1909 Dr. William Healy, a practicing neurologist, founded the Chicago Psychopathic Institute and in 1917 became the first director of the new Judge Baker Foundation in Boston.

In the early 1920s the Commonwealth Fund in cooperation with the National Committee for Mental Hygiene (now the National Association for Mental Health) established demonstration clinics in many American cities. To staff them the Fund provided for the special training of teams of psychologists, psychiatrists, and social workers, and it supported clinics for periods of six months to two years in cities requesting the demonstration. Most of the patients were children referred by the courts. Later, in a five-year experiment, community clinics were established that emphasized work with other social agencies and with schools. The Fund anticipated that the communities would arrange to maintain their clinics by raising funds locally after seeing the demonstration.

Public interest in mental illness was stimulated by the publication of Clifford Beers's book, *A Mind That Found Itself* (1908), which was as important in the development of the mental hygiene movement and community psychiatric services as the memorials of Dorothea Dix at an earlier period had been in humanizing the care of the mentally ill. The mental hygiene movement made a plea for the training of medical specialists to treat emotionally disturbed persons *before* their illness demanded hospitalization. As a result, ambulatory care "stimulated by new concepts of the nature of mental illness and the discovery of new therapeutic procedures, became as characteristic of the twentieth century as the insane hospital was of the nineteenth" (Hollingshead and Redlich, 1958, p. 144).

World War II dealt a severe blow to mental hygiene clinics in general and to the traveling clinics in particular because of shortages in personnel. However, the end of hostilities brought a renewed community concern about psychiatric problems, stimulated by the work of the Veterans Administration Clinics with discharged veterans and by that of the National Institute of Mental Health (NIMH), created in 1947 under the National Mental

Health Act of 1946. Indeed, the increase in psychiatric clinics since World War II has been impressive. Of the more than 1,200 out-patient clinics in existence in the United States in 1955, only 8 were in operation before the turn of the century. Sixty were functioning by 1920, 217 by 1930, and 372 by 1940. On the average, 15 clinics were opened each year of the war, that is, between 1940 and 1945. After 1946 the number of new clinics increased to more than 60 per year (Bahn and Norman, 1957, pp. 3–4). Thus, nearly two thirds of all clinics in this country were opened in 1946 or later. Perhaps the greatest stimulus was the federal support made available to states under the terms of the National Mental Health Act. More recently, the availability of NIMH funds for demonstration projects has stimulated experimentation with a variety of community psychiatric services.

In many states, separate bureaus or divisions have been established to foster and coordinate state-wide development of out-patient psychiatric clinics and mental health programs and facilities. State action in this field began in a few states in the 1920s and has greatly been expanded since the National Mental Health Act was passed in 1946. Each state now has a designated mental health authority responsible for the use of federal funds earmarked for community mental health program development.

PRIVATE PRACTICE

A detailed and authoritative history of the private practice of psychiatry remains to be written. In the 1800s most psychiatrists were superintendents or assistants on the staff of private and public mental hospitals. A few physicians, usually associated with medical schools and called "alienists," became especially interested in mental illness and served as expert witnesses and examiners in courts. In the late nineteenth century, with the development of pathology, more physicians began to specialize in disorders of the nervous system: neurologists began to treat patients with emotional disorders by talking to them, prescribing sedatives and tonics, rest and exercise, electrical stimulation, and massage. The term neuropsychiatrist came into use to designate the medical specialist dealing with nervous and mental disease. Many of the

great teachers and pioneers of modern psychiatry began their careers in neurology and/or neuropathology. Two were particularly
important, as their teachings laid the foundation for modern psychiatric practice outside the large and isolated mental hospitals:
Adolf Meyer, who held that the mental patient should be studied
and managed in his own community; and Sigmund Freud, who
laid the groundwork for dynamic psychiatry and many of our
present-day psychotherapies.

As the work of Freud and Meyer began to spread, more psychiatrists went into private practice, oriented to the community and
the medical schools rather than to public and private mental hospitals. However, information concerning the private practice of
psychiatry is extremely limited, and we make no attempt to collate this information.[4]

In this chapter we indicated some characteristics of the out-patient system of care in order to provide a background for the chapters that follow. There we shall discuss new developments in the
field of out-patient care. These developments represent current
attempts to deal with the shortcomings and are mainly concerned
with altering the conception of help and restructuring the nature
of out-patient care.

Chapter 4

Providing Immediate Help

Since the inception of out-patient psychiatric services, clinically trained professionals have been concerned with early diagnosis and treatment of mental disorder. Recently, they have been urging *immediate* help to individuals seeking or thought to require assistance for emotional disturbance.[1]

The current interest in immediate help has grown in part out of observation of the deleterious effects of present practices. Many persons who eventually require hospitalization were not given help at an early stage in their difficulties. Others, because of lack of early help, repeatedly resolve life crises in mentally unwholesome ways and chronically inadequate modes of functioning become stabilized.

Moreover, practitioners have begun to see the effects of this state of affairs on help facilities. For instance, they note the drain on social agencies when their services are depleted by a small number of families with multiple problems of a chronic nature (Buell, 1952). And some hospital psychiatrists believe that mental hospitals are overcrowded because many patients were not helped in the community before they actually needed hospitalization.

These observations point to the need for a community service freely available at the time of crisis or early manifestations of disturbance. Such a service would provide the help the emotionally disturbed person needs or would guide him to an appropriate facility.

The trend in the United States of providing immediate help for psychological disturbances is very new. As recently as 1956 a conference on community mental health programs reported that while "emergency treatment service on the spot is available in some European communities . . . firsthand experience with this kind of service in the United States is not yet available" (Milbank Memorial Fund, 1956, p. 154). American practitioners who have visited the Amsterdam emergency psychiatric service (Querido, 1955, 1956; Millar and Henderson, 1956) have been impressed with the value of the program and have been eager to develop a similar service in this country. Some English programs that combine early treatment and home visiting, such as those at Nottingham (MacMillan, 1958) and Worthing (Carse, et al., 1958; "The Worthing Version," 1959), also have stimulated the American practitioner to think of more immediate help. There still, however, are very few such programs in the United States. Nonetheless, some of the practitioners we interviewed maintained that adequate out-patient treatment requires such a service and that the introduction of immediate treatment may result in far-reaching changes in current practices.

The assumption has been that the sooner medical care is given, the better the prognosis, the more effective the treatment, the quicker the recovery, and the more economical the service. The hospital emergency room, battalion aid station, ambulance service, and first-aid training of Boy Scouts and Red Cross workers are concrete expressions of society's concern with sudden illness or injury. But in the case of emotional disturbance, the public sees the need for immediate intervention only when the person is a threat to himself or to those around him: it is the danger to the community that defines the situation as an emergency rather than the person's need. In a parallel way, the psychiatric system of care customarily mobilizes for immediate action only when such danger exists.

This situation appears to be changing. Programs of immediate help are now being planned; a few have begun operation in the past several years. Certain conditions in out-patient psychiatry aid this development.

First, practitioners are willing to experiment with different ways of giving treatment. For one thing, treatment in the community at the time of the crisis is now being tried. Many practitioners are coming to believe that immediate help in the individual's home can accomplish a great deal. Querido (1956, p. 162) has even said that "any removal of a mentally disturbed patient from his social background implies the side-stepping of the nucleus of the problem." At the very least, many practitioners find it valuable to investigate whether the patient can be treated immediately in his own surroundings before they take other action. Second, the relative flexibility of clinic and office practice, compared with in-patient treatment, encourages experimentation.

The newness of the few emergency services in this country makes it difficult to assess what facilitates as well as what hinders their development. There appear to be at least two major sets of obstacles: one is connected with present practices in the care of out-patients; the other with the individual involved. To the outside observer, the more obvious barriers are those inherent in the structure of out-patient care, especially the shortage of psychiatric personnel. Practitioners inundated with patients who present themselves for treatment have little time to seek out persons who are showing signs of disturbance.

Various organizational rules and administrative procedures in out-patient care delay treatment. For example, most clinics operate only during the day when it is difficult for a working man to attend, and rules of eligibility, processing procedures, and long waiting lists are also discouraging. In addition, the chaotic state of the referral system in most community agencies means that emotionally disturbed persons may be shunted from one agency to another before or without obtaining help.

In private practice, the psychiatrist's conception of his role serves as an obstacle to immediate help. For example, Henry A. Davidson (1956, p. 43), who conducted a survey of psychiatrists, reports that "willingness to make calls . . . correlates with low frequency psychotherapy" and that "one-fourth of the respondents said they would not make a house call no matter what the psychiatric emergency."

Occasionally, immediate psychiatric help is available on a private basis. But even for those who can afford it, the fee of the private practitioner may make many reluctant to seek help unless the problem appears very serious. Private practitioners carry few patients with low incomes, and many with middle incomes who could afford a specialist cannot pay for the services of a private psychiatrist even for short-term help.

Moreover, certain psychiatrists think only of long-term, insight-producing psychotherapy; most therapists give treatment only on a one-to-one basis and believe that dealing with the patient's family is an interference with therapy or, at best, a time-consuming "extra" service. These beliefs are not conducive to giving emergency or on-the-spot help.

The other set of obstacles to early psychiatric help—those related to the characteristics of persons needing help—may appear to the psychiatric professional to be the greater hindrance. It is now widely accepted that the value placed on help for emotional disturbance varies in different cultural and class groups and may determine the time it takes to get treatment.

Among some people the idea of psychiatric help is altogether disapproved of; others are barely aware of what psychiatric help is or what it might accomplish; and still others fear the stigma attached to psychiatric treatment. As a result, individuals or families often delay until the difficulty becomes a major personal or community problem (Myers and Roberts, 1959; Whitmer and Conover, 1959). Furthermore, there is evidence that most persons go through several redefinitions of their problem before they arrive at a definition of serious psychological difficulty (Yarrow, et al., 1955a). Often they completely fail to recognize that the trouble is "psychological" even after the patient has been hospitalized (C. G. Schwartz, 1957).

For the most part, immediate help programs are being developed by the social psychiatrist, the community-oriented social worker, and the psychiatrically oriented public health officer. In the sections that follow, we shall discuss the forms of their programs of immediate help and their implications for patient, community, and psychiatric practice.

Forms of Immediate Help

Current programs provide four modes of immediate help for emotional disturbance: new emergency services at conventional treatment facilities; on-the-spot treatment offered in the community; psychiatric "on call" information services; the development in various community caretakers of an emergency orientation toward emotional disturbance. In different ways each form attempts to eliminate or to reduce the various obstacles to early treatment previously discussed.

EMERGENCY PSYCHIATRIC SERVICE AT THE CLINIC

Some practitioners are now clearly aware of the obstacles to immediate treatment inherent in conventional out-patient facilities. But changes in practice rarely come about through the complete reorganization of existing institutions; rather, a new practice is introduced to fit in with the older, so that no one is aware that anything radical has occurred. This "evolutionary planning," as it is called by Lemkau (1957), seems to be the way in which emergency services at clinical facilities have developed.

Practitioners find good reason for not entirely revamping older practices. What may be an obstacle to one objective may be advantageous to another, equally important objective. Thus, even though a waiting list may impede giving immediately needed help, the fact that he waited may be of benefit to the patient. Some clinicians believe that patients who enter treatment after a waiting period value it more and therefore work harder at therapy than they would if offered it immediately. In any case, practitioners are reluctant to reorganize present clinical facilities until more is known about the most effective ways of running them, and in the end they have contented themselves with adding special features to existing operations to make help more quickly available.

One way of doing this is to add a special emergency service to a regular out-patient psychiatric clinic. In most clinics, appointments for initial visits are usually arranged by telephone, frequently as long as three to four weeks after the first contact. At that time, the patient is generally seen by a social worker who talks with him to get some idea of his problem, background, social history, and so on. He then may be interviewed by a psychiatric resident, fellow, medical student, or interne, tested by a psychologist, and in some instances, examined by a staff psychiatrist. After the information about him is processed, the psychiatrist determines the diagnosis and the disposition. If he is accepted for treatment—especially if recommended for individual psychotherapy, that being the most usual form of treatment in mental hygiene clinics—his name is placed on a waiting list. Then he may wait six months or a year or more before entering treatment; in all cases there will be appreciable delay.

A consequence may be a systematic selection of certain kinds of persons for treatment. Furthermore, those who drop from the waiting list may still be greatly in need of help (Morris and Soroker, 1953). Many may be hospitalized at some later point. But perhaps more important is the fact that what was initially a problem confined to an individual or family may develop into a disturbance affecting many persons. It is to reach the troubled person ordinarily by-passed by more conventional practices and to prevent his difficulty from becoming more extensive that clinics have initiated emergency psychiatric services.

Sometimes an emergency service is found operating in connection with the out-patient psychiatric clinic of a large medical center (Zwerling, 1958; M. D. Coleman, 1958; M. D. Coleman and Zwerling, 1959). In one such service members of the clinic staff (third-year residents and fourth-year fellows) devote one day a week to emergency duty, seeing without delay anyone who presents himself. Interviews vary from a few minutes to an hour. After the initial interview, the patient may be able to handle his difficulty without further assistance, but he is assured that he may return for help if needed. More often, four or five emergency interviews are scheduled with him and his family to advise on the immediate problem, to give tests, and so on. If longer therapy is indicated, the patient is referred to the regular clinic for intensive treatment. The Emergency Clinic operates daily from nine to five, on Saturday mornings, and on some evenings. Patients who request help at other hours are directed to the Emergency Ward, which is staffed around the clock by residents, one of whom may handle the situation in a single interview or by referral to the Emergency Clinic for an interview as soon as possible. Where necessary, he can hospitalize the patient on the ward or refer him to the out-patient clinic for tests. The same choices are open to the psychi-atrists in the Emergency Clinic during the daytime.

Although a detailed and long-term evaluation of the service is yet to be made, the clinic staff believes that five types of cases receive striking benefits from it: the anxiety-ridden or hysterical given an authoritative explanation of anxiety symptoms as fear equivalents; the guilt-ridden given an opportunity for catharsis and forgiveness; the angry individual whose feelings are permitted expression; the dependent one who derives support from quasi-magical authority figures; and the obsessive-compulsive given help in bolstering crumbling defenses.

Flexibility of operating procedure is perhaps the most impor-tant asset of emergency psychiatric clinics. In a sense, they serve as a general psychiatrist, seeing all kinds of persons with all sorts of difficulties, providing immediate help during crises, continuing emotional support following the crisis, determining the most ap-propriate long-range treatment or help and obtaining it for the patient, and standing by in case of further need. A variety of alternatives are available to the attending psychiatrist: he can have the patient admitted to either a closed or open ward in the hos-pital, to a day-care or night-care program, referred for long-term psychotherapy at the clinic or for service at a number of commu-nity health and social agencies, scheduled for a number of visits at the Emergency Clinic, or discharged.

Special procedures of admission that eliminate the long wait for therapy are a second provision in the Emergency Clinic for giving immediate help. For years practitioners have insisted that the patient should receive help the moment he contacts the clinic or hospital and that the very first interview should be therapeutic, then and there. But, particularly in clinics, no matter how well managed, this always seems to call for more help than is at hand.

A solution found by some clinics is to assign individuals await-ing individual therapy to psychotherapeutic groups. Those in need of help thus receive it immediately with little formality. These treatment groups have other advantages. For one thing, they can help determine who is a suitable candidate for individual treatment. The patient joins a group where continuity of therapeutic culture is possible, as members enter and leave at different times. Sometimes he may be one who feels more at ease with group than individual therapy because of the support derived from peers (Peck, 1953). Many patients elect to remain in the group even when individual therapy has become available, and some receive group and individual treatment simultaneously.

Group treatment is used, too, as a device for giving immediate help to parents of children waiting for treatment (Ginott, 1956). In one clinic (Hallowitz and Cutter, 1954), during the intake phase, parents are helped, individually or in joint sessions, to work on their problems with their child. As a result, only about one half of the cases in which full treatment was anticipated turn out to need more help. The waiting period was thus reduced from six to four months, and all the parents received some immediate assistance.

Moore and Albert (1959) describe the attempts of a small mental hospital to solve the problem of the waiting list. It aims at circumventing hospitalization by providing immediate care, either in the patient's home or at the hospital. This service, however, resembles an out-patient clinic rather than a program of emergency care. The authors report that they have been able to see only about half the patients on the hospital waiting list and of these, about one third can be saved hospitalization by being given immediate attention. Another one third is found to require inpatient care, while the final third needs only out-patient care—presumably that given in conventional treatment facilities—or referral to some agency other than a mental hospital.

There is a third way in which an emergency service has been added to a treatment institution. Some general hospitals offer psychiatric emergency help as part of their emergency services. Ordinarily, psychiatric units of general hospitals handle some psychiatric emergencies, but few encourage the community to use the hospital in this way. At present, a small number of hospitals are experimentally reversing the policy.

At one general hospital we visited, a psychiatrist—usually the resident on the psychiatric ward—sees an emotionally disturbed person who comes to the emergency room and if necessary, admits him to the psychiatric section of the hospital. Otherwise he is given whatever immediate help is appropriate, including suggestions as to the course he might pursue in getting help.

PSYCHIATRIC HELP ON THE SPOT

On-the-spot help for psychological disturbance is not, in itself, a new idea even in the United States. Alcoholics Anonymous has given this kind of help for many years, as did Recovery, Inc., a self-help organization, when it was started by a psychiatrist in the late 1930s (Low, 1949).[2] These two are privately sponsored, cover only a small and limited proportion of the emotionally disturbed in the community, and, though in its early days Recovery, Inc., was directed by a psychiatrist, neither it nor Alcoholics Anonymous has developed within the mainstream of psychiatry. The programs we shall discuss below differ from them in several respects. They represent a development in the field of social psychiatry. They are directed by psychiatrists and firmly anchored in medical practice. They deal with various types of emotional disorder and give full coverage of a community, whether of a small section of a city or of an entire municipality. Finally, they utilize the range of alternative treatment and social services considered necessary for adequate therapy in the community.

The best developed example of the municipal emergency psychiatric service is that of Amsterdam (Querido, 1955, 1956). Like other on-the-spot programs, it offers immediate mobilization of psychiatric help and management of the case outside a clinical setting. The service gives social rather than medical treatment in the strict sense: neither medicine nor psychotherapy is offered during the emergency call to the home. Rather, the service seeks to diagnose the difficulty, to handle the problem on the spot or to decide what kind of help is needed, and to establish the individual as patient or client in the appropriate facility. Thus, its function is "first aid" rather than definitive treatment. The fact that it originated in a service handling the distribution of beds in a mental hospital gives it an added advantage, for it has at its disposal the central file of all those hospitalized in government mental institutions. If the person calling the service is already known, the problem may be handled by telephone. If he is unknown to the service, the psychiatrist is "bound to go out and investigate."

From one point of view, the extensive scope of the Amsterdam service is its most significant characteristic. It is set up to deal twenty-four hours a day with the psychic emergencies of a city's entire population of 860,000 and to give attention to the emotionally disturbed for whom help is requested without regard to finances, psychological condition, or social class.[3]

In this country a program (to be described in the next chapter) somewhat similar to the one in Amsterdam, the Psychiatric Home Treatment Service of the Boston State Hospital (Perry, 1959; Rolfe, 1959; Friedman, et al., 1959), was established in 1957. It is concerned with the issue: can persons ordinarily hospitalized in a state mental institution be treated in their homes? One aspect of the service is to provide on-the-spot psychiatric attention in an emergency, by dispatching a staff member immediately to the home. In some cases, appointments for home visits are scheduled. At present, this program is confined to one section of Boston, and, unlike the Amsterdam service, it does not operate around the clock. As yet, it has not become an institutionalized part of the hospital; operating as a demonstration project, its continuity beyond the period of its grant is not yet established.

The trend toward providing on-the-spot help is leading to the development of a variety of programs, some only indirectly connected with a psychiatric service. For example, an organization known as Rescue, Inc., is operating from the Boston City Hospital to prevent suicide. In its first five weeks, it was in contact with 356 would-be suicides, all of whom were dissuaded (Boston Daily Globe, April 12, 1959). Though psychiatric consultation is available, the mainstay of the program is a priest whose car is equipped to receive telephone calls, and who, when called, talks to the person contemplating suicide or visits him.

On-the-spot psychiatric emergency service and emergency service at the clinical facility have a number of elements in common. Both give help without delay or formality. Both channel persons into the needed facility for treatment. And both serve as case-finding services for the community's institutions offering treatment, bringing in many who would not at that point come to the attention of a helping agent.

But they differ in two important respects. First, help given in the situation in which the emergency has occurred makes it possible to assess how various persons, in addition to the patient, are involved. Perhaps most important, the family may play a role in helping the patient, a role often denied them in more conventional treatment. A second difference is that one type of service requires the helper to go to the patient, whereas in the other the patient seeks the service. In general, it seems that coverage will be reduced if help depends largely on the patient's seeking it. In this respect, treatment in the community may be more of an innovation and reach a different population of disturbed persons than emergency treatment in clinics. When the service goes to the patient, less effort is required of him and his family and more is required of community caretakers.

On the other hand, on-the-spot services may have disadvantages. If such a service aims at assessing the possibility of keeping that patient at home, it encourages the tendency to believe that the patient is always better off with his family than in the hospital. As Perry (1959) indicated, "hospitalization as a therapeutic maneuver is much less of a problem if one does not have the mandate to prove or disprove the feasibility of home care for patients who would otherwise conventionally be hospitalized."

While there are differences between on-the-spot services and those given at treatment institutions, one must not assume that they necessarily will differ markedly from each other. To the extent that a community service carries on the methods of the consulting room in which one person is the patient, it will be similar to the more conventional modes of therapy and to that extent will be unable to utilize the strategic advantage of its special situation.

"ON CALL" INFORMATION SERVICES

Ignorance of where to turn for help is one of the major impediments to immediate help. Not only do the disturbed person and his family lack information about where to turn, but very often the family doctor treating the patient does not know himself where immediate psychiatric help can be obtained. Of course, failure to recognize that the patient is emotionally disturbed or mentally ill on the part of the family or general practitioner is equally accountable for delay in securing treatment. Hollingshead and Redlich (1958) point out that "perceptions of the psychological nature of personal problems is a rare trait in any person and in any class" (p. 172), though "persons in the higher classes are more perceptive of disturbed behavior and of the potential help psychiatry offers than persons in the lower classes" (p. 188).

It seems likely, however, that as psychiatric services become more widely accessible and accepted, physicians, other community caretakers, and families will be more likely to adopt the psychiatric view of emotional disturbance. Prompt information on how to secure help may increase the likelihood of early treatment. Many professionals feel the need for a central information service that could be called upon at any time by those in trouble. The problem of locating the appropriate agency is particularly acute in large cities where the multiplicity of institutions often leads one on a confusing and disappointing search.

The demand for better channels of information has prompted efforts to establish "on call" information services. Some practitioners think that the telephone number of a psychiatric information service should be prominently listed in the telephone directory along with fire and police departments and other emergency services, and some believe the service should be available twenty-four hours a day. Such conveniences do exist in some American cities, though they are not well known. In Philadelphia the Mayor's office has an information center to which anyone in the city may bring his problem; many inquiries are referred from there to the city's Division of Mental Hygiene for appropriate help. The Mental Health Association of Delaware distributed pamphlets inviting the reader to use its free information service, giving a telephone number to call "for an early appointment." The Vermont Alcoholic Rehabilitation Commission inaugurated a telephone recording service to spread information about alcoholism to people in the Burlington area and make known the facilities available in Vermont for helping alcoholics, and to bring hitherto unknown problem drinkers into the Commission's office for consultation and treatment. In New York City the Manhattan Society for Mental Health maintains an information service and directs callers to various resources, including more than one hundred private psychiatrists available for immediate consultation. Their names are on file with the Society, and the caller is given three names.

Most of these information services, however, operate only during certain hours. What is more important, they do not and cannot provide emergency psychiatric services, as such. They merely tell what is locally available. The basic problem of getting individuals into treatment or other kinds of help very early in the course of their difficulties cannot be solved merely by providing information about resources. Many will not call the service at all, or, if they do, they will not go on to get in touch with the recommended agency. And, even when they do so, the agencies are not geared to giving immediate help. Information services of the kind described above will lead to immediate treatment only if the agencies of treatment themselves are able to provide it when requested.

EMERGENCY ORIENTATION
IN COMMUNITY CARETAKERS

Sometimes an emotionally disturbed person fails to get immediate help because community caretakers do not define his difficulty accurately or do not think he requires the immediate attention of a psychiatrically trained professional. Unless his behavior is grossly deviant, he will be referred by the community caretaker to some psychiatric or social agency to wait his turn. If his behavior is bizarre and the caretaker is the police, he may be arrested and held in jail, particularly if he is of the lower class (Hollingshead and Redlich, 1958, p. 184). Thus, many practitioners feel that, if emotionally disturbed persons are to receive both early and immediate psychiatric care, it is necessary to reorient community caretakers to this objective and to help them provide emergency help in certain situations.

As far as we know, there is no program devoted exclusively to developing in all community caretakers the appropriate orientation to an emergency. Rather, work of this kind becomes one of the functions of the immediate care programs described above. The professionals in them are aware of the importance of educating community caretakers to emergency treatment since their patients are generally secured through referral. The nonpsychiatric community helpers are important referring agents and, therefore, can be a major link between the disturbed person and the treatment facility.

An orientation appropriate to emergency help may be instilled in community caretakers in a number of ways. Querido (1956, p. 168) points out that "every time the [Amsterdam] service comes into action, it teaches by example how to deal with the mental patient." When, for instance, the psychiatrist in a home treatment program demonstrates that tension may be reduced by treating the patient with understanding and honesty, without fear or force, the police, the physician, and others on the scene will be impressed with what such a program can do and will be more interested in making referrals.

In some places consultation is supplied to community caretakers (Milbank Memorial Fund, 1956; Caplan, 1959) either as a routine service or as a special undertaking in an emergency. It involves not only imparting information about local resources and about mental illness itself but also making the caretakers themselves aware of how their own reactions to deviant behavior affect their definition of the situation and partly determine the person's fate.

Consultants also try to increase the caretaker's skill in making referrals selectively (once they have defined the difficulty as psychological disturbance), and they impress upon the caretakers the unwisdom of referring every emotionally disturbed person for psychiatric, or even professional, help. With help from the caretaker, some persons may be able to work out their own problems, and this is more probable, of course, as caretakers become more skilled themselves in handling the emotionally disturbed.

Discussion

As we have noted, programs of immediate help are not well developed in the United States. Probably more important than limitations in clientele, hours of operation, or areas served is that help usually is given only to those who request it. The emotionally disturbed person who does not know where to get help or does not seek it usually fails to get immediate assistance.

Many American practitioners are interested in overcoming these shortcomings. The Amsterdam service has been of interest to them because it does not operate under the limitations of our emergency care programs; it covers an entire community, operates twenty-four hours a day, and offers or channels individuals to treatment and social service. In the thirty or so years of its operation, it has developed considerable breadth of function and offers the following advantages: It sees the disturbed person in the community, when he is not known to the service, and arranges for the needed help immediately. By referring him to clinic or hospital, it establishes him in a regular psychiatric institution in the community. It has a home treatment aspect, functioning where the difficulty has developed, dealing with family as well as patient. Thus it is able to see the various components of the precipitating situation. It overcomes the limitation of conventional arrangements by active case-seeking. Thus it is able to help the seriously emotionally disturbed who do not seek psychiatric help or do not know where to turn for treatment. It is an information service, orienting the disturbed person and his family to facilities available to them and helping them decide on the best way to attack their problem. It performs an educational function, helping people to accept mental illness and to aid the emotionally disturbed person. Community caretakers, as well as families, benefit from the practical, on-the-spot help. By maintaining an index of persons formerly helped and those in mental institutions, the service can give continuity of care. The disturbed person often can avoid the time-consuming and generally unpleasant process of being "admitted" repeatedly.

One of the problems plaguing practitioners who treat emotionally disturbed persons has been that of getting help before the disorder becomes chronic. The Amsterdam service demonstrates that the weak first link in the conventional system of psychiatric out-patient care can be strengthened by adding an emergency service to existing institutions. Querido emphasizes, however, that this service does not replace the community's agencies: it supplements and strengthens them and makes referrals to them more appropriate and admission into them easier, more expeditious, and less painful.

Because the Amsterdam program is so much more comprehensive than similar programs in this country, it can serve as a point of departure for discussing the instituting of services for immediate care on a broader scale in the United States. It might be well for practitioners who are eager to develop such a program to be aware of the inevitable changes in assumptions and values and the problems and consequences that may eventuate.

THE DEFINITION OF A PSYCHIATRIC EMERGENCY

Many, if not most, practitioners currently cling to the conception of a psychiatric emergency as existing when "it is responsibly believed an individual is mentally ill and because of this likely to cause injury to himself and others" (Baltimore Council of Social Agencies, 1957, p. 17). This criteria of a clear and present danger has served conventional psychiatric practice. But is it adequate or appropriate for programs of emergency care? Many who are neither threats to themselves nor to the community may, nevertheless, need emergency help. The number of persons seen as needing emergency help will be large if we accept the idea that psychological suffering is just as serious and in need of immediate alleviation as is physical suffering, and the sooner both are treated the less misery for the afflicted and the greater the possibility of preventing continuing suffering and future deterioration and of producing recovery.

If this rationale for altering the conception of a psychiatric emergency is accepted by practitioners, what criteria for admission to an emergency treatment service may be used?

A number of alternative criteria can be considered. Emergency care may be given on *demand,* that is, to anyone who asks for it. It may be given on the basis of *need,* that is, on a professional's evaluation that the person requires immediate help. It may be given on the basis of possible *benefit,* that is, on a practitioner's judgment that the person would make use of help and show improvement in psychological or social functioning as a result of it. Whatever criteria are used in admissions to emergency care, altering the conception of a psychiatric emergency to include more people inevitably brings with it the problem of providing an adequate supply of professional helpers. Under these new conditions, the imbalance between help-seekers and help-givers will become even more serious than it already is.

Equally serious is the possibility that a widespread acceptance of the idea of seeking immediate assistance for psychological disturbance may lead to an "illness-orientation" on the part of many individuals. As a consequence, ordinary problems in living may be interpreted as psychiatric problems calling for professional help rather than requiring solutions in the ordinary course of living; and a tendency may develop to read sickness into ordinary human suffering. These dangers are especially great when there is no clear-cut definition of mental illness and no sharp dividing line between ordinary everyday emotional disturbance and that which requires or could benefit from professional intervention. Moreover, there is always the danger that both professional and lay persons oriented toward discovering mental disturbance may interpret nonconforming, culturally alien, or socially disapproved behavior as "sick" behavior and see those who exhibit it as candidates for immediate help. For cultural values enter into the definition of mental illness, and it is middle-class practitioners, whose values and orientations in many instances differ radically from those of the persons they are evaluating, who make the diagnosis of mental illness.

These possibilities should not deter the development of services for immediate help for the emotionally and mentally disturbed. However, we do suggest that they be watched for and that one way of guarding against them is to make clear the distinction between the kinds of emotional disturbance and problems of living that are appropriately the province of mental health practitioners and those that should not be regarded as illness nor made the occasion of professional help.

ATTITUDES TOWARD HELP

Whatever criteria are established for admitting persons to emergency psychiatric care, the service will have the problem of recruiting clientele. Present programs tend to give immediate help only to those who seek it, leaving the initiative to the person needing help.

There are several rationales for waiting till the individual makes the approach himself. First, it is assumed that a willingness to seek help means he will probably benefit more from it. Second, some argue that even if he continues to suffer, he has the right to go without help if he wishes. Finally, with the pressure of demand on treatment facilities and the chronic shortages of personnel, practitioners are not eager to increase their already excessive case-loads. However, waiting for the individual to take the initiative provides emergency help for only the one category— those who want and seek it. The result sometimes is that professionals direct a good part of their skill and time to the chronically dependent. For these persons, the problem of the immediate care service is to discover how to reduce their dependence and encourage self-reliance in the handling of their problems.

Meanwhile, the service leaves untreated other categories of emotionally disturbed persons in need of their help: those who do not seek help though they want it and might accept it if offered; those who do not think they need help but might accept it if persuaded; and those who do not think they need help and would refuse it under any circumstances. It might be that to attract the first two categories of potential patients, greater initiative is called for from professionals.

If emergency care is to develop the greater coverage some professionals feel necessary in view of the extensiveness and degree of disturbance in our society, then aggressive casework is unavoidable. It is then important to make explicit the possible problems and consequences involved.

Many disturbed persons resist treatment because they place value on self-help. They see emotional disturbance, problems in family life and internal psychological difficulties as personal and private, not the affairs of outsiders, whether professional or lay persons. But self-help, while it may generate processes of self-healing for some, is risky for others—those individuals who in time grow worse, with increasing destructive effects upon themselves and others. In many instances, of course, it is difficult to predict into which category a case falls—that is, whether he will rise to meet his problems or sink under them. However, the emergency care service might make its best guess and try to recruit the latter population by aggressive means. In doing this, it will have to handle those who insist on self-help and continue in denial of illness while at the same time it avoids fostering dependence of those who are ever ready for help.

A major problem an aggressive emergency or immediate help service will have to face is how much persuasion or coercion to use in recruiting patients, especially those persons who appear unmistakably in need of their help. At this point, the individual's right to self-determination in regard to his psyche and emotions enters in, that is, his right to refuse the help of an expert if he so desires, and his right to reject the professional's definition of him as one who needs help. The problem is to determine which set of values will prevail, under what circumstances, and in regard to what persons and what kinds of illness or deviant behavior. The problem becomes especially critical when there is a tendency on the part of the professional to interpret class-related behavior, for example, beating one's wife, as psychopathology or to see an individual as sick and in need of immediate psychiatric help because he does not agree with the professional's values, as, for example, the juvenile delinquent.

THE ROLE OF THE HELPER

The development of extensive emergency care services requires a redefinition of the role of helper. Conventionally, he waits for the patient to turn up and specifies the time and place of treatment— all which is unsuited to emergency care. In the latter context, the helper may have to make himself more responsive to the patient's needs and requirements than is generally the case.

For example, the psychiatrist, rather than seeing the patient by office appointment, may have to go to the patient's house or to some other place in the community. Similarly, arrangements might have to be made to see patients whenever they appear at the emergency treatment facility. This kind of care, therefore, requires readiness to cope with the unscheduled, the unexpected, and the unroutinized. This means the practitioner will be inconvenienced; he will have to work at odd hours, handle difficult, sometimes unmanageable, cases outside of the clinical environment, and, in general, orient himself and his activities to a different mode and round of professional life than he customarily enjoys.

The role of psychiatrist might have to become more generalized, in comparison with its present high degree of specialization. He may have to deal with a variety of disturbances, utilizing a number of treatment modalities. He may even have to become something of a sociologist in order to understand the strange behavior and values of various subcultural groups. Understanding it, he may then be able to fit his therapy to the patient's social background and family. Instead of treating individuals he may have to manage a group, say, the family. These new conditions may lead to conceptions of treatment and intervention hitherto not considered appropriate to the psychiatrist.

In the same way the psychiatrist's relations with other professionals may have to change. He may have to spend a larger portion of his time as a consultant to community caretakers and others and less in direct relationships with patients. As a result, the sharp distinction between the psychiatrist, nurse, social worker, and psychologist may be blurred as they may perform many of the same functions. Thus, it may be necessary to redefine what functions are distinctive to each and what are common to all.

Any alteration in the role of one helper will inevitably affect the complementary roles in the emergency care service. And changes in roles also will inevitably effect the total system of emergency care. Attempts to anticipate and develop awareness of the potential changes might lead to preparations for meeting problems that can be expected to arise.

MODALITIES OF HELP

If emergency care services are to attempt widespread coverage, some current conceptions of therapy may have to be modified. In view of existing and anticipated shortages in personnel, depth and long-term therapy may have to be secondary to rapid help. One is then committed to the belief that it is just as important to change disturbed social behavior (sometimes called symptoms) as it is to change underlying personality dynamics. By the very nature of its operation, the service of immediate care will have to rely most heavily on brief, quick-acting procedures and management of the patient's social situation instead of on intensive psychotherapies.

Psychiatrists have struggled for a long time to develop therapies that are both brief and effective. The complaint against brief therapies has been that they sometimes bring no benefit at all and, even when successful, they only alleviate symptoms, leaving the strong probability that illness will recur. Some professionals hope that in programs offering immediate care brief therapies will be employed at more auspicious times than is usual—either early in the course of the disturbance or at a critical point when the patient is more amenable to help. With this appropriate timing a small amount of professional help then might bring about a significant and lasting improvement.

The same arguments are advanced for the use of such quick-acting treatments as hypnoanalysis, drugs, and other physiochemical agents. In addition to bringing relief of symptoms and changes in behavior some practitioners believe that "quick-acting methods can prevent a deeper neurotic or psychotic fixation" (Meerloo, 1956, p. 118) and that reversals can be made in the course of the disturbance through such dramatic intervention.

The Amsterdam Service is primarily concerned with "adjusting the social pressures to the needs of the patient" rather than with medical treatment (Querido, 1956, p. 173). This may mean referring the person to a treatment center, a mental hospital, or a social agency or undertaking to re-establish him at some minimal level of social functioning. Or it may involve an attempt to bring about some equilibrium in a disturbed family situation as a precondition or a form of helping the member who is identified as the patient. Such efforts at social management rest on the idea that creating favorable social conditions for the patient may be the most effective treatment or, at any rate, the *sina qua non* of effective subsequent treatment. However, if the manipulation of the social as well as the psychological becomes the province of the emergency care service, the modes, limits, and responsibilities involved will have to be clearly defined in order, among other things, to safeguard the patient's and the family's rights.

FUNCTION AND STRUCTURE OF THE FACILITY

The type of help required in immediate care, the possible changes in the roles of helper, and the innovations in recruiting clientele all point to the probability that the organization of the facility for immediate treatment will differ from that of the conventional out-patient clinic. This will be reflected in its internal organization, its place in the larger system of help for the emotionally disturbed, and its relationship to other community agencies.

If an immediate care service is to maximize the help it offers to the emotionally disturbed, it must be known to potential clients and community agencies, its services must be accepted, it must be accessible, and it must be ready to give care as soon as possible. In practice, this means it must be more mobile and more flexible than the out-patient clinics, more experimental, and more ready to accept and exploit unorthodox procedures. In addition, it will have to deal with questions such as: How much and what kinds of responsibility will it accept for the patient and his family? In what ways will it share this responsibility with other practitioners and agencies?

The place of the immediate care service in the total system of help for emotional disturbance and its relation to other community agencies cannot be determined a priori. For example, whether an emergency service should be independent, attached to in-patient or out-patient facility, or a mental health center can only be decided when experience has accumulated with various organizational patterns. It may be that no one form of organization is suited to all communities. What is more likely is that a variety of organizational forms are required if one is to meet the quite different emergency situations produced by heterogeneous communities.

Chapter 5

Extending Out-patient Services
in the Community

Recently some professionals have become aware of the necessity
for supplementing conventional out-patient psychiatric services by
broadening the base for helping emotionally disturbed persons
outside of mental hospitals.

Ordinarily, psychiatric out-patient services are given under
what appear to be narrowly defined conditions, well known to
students of the field. Treatment for emotional disturbances is seen
as a medical specialty, to be practiced by qualified physicians and
by other trained professionals under medical supervision in a
clinical setting, either a private office or an out-patient clinic. The
roles of therapist and patient are regulated by certain assumptions
and rules: for example, therapy is to be initiated by the person
seeking help from the practitioner. If the practitioner accepts him
as his patient, he treats him at a clinical facility in the hours set
aside for treatment, the treatment being the transactions that take
place between therapist and patient in face-to-face relationship.

Most practitioners feel that under these conditions they are able
to deal with a range of emotional problems and with a variety of
treatment modalities. And they would say that the major limitations lie outside the out-patient system—in the patient's resistance
to therapy, in economic considerations, and the like. However, an
increasing number are coming to believe that important limitations reside *within* the out-patient system itself. They contend
that present conditions of treatment are overly restrictive, limiting both the nature of the treatment process and the number and
kind of emotionally disturbed persons treated. The organization
and the orientation of out-patient care give rise to differential

opportunity to receive help for various segments of the population, differential acceptance of help by those who get as far as the treatment facility, a significant rate of drop-outs among those who begin treatment, and a rate of improvement that leaves much to be desired. These are seen as basic defects by some practitioners.

Dissatisfied practitioners maintain that differential accessibility to psychiatric out-patient treatment is partly a result of the manner of patient recruitment, and they point to recent research documenting the ways in which the better-educated and those with higher incomes are favored and those with less education and low incomes are disadvantaged in being offered help.[1] They also note how differential admission to treatment follows the same direction. Thus, of those who manage to reach a treatment facility and make contact with one of its staff, there are many who do not receive treatment: they are either excluded by the agency or drop out on their own initiative. Although criteria of eligibility, policies, and goals vary somewhat among out-patient clinics, many in the end exclude from psychotherapy psychotics and those with poor motivation or little capacity for verbalization—characteristics that correlate highly with low income and little education. Observers do not so much deplore the fact that exclusion is built into the system, recognizing that there must be some degree of exclusion in view of the unfavorable ratio of therapists to potential patients and the limitations of current methods, but that exclusion operates along class and ethnic lines. These critics also raise questions about the benefit patients receive from contact with existing facilities. Why do many drop out of treatment prematurely? What interferes with helping those who continue in treatment? They seek answers to these questions in the assumptions, expectations, and rules and regulations of the out-patient system. This is not to say that they are unaware of the contribution of the disturbed person himself to this state of affairs— his unwillingness to seek help, his lack of motivation to continue treatment, or his inability to verbalize his difficulties. But they regard the fact that a major form of out-patient treatment—psychotherapy—is offered primarily to the better-educated in the middle and upper classes as a commentary on both the inability of the lower class to use what is available and the failure of the system to develop treatment suitable to the lower class. But they differ from conventional practitioners in their strategy of trying to introduce changes in the system as well as in the patient.

The extensions of out-patient services described below are based on certain broadened conceptions of help for emotional disturbance to be discussed at length in Chapter 6. The increasingly accepted view that a greater number of human needs ought to be provided for by industry, labor unions, and local agencies is resulting in their developing a variety of social, educational, and health services as well as in the increase in the government's responsibility for health and welfare. Granger (1954, p. 71) points out that the "enlarged role of government in welfare may be regarded as the most dramatic social development of this century," and the trend may be expected to continue. Although provision for the treatment of emotional disturbance has not kept pace with developments in public assistance, social security, unemployment compensation, aid to the handicapped, maternal and child health, and other public health services, it is following close on the heels of these expansions in government responsibility.

The heightened concern with mental health problems and the attempts to develop facilities to deal with them seem, moreover, to be related to a broadening conception of how help for emotional disturbance can be given. Hollister (1959), for example, points out that much of what has been done in the past has been based mainly on the premise that help could best take place in individual psychotherapy, an assumption which, in turn, rests on the more basic assumption that the forces causing illness are primarily endogenous to the individual. But recently more weight is being given to the view that the ability to deal with stress does not depend only on the psychic strength of an isolated individual but also on his interaction with others. Thus, there is greater interest in discovering ways of using interaction in group settings, of managing social settings, and of training community helpers to bring about therapeutic effects.

In this connection, the idea of the life crisis as a strategic time for intervention in emotional disturbance has opened the way for a number of new practices. The helper tries to reach the emotionally disturbed person during the crisis, when it is assumed that help will be most effective. Thus, the requirement that the helper be more available to the emotionally disturbed person led practitioners to offer help under a wider range of conditions than is usual in out-patient psychiatric treatment and to make use of a wider variety of helpers.

As interest in new ways of helping emotionally disturbed persons developed, psychiatrists began to broaden their substantive concerns. The recent interest in the relation of psychological functioning to social structure has stimulated them to consider how they might contribute to more effective handling of delinquency, crime, alcoholism, and other social problems that appear to rest in some part on psychological disturbances. Clinicians have come to view "treating the environment" as a serious and legitimate concern. They are interested in identifying the elements in a given setting that are nontherapeutic or dysfunctional, the junctures of the social structure that permit effective intervention, and the concrete ways that social contexts can be managed for therapeutic purposes.

Forms of Extending Out-patient Services

The programs devised by the practitioners' attempts to break down the limitations of the conventional psychiatric out-patient system take three forms: making treatment units mobile; expanding the functions of community caretakers; and building help for the emotionally disturbed into the institutions of everyday life. Underlying all three is the notion that help for emotional difficulty can not only be made more available but also that it can be given while the person pursues his normal life in his community. But each form concentrates on a different type of extension. Making treatment units mobile focuses on extending the clinical facility in space, that is, enlarging the geographic area covered. Expanding the functions of community caretakers is the extension of helpers' roles, either by broadening the conventional role of the clinician or by adding to the roles of nonpsychiatrically trained practitioners. Building help for emotional disturbances into the institutions of everyday life means extending the setting of treatment or giving help in community settings and places where it is not usually found.

However, not all these extensions are dramatic alterations in the way help for emotional problems is given. Some merely are continuations and enlargements of programs that have been operating for some time. Others are marked innovations. In our discussion, the forms of extending out-patient services in the community are ordered in terms of the degree of innovation involved.

MAKING TREATMENT UNITS MOBILE

The practitioner concerned with helping emotionally disturbed persons in sparsely populated areas of the country must perforce overcome the inaccessibility of treatment facilities. Regardless of the troubled person's motivation or the seriousness of his disturbance, help for psychological problems on an out-patient basis may be unavailable in his community or in any community within commuting distance.

The solution to his problem was first conceived of in terms of traveling treatment and consultation services for communities that were without adequate psychiatric resources. The result was the traveling mental health clinic (Hopple and Huessy, 1954; Hubbard, 1956), several of which were in operation in the United States in the 1920s though they did not develop extensively until after 1940.

At present, traveling out-patient clinics emphasize different functions, depending upon the sponsoring agencies and the interests of the members of the team. Whereas most traveling clinics offer a range of services, some emphasize clinical functions (treatment and testing) while others emphasize what has been called "psychosocial treatment" (J. V. Coleman and Switzer, 1951), affording consultation to community caretakers, in-service training, and so forth. These psychosocial services may be undertaken because the team is unable to offer direct treatment (W. H. Brown, et al., 1957), although some students of the field maintain that psychosocial help and not therapy is the proper function of the traveling team.

A number of practitioners take issue with the view that the traveling team is an effective way to deal with the psychological disturbances of rural populations.[2] They maintain that the basic problem is not inadequate psychiatric service but a lack of health and welfare services of all kinds. They argue that if these services were available, problems (including emotional disturbance) could be handled before they become chronic. This means that many disturbances might be dealt with before they require psychiatric attention, thus reducing the need for psychiatric services. Establishing more rural clinics will not solve this problem. What is needed is the improvement of family casework, welfare, and public health services, the development of health centers, and the training of community workers to deal with emotional problems.

The practitioners espousing this view believe that traveling mental hygiene clinics may make a beginning in this endeavor by generating community interest in better health and welfare services in general and by demonstrating that community workers can be trained to handle emotional difficulties. But a more adequate approach to the problem of emotional disturbance in rural areas requires the integration of a physical and mental health program.

Hunterdon Medical Center (Trussell, 1956) is an example of a rural health center with such a program. The intention was to develop a hospital that was more than a hospital and a mental health service that was more than a clinic. Thus, in addition to its traveling clinic, the Center has a number of unusual organizational features (affiliation with an urban medical school, opportunity for all local medical practitioners to affiliate with the hospital, provision for a variety of preventive medical services) as well as a mental health service that is integrated into the medical program. The premises of the mental health program reflect the orientation to preventive medicine: prevention and treatment are to be integral parts of the project; the duties of the mental health team are to be blended with the medical services; and a major function of the team is to assist community workers confronted with emotional disturbances to do a better job, providing direct treatment only in those situations that cannot be handled by less skilled workers. Thus, the Center's mental health team is involved in a range of activities, including classes for parents aimed at fostering better family relations; assistance to pediatric staff members in improving their management of their cases; evaluation of patients referred from the in-patient and diagnostic center; training and consultation for teachers, physicians, clergymen, public health nurses, and other community workers, and workshops to bring concepts of mental health before the public.

Thus, starting from the need to make psychiatric treatment more accessible to those in rural areas, practitioners have been led to extend their concept of treatment to include community programs emphasizing prevention.

Mobile treatment units are used in rural areas because treatment is geographically inaccessible; in urban areas they are used because treatment is psychologically inaccessible, for many persons do not seek help even though there are mental hygiene clinics, psychiatrists in private practice, casework agencies, and so on, at hand. Therefore some practitioners ask: If the emotionally disturbed person does not come to the clinical facility, why not bring the clinic to him?

They see three advantages in bringing helpers into an ordinary life setting. To some extent it eliminates much of the delay customary in conventional admission procedures. Moreover, the patient may be more willing to accept help that is brought to him than that given at a clinical facility. He may derive a greater sense of support and security by remaining in his own surroundings and may stay in treatment until its termination and participate more actively in it because the conditions under which it is given are more congruent with his life. Treatment in his ordinary life setting may often also be an alternative to hospitalization.

At present, the disturbed person's home is an important non-clinical setting to which treatment might be brought. Dealing with emotional disturbance in the home is not new, but, until recently, there was little attempt to do so on a regular basis. The public health nurse, who traditionally gives service in the home does not practice psychotherapy, though she may often refer patients for such treatment and support them in their attempts to get it. Occasionally, psychiatrists and psychologists do visit patients' homes, but, for the most part, they give treatment in a clinical setting.

As we noted in Chapter 4, home treatment services are not common in this country. However, the Home Treatment Service of Boston State Hospital (Friedman, *et al.*, 1960) can serve to illustrate their orientation, procedure and problems. Supported by NIMH as a demonstration project, its spirit is experimental, its staff small, and its activity restricted to a section of a large city. Although it is located on the grounds of a state mental hospital, it is a relatively autonomous unit.

Part of the clinical program is oriented toward emergency service for acutely disturbed persons, particularly in instances in which hospitalization might be avoided by immediate help. Another goal is to give temporary relief to ex-patients encountering stressful situations and to give continuing support to those who require irregular contacts with a helper. The Service also offers help to those who do not require hospitalization but are considered too sick to benefit from clinic treatment or will not seek or go on with it.

Patients are selected from the hospital's waiting list, others are referred by community caretakers, and some are self-referred or referred by their families. When a referral is made, a member of the Home Treatment Service may make an appointment with the family or he may appear at the patient's home unannounced. On the initial visit the psychiatrist and social worker (sometimes aided by a psychiatric nurse and a social scientist) determine the nature and extent of the disturbance and whether home treatment is needed or promising. If the patient is accepted for home treatment, the staff attempts to enlist the members of the family in the therapeutic endeavor. The staff deals with resistance to treatment or reluctance to continue with the Service as part of the problem of giving help, returning to the home even when services have been refused, reaching the family by telephone, or perhaps working through an amenable member.

The length of treatment varies with the case and with the staff time available. In many instances, short-term help (three to seven visits) is given to provide emotional support and to help patient and family resolve an acute situation. In other instances, help may be more extensive, the staff seeing the family weekly for a year or more. Here the goal is to reorganize family patterns of interaction to minimize or eliminate destructive relationships.

Home treatment sometimes involves several staff members who see the patient at the same time. Sometimes one helper sees him while another sees his spouse or parents. Occasionally, staff members hold meetings with the whole family. Here the concern is with opening channels of communication between them and developing understanding about the nature of their expectations of each other. This endeavor aims at altering family relationships in a direction that will not only alleviate the immediate emotional disturbance but bring about an enduring change in the emotional climate of the home and of the family's sense of relatedness. In some situations, family therapy of this type is carried on while the members are treated individually.

Whether an individual member or the whole family is treated, psychiatrist, social worker, nurse, and social scientist try to operate as a team, making joint decisions about the handling of each case. Although there is some role differentiation among them (the role of psychiatrist, especially, differs from that of the others), there is considerable overlap in function. Where it is appropriate, an effort is made to develop a "prescription" and "treatment" for the family as a whole as well as for the particular persons manifesting the most severe pathology—an aim manifestly different from treating only the individual patient.

Offering family treatment in the home provides the therapist with a number of advantages. It offers him the opportunity to observe family interaction and to take account of the various situations in which the family is involved. His presence in the home may mean that a helper is there at the time difficulties are encountered. The home treatment therapist, unlike the conventional practitioner giving out-patient treatment, may be able to work through emotional problems in the contexts in which they arise. In this sense, he shares the orientation of the group worker who approaches problematic situations through the "marginal" interview.[3] This involvement in actual situations means the therapist is both "talking and doing": that is, he demonstrates for the patient and his family ways of dealing with problems through concrete actions, the implications of which sometimes are quite apparent, as well as by "talking" about problems and ways of handling them. Thus, the therapist can become a realistic role model. Many practitioners believe that this may offer greater therapeutic opportunities to persons who do not seem to derive benefit when the therapist plays a more passive role.[4]

Family treatment in the home is enthusiastically endorsed by practitioners who see particular advantages in bringing a larger part of the patient's social field into the focus of treatment. Less attention is paid by them to the possible dangers or disadvantages of moving the clinical operation into life settings. Yet the invasion of privacy and sharing by strangers in personal and family decisions are two obvious characteristics of these programs that may have unfavorable effects.

In any case, the feasibility and practicability of family home treatment is still a major question. It may prove too taxing, complex, or time-consuming to be effective in more than a small number of families. Yet it may be the most effective way of learning about and dealing with the family milieu.

All these considerations concern practitioners who face the day-to-day management of home treatment. They are interested, especially, in learning what kind of family can benefit from this approach, what disadvantages it entails, and how these compare with its advantages.

Home treatment procedures still need to be worked out in greater detail. For example, practitioners need more experience with variations of family treatment before they can determine the extent to which the Service should take initiative in bringing people into treatment, the conditions under which it should accept refusals, and when it should persist in inducing families to enter treatment. More work needs to be done on staff roles, particularly on the relationship between the roles played by various members of the staff and changes in family dynamics. More needs to be known about the kinds of family diagnoses and plans for treatment that might be developed to suit varying cultural, class, and personality constellations and about the circumstances that determine when one should work with a single family member and when one should deal with the family as a unit. Lastly, the question of how to combine help for individual members with help for the family as a whole still presents knotty clinical and theoretical problems that practitioners of family treatment have only begun to study.

EXPANDING THE FUNCTIONS
OF COMMUNITY CARETAKERS

Perhaps the most significant extension of out-patient psychiatric services is the expansion of the roles of community caretakers. The grounds for using them to deal with emotional difficulties are their availability, their strategic relationship with disturbed persons, and the possibility of training them to handle mental health problems effectively.

Community caretakers are available in the sense that they are present, for few communities are without a physician, a public health nurse, a school teacher, and a clergyman, though many have no psychiatrist, clinical psychologist, nor psychiatric social worker. Community caretakers also are available in the sense that they are in the "helping" professions and are interested in doing something about their clients' emotional problems as well as the problems falling in the caretakers' own province. A large number are willing to undertake training and consultation to learn more about emotional disturbances and how they may be helpful.

The caretaker often has continuing contact with his charges and thus is in a strategic position to identify emotional disturbances early in their development. Whether he ignores the emotional upset or tries to do something about it, his association with the disturbed person may directly or indirectly influence the course of the pathology.

Practitioners hoping to train community caretakers stress that they are not attempting to make them "junior psychiatrists." The public health nurse still is expected to function as a nurse; the caseworker as a social worker. But since emotional disturbance may be a concomitant of the problems legitimately in the caretaker's province, it is believed possible for him to deal with both. In this sense, expanding the caretaker's functions means helping him to take account of emotional disturbances encountered in his work with clients and patients. The current conception is that the caretaker should know which difficulties he can handle, what are his limitations, and how to deal with problems within his competence.

The caretaker already has an established contact with his client or patient; thus, if he can deal with the emotional upset while handling the manifest problem, the need for the intervention of psychiatrically trained practitioners may be eliminated. But perhaps the crucial point is that the caretaker often is in contact with persons during various life crises when, as some students of this field now believe, minimal intervention, properly timed and handled, can have beneficial and lasting therapeutic effects. Interventions by the community caretaker may turn out to be so economical of time and energy that he can give help to large numbers of the emotionally upset.

Finally, it is feasible to train caretakers to handle certain emotional disturbances because, for one thing, there are many continuities between what they are being asked to learn and the professional knowledge and skill they already command. This particularly is true of those trained in medical, psychological, or social services. In the second place, this new learning of caretakers can be made part of their daily work. The caretaker is not asked to undertake a long period of training nor to enter a formal program: training occurs through consultation and group discussion and can be developed in the work situation and tailored to suit the needs of the agency and the caretakers involved.

We shall focus here on the effort to use three classes of community caretakers in community mental health work, though with equal justification we could have included others, such as the clergyman and the teacher. However, since they are subjects of Joint Commission monographs (McCann, 1962; Allinsmith and Goethals, 1962), we shall restrict our discussion to the general practitioner, the public health nurse, and the social caseworker.

Many psychiatrists would maintain that of the community care-takers available, the physician is the best qualified to deal with emotional disorders. Physicians are considered so potentially sig-nificant in this regard that the Eighty-fifth Congress of the United States appropriated more than $1 million to give psychiatric train-ing to practicing physicians who wished to use psychiatric knowl-edge and skills in their own field or to become psychiatrists. In 1959, for the first time, funds were available through the National Institute of Mental Health to training institutions giving psychi-atric postgraduate courses to general practitioners and other non-psychiatric physicians. The American Psychiatric Association has investigated ways in which physicians might participate in the treatment of emotionally disturbed persons (Goshen, 1959); and the Division of Industrial Mental Health of the Menninger Foun-dation conducts an annual seminar in psychiatry for industrial physicians.

There are a number of reasons why the nonpsychiatric physi-cian is seen by psychiatrists as particularly equipped, by training and function, to provide help for a person with mental and emo-tional disturbances. The physician, for one thing, is uniquely qualified to use somatic therapy, such as drugs and shock. Many who come to his office suffer from mental disturbances exclusively or from emotional disturbances that accompany their physical ail-ments. Often the physician is the first professional person con-sulted when a person begins to seek help for his disturbance. The physician also has the advantage of knowing his patient well and of having an opportunity to see significant alterations in his emo-tional states. And, of course, the authority and the trust a patient invests in him provides the physician with one of the important conditions for effective intervention. For another thing, when the physician helps the disturbed person, it is not likely to be seen as "psychiatric treatment" and, therefore, may be more acceptable than the services of the psychiatrist to whom the patient might be referred.

But some experts in the field maintain that many general prac-titioners are not trained to be effective psychotherapeutic agents.

A conference of the Surgeon General of the Public Health Service with state and territorial mental health authorities (U.S. Public Health Service, 1959) noted that "most general practitioners need training in mental health, especially those located in rural areas." In particular, they are reportedly to need training in the administration of tranquilizing drugs, now widely dispensed. Orlund (1959) notes that the extensive use of drugs may provide relief to patients suffering emotional disturbances but prolonged use may make them indifferent to their problems and to the realities of life, foster dependence upon the physician, and lead to a perpetuation rather than a solution of conflicts. But his injunction that the administration of tranquilizers should be accompanied by psychotherapy cannot be implemented by most physicians, however well qualified they are in medicine.

There are differences of opinion on what should be the objectives and character of general practitioners' training for dealing with emotional disturbances. One view is that they should be helped to work more effectively with emotional problems in general by increasing their skills in differential diagnosis, in making referrals to psychiatrists, and in providing supportive help for nonpsychiatrically ill patients. Another is that they should be trained to deal with specific psychiatric problems, for example, psychosomatic disorders and alcoholism. Psychiatrists disagree on the advisability of encouraging the general practitioner to engage in any form of psychotherapy.

Psychiatrists interested in training general practitioners must deal with the latters' feelings of competence to handle emotionally disturbed persons and their attitudes toward receiving psychiatric consultation and training. Two studies of general practitioners (Korkes, 1957; Lemere and Kraabel, 1959) indicate that, whereas a large proportion believe they are competent to deal with the emotional disturbances of their patients, many would be willing to participate in a seminar in psychiatry. The implications would seem to be that practitioners might undertake psychiatric training if it is presented to them on their own terms and in ways that do not question their assumption of competence to deal with the psychiatric problems they encounter. In whatever way it is presented, the training program would have to contend with the indifference or hostility toward psychiatry and the lack of interest in treating emotional problems that persist among general practitioners, particularly among older physicians.

The public health nurse, according to Caplan (1954), is "closer" to the patient than is the physician. She goes into the home, the school, or the well-baby clinic, where her contact with the patient can be constant and continual. She also is close, sociologically speaking: the patient regards her as of the same status as himself and finds it easier to communicate with her than with professionals of higher status. Lastly, she is closer psychologically to the patient, involving herself in his life more directly. Thus, Caplan argues that the public health nurse is particularly well placed to identify crises involving emotional disturbance, motivate the patient to seek the right help, interpret patient and physician to each other, bolster the former's morale and mobilize sources of love and support by explaining the patient's problem and needs to the family, and teach both family and patient certain ways of dealing with specific problems, for example, how to handle a sick child.

In contrast to the work with the general practitioner, the efforts to enlist the public health nurse have been directed at making her an assistant to the patient's psychotherapist rather than the actual therapist herself. She is expected to be therapy-oriented but not to conduct formal treatment. However, she is expected to help those who would not be classified as psychiatric patients but are for the moment defensive, hostile, depressed, or discouraged.

Traditionally, the public health nurse has dealt with emotional problems of the families in her caseload. What is new is the systemic attempt to help her use her nursing techniques in more sensitive ways. As a result, for example, she is being trained to distinguish between the treatment accorded one who needs direct reassurance and one who should be given emotional support indirectly.

The involvement of the social worker in the handling of emotional disturbance of her clients derives from her specialized training rather than from her special position as regards her clients,

as in the case of the public health nurse. In theoretical orientation, she usually is closer to the psychiatrist than is either the general practitioner or the public health nurse; thus she is able to
use psychiatric consultation in her work without basic revision of
her viewpoint.

J. V. Coleman (1949) has commented upon the similarity of
casework and psychotherapy as disciplines offering help to persons
in emotional distress. For example, both require skill in inter-
viewing, the ability to inspire confidence, and recognition of the
role of emotional and unconscious processes in attitudes and behavior as well as the force of intrapsychic resistance and the limitations of personality structure or life situations. In both casework and psychotherapy there is a selection of the problems to be
dealt with. Both give emotional support for immediate and acute
anxiety, and both consider problems of transference important
though they handle them differently. But, of course, although both
deal with emotional difficulties, casework generally is directed at
helping clients find solutions to their problems within the framework of their pattern of functioning whereas psychotherapy attempts some restructuring of personality through a corrective emotional experience. Some practitioners see the inclusion of mental
health work as a logical extension of casework. Some casework agencies now explicitly deal with problems of the emotionally disturbed
client and argue for the greater suitability of casework treatment
as compared with psychotherapy for certain of their clients. Increasingly, mental health consultation is offered welfare workers
in an attempt to help them handle the emotional as well as the
welfare problems of their clients. But the issue in using caseworkers in this connection is that the similarity of casework and psychiatric treatment threatens to create problems of competition
between the two closely related specialties. The complementarity
of the public health nurse's referral-interpretive-supportive functions to the psychiatrist's treatment function does not as neatly
characterize the relations of social worker and psychiatrist. At the
same time, the similarity between the roles probably has increased
the opportunities for the social worker to participate more extensively in treatment.

It is important to note here that changes in the role of psychiatrist are necessary accompaniments of this trend to include the community caretaker in mental health work. If the latter is to be trained, the psychiatrist must devote less time to treatment and more to consultation and teaching.

BUILDING HELP FOR PSYCHOLOGICAL PROBLEMS INTO NONTREATMENT INSTITUTIONS

Building help for psychological problems into nontreatment institutions extends giving help one step further, for here treatment programs are set up where they did not exist. The mental health experts hired by these institutions have wider functions than they have in either of the forms previously discussed; moreover, the added enterprise means that persons whose role has not included giving help are asked to become helpers.

Many professionals now believe that all community organizations should take account of emotional problems. Primary and secondary schools, colleges, churches, military establishments, large industrial and commercial concerns, labor unions, and penal institutions now assume some responsibility for insuring the psychological well-being of their members. Organizations are hiring their own experts in psychological problems as regular employees. Although most of them are part-time, they are regular employees, not occasional consultants. As employees they have responsibilities for taking action within the limits imposed on them by the organization; as regular participants they have the obligation to provide a service that fits the needs of the organization. The service reaches its fullest expression when the experts also have a staff or utilize others in the organization to implement their programs.

But even though professional helpers are hired, it does not mean that help has become the primary concern, nor that the help is the same as that provided in treatment settings. When a helper is added to an organization whose central concerns are not therapy, there will be an accommodation: the conventional role of helper changes somewhat, and the organization changes certain practices to make it possible for the helper to function in it. The hired psychological expert faces two general problems: he must bring key members to see the importance of giving help for emotional problems and of supporting his program, and he must devise ways of giving help within the framework of the organization. This task is more difficult in organizations such as reformatories or factories than in schools or churches because the former have traditionally functioned in ways that are incompatible with treatment, and treatment cannot merely take its place alongside other activities. If treatment is to be given, some transformation in the way the organization goes about its business is required. Bringing these changes in the organization about is sometimes the major problem in introducing help.

To make help for emotional problems available in industrial organizations and agencies of social control is the farthest extension of the out-patient system. Despite differences in purpose, ideologies, and organizational structures, the trend toward giving help in these contexts is similar in that both have emphasized a mental health program rather than merely the setting up of conventional out-patient treatment units. This has been interpreted to mean: developing appropriate procedures in the setting, such as on-the-spot help and informal counseling; training supervisory personnel to deal with the emotional problems of their subordinates; altering elements in the situation so as to prevent the development of emotional disturbances or the exacerbation of existing ones; and consulting with or advising higher officials, such as wardens or top management, on policy decisions and matters relating to emotional well-being. Thus, though some treatment is given, the general objective is to avoid or minimize emotional disturbance by infusing therapeutic attitudes and behavior into everyday actions and to blend the orientation toward help with the orientation determined by the organization's functions.

Industrial mental health is a field in which the mental health specialist shows increasing interest. Yet of the 183 members of the American Psychiatric Association employed by industry, only a dozen or so devoted full-time to this work in 1960 and equally few clinical psychologists and social workers were involved (Maisel,

1960; Levinson, 1959). Nonetheless, the programs directed by these few suggest the direction in which industrial mental health is likely to take.

The expense of treatment is probably only one factor limiting its use in industry. Because treatment can be offered to a small proportion of all in the firm, the mental health expert may make mental health rather than emotional disturbance his primary focus. Reasoning that he can help a larger number of persons and be of greater use to the organization, he turns his attention to making work relationships more satisfying. Thus he has become involved in such diverse activities as evaluating employees' aptitudes and interests; placing them in appropriate jobs; training foremen, other supervisors, and executives to be better leaders, increasingly sensitive to the needs of subordinates; consulting with industrial physicians on psychologic aspects of patients' complaints; and advising top management on policies to minimize stress.

Some programs set up by human relations experts emphasize the use of nonprofessional personnel, such as foremen and supervisors. Western Electric's Hawthorne Plant has trained its own counselors to give on-the-spot help to line employees. They are instructed in interview techniques and psychological functioning and are assigned to departments or plant areas to discuss with the employee any problems or experiences he wants to talk about. Since they are not professionally trained, they are not to diagnose, treat, or advise but merely to offer employees opportunities to ventilate their problems and to mobilize their own strength. To make it possible for them to establish the necessary relationship with workers, the counselors operate independently of the medical department (which is responsible for referring ill persons to treatment elsewhere) and of the personnel department (whose responsibilities include evaluating and placing job applicants and employees) (Wilensky and Wilensky, 1951).

Though few in number, mental health experts are now found on the staffs of prisons, reformatories, parole agencies, juvenile courts, and police departments. (Silver, 1959; Wilson, 1960; Gibson, 1954; and Kahn, 1953.) Here extension of out-patient psychiatric services is characterized by the attempt to provide treatment for the emotionally disturbed and by the broader interest in increasing the therapeutic value of the institutions. The specific aim may be diagnosis and treatment or referral of the emotionally disturbed person to treatment; it may be training other workers to approach their charges in more psychologically sophisticated ways; or it may be advising those in authority in the handling of lawbreakers so that emotional disturbances may be prevented, or detected and treated. More important is the psychological expert's implicit or explicit concern with affecting the entire setting. In general, he tries to minimize the punitive and custodial processes and to maximize individualized care and rehabilitation.

Lack of trained personnel obviously limits the development of mental health programs in nontreatment institutions. However, even if this were not so, it might be difficult to develop the kinds of program that mental health professionals have in mind, especially when the institution's main functions are unrelated to or incompatible with treatment. In his analysis of the prison, Cressey (1960) describes some features that prevent the prison from becoming a therapeutic milieu: in effect, because prisons have custodial as well as punitive functions, both of which require strict enforcement of rules, individualized handling of inmates according to their needs is difficult to achieve. Yet we are not implying that the mental health expert can have no impact on nontreatment organizations. We are merely pointing out that because his values and his conceptions of his role may not be readily acceptable to the institution, his therapeutic influence will not be widespread nor immediately felt.

Discussion

As innovations are introduced to solve problems inherent in the present system of treatment, practitioners find that new and equally difficult problems arise. It is as if the remedies for one set of deficiences breed another set just as difficult to cope with as the first. For example, the psychiatrist attempting to increase the supply of helpers by drawing upon general practitioners, must face the difficulties of advising them on how to deal with psycho-pathological processes that are ordinarily beyond their ken.

Two general issues seem to be involved in extending out-patient services in the community. The first concerns the changes required in psychiatric practice and in related specialties if the defects the practitioner seeks to remedy are to be overcome. The second is related to the changes in other aspects of our society implied by these programs. The extent of these two types of change will largely determine how effective these programs will be.

One important aspect of the first issue is the adapting of practices to the groups who are to receive help. Psychiatrists and particularly social workers have long been aware that treatment, casework, or, indeed, any kind of help does not operate in a cultural vacuum—that the attitudes of the clients the professional seeks to help may decide whether the offered help is meaningful to them and whether it is effective, not to mention whether it is sought or the relationship continued. Even though courses in sociology and anthropology are increasingly common in medical, social work, and nursing schools, help practices as a rule do not take this point into account. There are, of course, some exceptions. Group workers with juvenile gangs and caseworkers handling uncooperative families are sensitized to their clients' values and attitudes. But the fact remains that at least in the programs described in this chapter, subgroup norms have been neglected. For example, Etzioni (1958) notes that most human relations programs in industry operate on the assumption that workers prefer democratic to authoritarian supervision, welcome responsibility, and prefer mutual understanding to griping. In short, the assumption is that all workers share the middle-class ethos that underlies much of psychotherapeutic work. But he finds evidence that workers from traditional societies and those from certain subgroups in our society may be most satisfied and effective under paternalistic or authoritarian supervision.

But if a professional acts on such knowledge and alters practices to make them better suited to his clients, for example, introducing more authoritarian relationships into organizations, his colleagues might charge him with engaging in activities that are non-therapeutic, unprofessional, even unethical, or outright damaging to clients. Even if a group of professional workers could agree on modifications in goals and practices, the sponsoring agency might not concur, nor is it likely that other professionals or members of the community would support them.

Another important aspect of extending out-patient service is that of changing traditional roles. As the general practitioner, the public health nurse, and the social worker become more involved in mental health efforts, it is the boundaries rather than the core of their roles that change. That is, their roles widen as they take on functions conventionally considered those of the psychiatrist. But he, too, is enlarging the boundaries of his role as he assumes teaching, consultation, advisory and even supervisory functions in connection with the work of others and as he reduces the time he gives to direct clinical work with patients. These changes are not dramatic at present, nor are they extensive. But the central problem connected with them can most clearly be seen in certain interdisciplinary team programs that operate on the assumption that all members of the team have important functions in regard to treatment. If nonmedically trained workers regard their roles as essentially the same as the psychiatrist's, he is likely to make it clear that, while he may share certain peripheral functions, he will retain responsibility for the treatment of patients as his sole prerogative and preserve treatment as a medical function. He may agree to alteration in the boundaries of his role, but he is adamant about preserving its core. From his point of view, the question is how to share parts of his role and at the same time to retain his unique functions. And to the community caretakers, expansion of their role to include helping emotionally disturbed persons also presents a problem. They, too, want to preserve the core of their role, yet to assume new functions. The question for them is how much can their role be changed while they still carry out their traditional functions.

It may be that the psychiatrist's concern with the issue of changing role boundaries is related to the threat to his traditional functions. Psychiatrists are so intensely involved in debate about changing role boundaries because the projected changes highlight one of the major dilemmas of the out-patient psychiatric system, namely: How can the continuing shortage of treatment personnel be met by enlisting the social worker, clinical psychologist, public health nurse, or general practitioner without rendering their roles functionally indistinguishable from that of the psychiatrist?

One way out of this dilemma is to train community caretakers to do preventive mental hygiene only while treatment for serious emotional disturbance is retained by the psychiatrist as his unique function. He can remain the sole professional competent to treat these disorders while, at the same time, hoping that the future demand for treatment personnel may be reduced. To this extent, the mental hygiene movement can be viewed as an attempt to solve the problem of increasing opportunities for help without using nonpsychiatrists to give treatment and without altering conventional professional roles too drastically. Of course, this is all based on the assumption that a clear differentiation can be made between incipient and mild disturbances for which preventive help is needed and serious disturbances for which treatment is needed.

A third problem is that innovations have created incompatible functions for the helpers, especially in organizations in which the primary activities are not consonant with treatment. For example, the position of the foreman in the factory frequently is considered a difficult one, lying as it does between management and the worker. Introducing a human relations program in industry makes the role of the foreman more stressful; attempts to increase his sympathetic understanding and help his subordinates while acting as their direct supervisor requires him to behave in contradictory ways. McMurray (1959), speaking for one point of view in industry, argues that a man cannot "wear two hats," and that, while foremen may be expected to understand that a worker has problems, they cannot be expected to serve as their counselors. The supervisor is a line administrator, and he should not be expected to be anything else.

According to Cressey (1960), the same incompatibility in function can be observed in treatment-oriented prisons: when prison guards are expected to be treatment-oriented as well as custodially-oriented, a certain confusion in their role is introduced. Guards attempt to resolve the conflicting requirements not by abandoning punishment for misbehavior or uncooperativeness but by dispensing punishment more arbitrarily, according to their personal whims. Significantly, they can be neither effective custodians nor therapists. According to Ohlin, *et al.* (1956), the social worker–parole officer faces essentially the same dilemma but in reverse. He attempts to pursue a treatment orientation but is also expected to perform a control function. He, too, fails to be the kind of helper prescribed by his profession.

The basic difficulty here is that innovations in the roles of prison guard, factory foreman, parole officer, and similar caretakers have been introduced without concern for the larger structure into which the new role is expected to fit and without considering the structural pressures on the helpers. The assumption seems to be that the individuals in these settings must be changed: for example, if a superior is not helpful to subordinates, it is because of some personal propensity. That is, if the prison guard, the parole officer, or the policeman on the beat handles lawbreakers in a "tough" way, it is primarily because he lacks "understanding" of the violators' problems and of the dynamic psychological reasons underlying their behavior. The assumption is that this can be corrected by training or consultation programs.

What has been overlooked is the fact that persons in these positions in society are expected and even pressured to behave in the ways they do. This is not merely a question of the right training. Cressey (1960) notes that

even if guards and foremen were replaced by professionally trained specialists, the problems stemming from the attempt to administer treatment in a punitive setting would not be resolved. The handling of prisoners as individualized treatment cases . . . is limited by the necessity of meeting the inmate community's demand for justice and the employees' needs for cooperation of inmates [p. 101].

This is a problem that cannot be handled only by training individuals; it requires working on the social structural problems involved.

The second general issue raised by all these innovations in

professional practices concerns the changes in social institutions implied by the new conceptions of help. Here we merely wish to point out that the practitioners involved in some of these new programs often seek to bring about changes not only in the way the professional or nonprofessional helper goes about his business but in the goals and structure of our institutions.

This is not to say that this is specifically recognized by most practitioners engaged in the programs we have described. On the contrary, they ordinarily state their objectives more narrowly. They would say, for example, that they aim to develop psychological understanding among key persons in a given organization so that these workers might have more therapeutic effects on the persons with whom they have contact. Or, they might see their objective as training a particular group of professionals so that they can be more effective in their work. Only occasionally do they state their goals as clearly as do Markey and Langsam (1957) when they indicate that, by introducing a psychiatrist in the juvenile court clinic, they hoped to "change the basic court milieu in such a way as to make the court experience a therapeutic one."

But whether it is recognized or not, to extend help into ordinary life settings is also an attempt to change them basically. For example, the attempt to replace the custodial, punitive orientation of prison guards with a conception of rehabilitation through training and attention to individual needs really involves altering the way in which prisons are managed and the inmates' dissatisfaction, misdemeanors, and so forth are dealt with. In short, what appears on the surface as an attempt to change the role of guard may actually end in transforming the prison. And since the role of members of organizations is not simply a function of individual choice or propensity but of pressures in the organization to operate in certain ways, any effort to change roles by training individual workers is not likely to succeed completely. This is not to say that institutions cannot be changed, but that the mechanism of change must be appropriate to the social context.

The mental health expert who perceives that changes are not occurring in the way he would like may be at a loss to account for it. He often concludes that he could do a better job if more professionally trained personnel were available, or if he had more money. But we suggest that the causes for many of these failures are embedded in the social structure. An analysis of the social structure might serve several purposes. It might suggest not only which programs might succeed and which might not, but it might reveal what areas could be successfully attacked first and what are best left till later. It might indicate, moreover, how programs could be introduced, what is required to maintain them, and what problems to anticipate. Finally, it might provide him with a clearer notion of the limits in which his program is operating so that his expectations might be more realistic.

Chapter 6

Broadening the Conceptions of Help

Before the growth of modern psychiatry what we now refer to as mental illness was often treated by supernatural means or by imprisonment. Since its definition as a medical problem, specific treatments have included: blood-letting, hydrotherapy, surgery, endocrine preparations, and vitamins. With the growth of a more sophisticated understanding of mental illness emphasis has been placed on understanding the patient by studying his life history, his psychological and social relationships, and his social environment and on the use of this knowledge in treatment. This orientation is what we have called "broadening the conceptions of help."

Today many experts see mental illness as a resultant of multiple factors, organic, psychological, and social, intricately interrelated. With the development of more complex theories of the etiology of mental and emotional disturbance and the notion that many factors may effect therapeutic progress, the idea has taken form that these disturbances may happen to anyone, given sufficiently stressful circumstances.

Physical treatment and psychotherapy still constitute the main therapies for out-patients, but a considerable number of mental health workers are interested in instituting treatment based on broader conceptions. They accept the fact that they are dealing with a complex interaction of biological, psychological, and sociological conditions and consequently argue that treatment should be designed from all three points of view.[1] Their view implies a distinction between treatment and help, the former referring to conventionally accepted clinical procedures, the latter to the large variety of attempts, ordinarily conducted outside of the clinical setting, to influence emotionally disturbed persons in a therapeutic direction. Following this, in our discussion we shall use "help" as the more inclusive term and "treatment" in the restricted sense noted here.

The newer conceptions of help include considerations such as a wider arena within which help might proceed, a different conception of who and what is to be helped, and a different view of the conditions and processes that affect therapeutic progress. In addition, those offered help are not only those formally defined as patients, but anyone suffering psychological stress or an emotional crisis, such as may occur in migration, disaster, bereavement, or retirement.

Thus, broadening the conceptions of help involves some reorientation. From looking upon the process exclusively as a clinical activity, directed at a disease entity, and undertaken within the boundaries of the conventionally defined therapist-patient relationship, the change is to seeing it, in addition, as a sociopsychological process that attempts to deal with problems in living that are not necessarily serious or well-defined emotional disorders. Some practitioners using these conceptions believe that their help processes are sufficiently specifiable and manageable to have therapeutic effects. Others see this kind of help as just as specific as psychotherapy but as dealing with a more limited range of phenomena, for example, with a particular problem or segment of the personality. And they see it as just as capable as psychotherapy of producing stable changes.

In this chapter we focus on the re-conceptualization that underlies these programs, and we use specific programs only as illustrations of the conceptions.

When practitioners discuss broadening the conceptions of help, directly or by implication, what they are doing is altering a number of notions related to the process of helping; that is, they are concerned with ways of re-conceptualizing the unit of help, changing the definition of patient and object of help, expanding the role of helper, and re-orienting their approach to help processes. The four objectives are interrelated and together constitute the theme "broadening the conceptions of help." We discuss the four separately, but it should be clear that an understanding of any one of them calls for seeing its relation to the other three. Thus, for example, the conception "unit of help" can only be fully understood when seen in connection with the conceptions of patients, helper, and help processes.

The Unit of Help

A number of practitioners would like to see help for emotional disturbances patterned more closely on the general medical model. They believe that greater precision in identifying mental illnesses or in classifying mental disturbances into discrete and mutually exclusive categories will lead to the discovery of specific procedures for treating each category.

Other practitioners advocate what appears to be the opposite: that the unit of help be conceived more broadly and its boundaries enlarged to include not only the individual, but his environment and the transactions that take place between him and it. This view underlies some of the programs we have described in previous chapters, and we shall therefore analyze it in some detail.

The gradual movement in medical thinking away from the view of a diseased entity or part as the unit of treatment is reflected in such phrases as "treating the patient as a whole" and "what should be treated is a person with an illness rather than an illness in a person." Some practitioners have been led to an even broader notion of the unit of help than "the whole person," a conception that takes into account a greater number of variables and deals with a more complex unit than the single individual. It includes not only symptoms, psychodynamics, and interpersonal relations, but also sociocultural contexts of varying size, organization, and purpose. Thus, the object of their help is the identified patient, his significant others, his social network, and general social context.

When the unit of help is seen as some aspect of the social environment, practitioners tend to focus on three aspects: the intimate primary groups, particularly the family in which the patient is continuously and deeply involved; the secondary groups such as fellow workers and employer, which form an important part of his life apart from his family, and his inclusive milieu—his subcultural group, his community, or the institutions and even the society of which he is a member.

Practitioners who see the family as the unit of help operate on the assumption that family interaction is primary in contributing to emotional difficulties. A logical corollary is that changing the relations within the family will change the patient and alleviate his disturbance. From this point of view the family unit is a set of dynamic forces and patterns as important as the psychodynamics of individuals. Plans for help would take into account the family's sociocultural characteristics, such as the degree of solidarity, its values, its tolerance of overt aggression and sexual expression, and its anxiety concerning mental illness itself. The goal is to identify the destructive elements in family relationships and then to utilize specific techniques of intervention to alter them. The techniques will vary with the practitioner's conceptions of how the family should be worked with as a social unit.[2]

Mental health workers who focus on secondary groups as the unit of help have in mind work settings, schools, social clubs, and the like, which they are interested in influencing directly or indirectly, formally or informally. These contexts are not as affect-laden as the family but are nevertheless significant in a person's life. The practitioner seeks to generate therapeutic processes within them.

The broadest, and at the same time the vaguest, units of help some out-patient practitioners seek to encompass are communities, subcultural groups, and certain sociocultural processes in institutional and societal life. In the belief that stable and recurrent patterns of activity, such as assumptions, beliefs, and "taken-for-granted" social processes, contribute to the perpetuation of certain kinds of mental disturbance, they seek to develop selective modes of intervention. This intervention may take any of three general forms: an attempt to change the person's participation in the social setting; an attempt to minimize or reduce what are thought to be the noxious influences therein; and, as with the prison or the school, an attempt to influence the setting to become a therapeutic milieu.

The idea that a person's emotional disturbance is influenced by an ever-widening circle of social contexts may be theoretically valid, but it is difficult to establish its validity and to show specifically how these influences operate. Perhaps more difficult is the problem of intervention when the units of help are conceptualized in this way. Intervention means some degree of change in on-going institutions and community or societal processes, and these changes may not be readily acceptable to the community. In addition, there are problems of working out the boundaries of the unit of help, knowing when and how to deal with it, and determining whether to be concerned with a number of units simultaneously or separately. Criteria are needed for determining when the family should be the unit of help, when the neighborhood is the appropriate focus, and when it is more profitable to work with the other wider social entities. The question of dealing with the context selected involves determining which modes of intervention can be best used and what the roles of helper and "helpee" should be. Practitioners are still unclear about which conceptualization of the unit of help would lead to the discovery of more adequate types of interventions.

The Object of Help

One implication of this discussion is that families, communities, or total societies as well as individuals may be designated as "sick" and therefore be potential objects of therapeutic effort. This contrasts with the conventional view in which practitioners treating emotional disturbance identify one person as the patient and, at the most, view significant members of his family and social network as helpful intermediaries.

Conventionally, a psychiatric out-patient is identified by a qualified diagnostician as emotionally disturbed, or mentally ill, and in need of help. The patient confirms the definition by agreeing to enter a treatment relationship, and he submits to the therapeutic process in the hope and expectation of alleviating his difficulties. His obligation is to accept the role, carry out its functions as prescribed for him, abide by the rules, accept the therapist in his role, and submit to therapeutic ministrations conceived and effected by the therapist. Not content with restricting the object of help to a person formally defined as a "patient," some practitioners, implicitly or explicitly, are developing instead a concept of the object of help that permits the disturbed person to receive help without necessarily being defined as a "patient."

One example of this is the help sometimes given the emotionally disturbed student by school teachers as part of their regular classroom activity.[3] This means that the teacher not only teaches a given subject but manages the students in ways intended to have therapeutic effects. Mental health consultation services to schools are specifically designed to aid the classroom teacher in this role. At least three aspects of the patient role are altered. First, there need be no consent on the part of the person that the helping relationship should be undertaken, and in many instances he is unaware that he is being helped. Secondly, the person may not be formally defined as an object of help. The distinction between persons being helped and others in the same situation who are not the specific objects of help is deliberately blurred. The beneficiaries are truly unclear since students other than the emotionally disturbed one may benefit from the teacher's efforts. Thus, in contrast to those who become patients, the one who is being helped is not in a special social role. All that is required is that he be present in the helping context and function in the role of student. Thirdly, the reasons for which a person is given help are neither as clear-cut nor as narrowly defined as those connected with conventional treatment of mental illness: ineffective functioning as student or worker, a life crisis, or deviant behavior, such as delinquency, economic dependency, vagrancy or alcoholism—all might qualify him for help.

The Helper

In the same way that some persons receiving help for mental or emotional disturbance need not acquire the patient label, some helpers do not play the conventional role of therapist. There are at least eight ways in which they may differ.

1. The person giving help may not publicly and explicitly be designated as a helper for emotional disturbance, as, for example, the public health nurse who tries to help her emotionally disturbed patients in the course of exercising her regular functions. In this case the role of helper (for emotional disturbance) is covert and not recognized as such by the one being helped.

2. The helper may not be a person for whom helping the emotionally disturbed is a central activity. As in the case of the school teacher, the helping role is secondary and peripheral to his central function.

3. The role of the helper may not be as formal and in its performance the helper may not be as socially distant from the "helpee" as the conventional therapist would be. For example, the "companion" used by psychiatrists to keep an emotionally disturbed person out of the mental hospital carries on highly informal friendly relations with the person being helped.

4. The role may be played by persons who have no professional training and skill. Their helping potential is seen by professional practitioners as residing in the kinds of interpersonal relations they might have with the object of help.

5. The helper's relationship with the disturbed person may not be restricted to a particular time or to a narrow aspect of his life. The helper may participate in a variety of life experiences with him during the day or at night.

6. The helper may be active and aggressive in bringing help to emotionally upset persons, as in the Home Treatment Service.

7. The helper need not be a single individual but may be a number of individuals operating as a team.

8. A helper may be an expert who is not in direct relations with the disturbed person but manages and guides the helping relationship through an intermediary who is his therapeutic agent.

The Help Processes

There are at least three major ways in which the conception of direct help has been modified: (1) the help process may be covert; (2) it may be informal; (3) it may take the form of activities other than discussion or medication.

In contrast to conventional therapeutic modalities where the therapist-patient relationship is explicit and consented to by both parties, the helping process may be covert in some programs (especially where a community caretaker is the helper). Where this is the case, it can go on at any time or in any context that suits the purposes and convenience of the helper.

Conventional individual or group psychotherapy is a formal procedure in which social distance is maintained between therapist and patient. But, with the introduction of home treatment and with the use of companions for emotionally disturbed persons, it has become more informal, approximating ordinary social intercourse, and with the technical aspects less prominent as vehicles of helping the disturbed person. Such informality encourages the reduction of social distance between the participants, and help may be given in surroundings and under conditions that are more familiar and more "natural" to the person than is the clinic or office with its timing and duration becoming more flexible.

In contrast to the treatment modes that rely on medication or verbalization, some practitioners conceive of help as a form of social action. They conceive of their function as discovering, facilitating, and creating the appropriate interpersonal and group activity that will be therapeutic for disturbed persons. One practitioner, for example, established shops and facilities for work and recreation to teach his patients new skills and thus increase their self-esteem, to have them form new friendships, and to help them share in the collective activity of a small community.

Finally, the conception of help is being broadened through the attempt by mental health experts to influence disturbed persons indirectly through intermediaries and the modifications of social contexts. The consultation process is a primary instrument for these indirect forms of help.[4] In specific programs, a caretaker may be given consultation on how to manage his relationship with an emotionally disturbed person or on how to deal with a personal crisis of his own that is making it difficult for him to provide the necessary help. Finally, consultation may be provided authorities on the effects of the social structure or their administrative policies on the emotional life of persons working in their institution.

Chapter 7

Problems and Issues of
Out-patient System

The practices and programs associated with the themes of concern that relate to out-patients—providing immediate help for the emotionally disturbed, extending out-patient services in the community, and broadening the conception of help—have been adopted to meet persistent problems. The most pressing of these are: shortages of trained personnel, poor results with certain kinds of patients, an inordinately long interval between manifestation of emotional difficulty and the seeking of help (also between manifestation and the receiving of help), uneven distribution of resources, and rigid practices of practitioners and clinics. These problems actually fall into two broad classes: providing adequate coverage and providing effective help. Our thesis is that these problems are in large part a product of certain conceptual and structural aspects of the conventional social system within which practitioners operate. In this chapter we suggest some characteristic ways in which these conventional structural features perpetuate inadequate coverage and add to the difficulties of providing effectively for many persons who enter treatment.

Effective Help

One major feature of the out-patient system is the undeveloped state of knowledge, a deficiency evidenced in a number of ways. First, there is little validated knowledge about the treatment modalities that are consistently effective and successful. In the absence of conclusive evidence based on carefully controlled studies, practitioners are claiming success with all kinds of techniques and base their treatment preferences on experience, ideology, faith, and selective perception. Secondly, there is still much uncertainty about the general and specific agents and processes that contribute to improvement in patients (Frank, 1959). It is not known, for example, to what degree effective therapy is due to nonspecific agents, such as faith and trust in the therapist, to the latter's training and experience, and to unplanned ordinary human experiences that arise in the course of interaction. Thirdly, only a few modes of treatment are accepted and demonstrated to be specifically effective in particular types of disorders; in most emotional disturbances there is no agreement as to the best approach with any particular kind of patient. This is so for a number of reasons among which are the inadequacy of the classification system and of the frame of reference and the difficulty in isolating the relevant units of treatment.

Another feature of the conventional system that may limit effectiveness of treatment is the dominant conceptual orientation and the consequent restrictions that flow from it. Conventionally, mental illness or emotional disturbance is viewed by practitioners as a disease or as an entity within the individual that needs to be altered or removed. Thus, for one thing, they attack the pathogenic state and confine treatment to the individual designated as the patient in isolation from his living context, as if he were able to receive therapeutic benefit only in the confines of the consulting room. This inhibits intervention in the social (that is, the familial, occupational, and recreational) life of the patient. In the second place, this point of view ignores the possibilities of intervention in institutional organization. We suggest that ineffectiveness in treatment may be attributable, at least in part, to failure to pay sufficient attention to these two types of social contexts.

It is commonly assumed that help for emotional disturbance is not as urgent as physical illness, that such disturbance does not call for immediate action unless a social crisis is provoked. Whether this is actually believed by practitioners or whether it is a necessary concession to their inadequate numbers is not as important as the fact that the notion enters into the identification, processing, and initiating of treatment for out-patients. It fosters delay in treatment and may very well lead to an increase in the severity of the disturbance, with poorer chances of success in therapy and a longer time required for it.

The present treatment system not only operates in a way that seems to limit effectiveness of treatment; in addition, unclarified processes within it make it difficult to evaluate the success of present practices. There is little consensus on the criteria of success and failure in treatment. (Baumrind, 1959.) Moreover, the covert and private nature of treatment hinders evaluation. By and large, any particular therapeutic process or therapist-patient relationship is insulated within the confines of the practitioner's office, with the therapist primarily and the patient secondarily controlling any disclosure of information.

Adequate Coverage

The adequacy of coverage for psychiatric out-patients is mainly a function of the number of patients, of personnel to provide help, and of the length of time needed for effective treatment. Adequate coverage even more than effectiveness of treatment is largely dependent upon the nature of the system.

A conspicuous and continuing problem in out-patient care is the persistent and growing discrepancy between the number in need of help and asking for it and the number equipped to provide it. On one hand, an attempt is being made by mental hygiene organizations and professionals to decrease the stigma attached to mental illness and its treatment and to bring into treatment more persons who show signs of emotional disturbance. However, success in this venture is a mixed blessing. For a more accepting attitude toward emotional disturbance and its treatment may interrupt a "natural" regulator of demand for services. Stigma serves to restrict demand, and, as it diminishes, demand may be stimulated far beyond the capacity of current facilities to cope with it. Not only that, but in their eagerness to equate mental illness with "any other illness" and to encourage the disturbed to seek professional help, clinicians and mental hygiene personnel have not circumscribed the areas of psychiatric legitimacy. By leaving it broad and poorly defined, they encourage persons to seek help for a large variety of difficulties, a situation resulting in an even greater unmet demand for services.

On the other hand, while the demand is stimulated and increases, the supply of professional personnel lags behind and is expected to continue to be in short supply. (Albee, 1959.) In addition, the conflict between medical and lay psychotherapists and their controversy over the conditions under which lay therapy should be practiced may be preventing the most effective allocation and utilization of available professional personnel. Thus, inadequate coverage is a product not only of the shortage of trained personnel but also of the ways in which personnel are used. In this regard, one dominant clinical mode that has the highest prestige, is most acceptable to practitioners, is most sought after for training, and is best organized to spread its point of view and approach is the psychoanalytic or intensive psychotherapeutic mode. Here treatment is a clinical operation in which the patient and therapist must be in a one-to-one relationship at frequent intervals for a prolonged period of time. As a consequence, a great deal of professional time is spent on a relatively small number of patients. Even the "briefer" therapies are not sufficiently brief to compensate for the disproportion between demand for service and supply of therapists.

There are other shortcomings: the location of responsibility for out-patient care and the relations between agents and agencies.

Under prevailing arrangements of mixed public and private care for out-patients, there is no designated body responsible for the population in need. For the vast majority of *in*-patients the state or the county assumes the central responsibility, but there is nothing comparable for *out*-patients, although some states have declared their intention to accept responsibility for treatment of all disturbed persons. Instead, responsibility is divided among various organizations and institutions and among different professions and individual practitioners. The out-patient population—actual and potential—is handled in segments. Each agency selects for service that part of the population in need which it wants to serve, but the selection is not governed by any plan whereby the total population is divided up among them. This individualistic way of operating, as well as the small number of practitioners, results in failure to cover the population in need.

Private practitioners, private and public clinics, and family agencies operate in considerable isolation from each other. The private practitioner as an independent professional has his major ties not to clinics or agencies offering similar or related help but to his colleagues in the psychiatric profession and to his professional organizations. Clinics, as noted earlier, tend to be oriented to specific populations and to tasks they have carved out for themselves, without regard to either total needs or the ways in which private practitioners and other organizations do their work. And social agencies, too, frequently carry on with little connection with either of these two sources of help. All this independent and unintegrated effort gives to the psychiatric out-patient system a diffuse and fragmented character which rules out concerted action, addressed to the "problem as a whole."

A basic difficulty is that it is a system of care characterized by a significant discrepancy between means and ends. But more concretely there is an impressive gap between certain important values held by psychiatric practitioners and the instrumentation (treatment techniques, operational procedures, and so forth) used or available to achieve them. For example, on one hand, the psychiatrist is dedicated to the principle of providing out-patient care for all emotionally disturbed persons who need it. This looms large in his professional motivation, encourages him to expand existing treatment facilities, and to extend himself in many directions to administer the needed care. But, on the other hand, many of his practices limit coverage and restrict the search for better methods of treatment. The lack of fit between ends and means, or between treatment goals and practices, is an underlying problem practitioners are wittingly or unwittingly seeking to solve in the various new programs of out-patient care described in preceding chapters. Whether to find new knowledge, new ways of integrating agents of treatment or of supplementing the work of treatment personnel, the attempt is somehow to narrow the gap between ideology and practice. The difficulty, of course, is that attempts at solution are generally made by using the very organization that gave rise to the problems. This means that until there is a reorganization of the basic structure, including a resolution of some of the conflicts in value, problems inherent in the present organization of out-patient care will persist.

Part III

The In-patient System

Chapter 8

Characteristics of the In-patient System

The purpose of this chapter is to describe briefly the prominent characteristics, processes, and problems of the major type of mental hospitals, as an introduction to a subsequent discussion of recent trends, programs, and themes of concern in hospital practices.

Deutsch (1949) has well described the evolution of the care of the mentally ill from almshouses and jails to institutionalization in mental hospitals. In this dismal history there was at least one bright spot—the era of moral treatment during the first half of the nineteenth century. During this period, the very concerns that occupy today's practitioners—individualizing care, breaking down the barriers between hospital and community, and developing a therapeutic milieu—were also important to the then hospital superintendents. Patients were regarded as individuals and treated according to their individual needs; there was a steady communication and flow between the hospital population and the community, and superintendents set about making the atmosphere of the hospital kindly and conducive to recovery.

The mental patient load in the late nineteenth and early twentieth century paralleled the general increase in national population, and mental hospitals expanded in size and number. Professional and semiprofessional personnel, however, did not keep pace nor do they now. The size of the state mental hospital and the staff-patient ratio at present are facts widely deplored.

In addition, the growth of cities, technological and economic change, the development of psychiatry and allied professions, the differentiation of sponsorship of hospitals between private enterprise and federal, state, and local governments contributed to the development of present-day mental hospitals. So did the internal dynamics of the hospital itself. Thus today certain institutional "types" dominate hospital practice: the large state mental hospital, the Veterans Administration (VA) mental hospital, the small private psychiatric hospital, and the psychiatric section of the general hospital. While there are other in-patient institutions—among them psychopathic hospitals, military hospitals, psychiatric research and training hospitals, psychiatric receiving centers, and children's residential treatment units—the four mentioned types house all but a small fraction of the hospitalized mentally ill.

Hospitals within each of the four categories tend to resemble each other and to differ from the other types. For one thing, the hospital atmosphere seems to be generally more similar from one state hospital to another than between state and VA hospitals or between either of them and private hospitals. The same may be said of the social composition of the patient population, the organizational pressures affecting personnel attitudes and motivation, the specific problems of patient management, and the types of issues faced by the hospital administrators. For our purposes, the four well-defined hospital types represent the current organizational forms of mental hospitals in this country.

The Large State Mental Hospital

From the point of view of numbers of resident mental patients, the publicly supported county or state mental hospital is far and away the dominant organizational form, containing some 85 percent of the total population.[1]

These hospitals play a particularly important role in the care of the long-term patient. This role is perceived accurately by people in the community when they regard this type of institution as the accepted and customary place in which to maintain and treat a person with severe mental illness. In addition to the general fear and rejection of severely disturbed mental patients that strongly color the popular view of any institution specifically devoted to their treatment, the typical state hospital is characteristically forbidding in appearance, with its large masses of patients whose daily lives are scheduled and ordered to fit into institutional routines, its inadequacies and in such basic necessities as food and clothing, and its custodial and repressive atmosphere expressed in restraint, seclusion rooms, barred doors and windows. These features dominate the lives and activities of patients and personnel alike, and it is understandable that students and practitioners as well as laymen often see the state mental hospital as more like a prison than a general hospital.

The state-supported institution is required to accept as patients all legal residents who need in-service psychiatric treatment—both volunteers and the legally committed. A court officer or a policeman is the patient's frequent escort, and often he is unaccompanied by friends or family. Although the hospital is in a general state of readiness to receive and admit patients, it is not specifically prepared for any particular individual.

With this relative lack of control over admissions, the superintendent of a state mental hospital has little room for administrative maneuver. Anything that affects the incidence of mental illness or the probability that the mentally ill will come for treatment will have immediate consequences for the hospital administrator and his staff, affecting the pressure for hospital beds and the composition of the patient population. The administrator's freedom to release patients to the community is often more apparent than real. For, whereas only he has the formal and legal authority to determine whether a patient has recovered sufficiently to be discharged, his judgment of the community's receptiveness to ex-patients will enter into his decision. By and large, the patient is as little prepared for his return to the community as he was for entrance into the hospital.

The state hospital is accountable to the political administration of the state. It is more likely than other hospitals to be subjected to and responsive to local political, social, and economic pressures. "Incidents" involving patients or ex-patients might cost an administrator his job; or they may affect his budget or the hospital's reputation. Easiest for him is to develop "safe" custodial programs of patient care and treatment that conduce to little risk of incidents.

The state hospital has been used as a "dumping ground" for a variety of problem persons, particularly certain kinds of troubled and troublesome individuals in the lowest socioeconomic classes. The presence of these "undesirable" persons, combined with the high proportions of aged and chronic patients, seems to be particularly conducive to the custodial and apathetic atmosphere that is so striking a feature of state hospitals, even of the better ones. Achieving perceptible "movement" in chronic patients or rehabilitating antisocial individuals requires a great deal more in time, energy, and skill than is necessary for equivalent results with less difficult cases. These resources are in such short supply that the objective of improvement tends to be forgotten and most patients who require maximum efforts to show improvement receive at best the barest minimum of care.

The state hospital is often described as a self-contained community or subculture. It is often geographically isolated, and the attempt to provide for the total needs of its patient population primarily by its own intramural activities and resources causes it to become isolated from other institutions. This further accentuates the qualities of a mass organization, the atmosphere of apathy, and the repressive custodial orientation. These features comprise the major dimensions of the subculture, and through mutual reinforcement and the relative isolation from other social pressures they come to form a strong and change-resistant pattern.

The ward is the primary center of the patient's life. Because of the low salaries and undesirable working conditions, the attendants who preside over ward life are as a rule recruited from among the relatively uneducated and socially deprived or picked for their jobs by political patronage. It has been difficult to attract and retain stable and well-motivated ward personnel, and most descriptions of the "attendant culture" stress its negative impact on patients.[2] In recent years, a number of research projects as well as many practitioners have focused attention on the ward with the intent of maximizing its therapeutic benefits.[3]

Clearly state mental hospitals have not functioned primarily as active treatment centers. The prevalent modes of treatment reflect the need for the mass processing of patients in the absence of sufficient numbers of skilled personnel for either refined diagnosis or intensive treatment. The favored therapy in the past had been

shock treatments of one sort or another. Recently group and milieu therapies have been introduced as have the tranquilizers,
with the latter replacing shock as the predominant treatment
mode.

It is extremely difficult to evaluate the effectiveness of treatment institutions or of different forms of therapy. Systematic and
extensive research on these topics is still one of the necessary tasks
of the future. What we do know is encouraging: The probability
of the release of a mental patient within one year from admission
to a typical state hospital is increasing (Kramer, et al., 1955). On
the other hand, the probability of release in the second year of
hospitalization has only increased slightly. Information gathered
by the National Institute of Mental Health from nine states in the
Model Reporting Area indicates that there is considerable variation among states in the percentages of first admissions released
within one year of hospitalization. An adequate explanation of
variability in release rates undoubtedly will have to include, along
with the direct psychological effects of specific treatments, such
factors as family and community levels of tolerance and degrees of
receptiveness.

The Veterans Administration Mental Hospital

While there are some exceptions, VA hospitals tend to be
smaller than state-supported institutions. Many of them have been
constructed since the end of World War II, and they often resemble large general hospitals in architecture and interior decora-
tion.

The criteria for admission for treatment in a VA hospital—
veteran's status and a service-connected disability—result in a
patient population very different in composition than that found
in other psychiatric institutions. In the first place, almost all the
patients are men whereas often in state hospitals about half the
resident patients are women. Moreover, patients in a VA hospital
come from a wide geographical area (they may reside in any part
of the country) and a great range of communities. On the other
hand, that they have all had military experience may impose other

elements of homogeneity—age, for example. It is becoming increasingly rare for a "fresh" case to appear at a VA hospital, and the population tends to consist more and more of chronic patients and "repeaters."

Average expenditures per patient in VA hospitals is twice that of the state hospital. The difference is registered in the quality of food, the physical surroundings, and the material and equipment available for patient activities. It is reflected also in the relatively high staff-to-patient ratios, not only with regard to physicians and nurses but also for others, such as clinical psychologists and social workers. The emphasis given to the work of members of the last two professional groups contributes markedly both to the general atmosphere and the specific features of VA hospitals and serves to distinguish them in important ways from hospitals under either state or private auspices. Usually there is considerably more research and more interest in it in VA hospitals than in state hospitals. This seems due in large part to the special interests and training of the psychologists and to the official definition of their work as including research. The relatively greater stress on the "psychiatric team" and on group therapy also appears to be related to the more extensive and intensive use of psychologists. On the other hand, the special emphasis on aftercare programs and the concern about the outside world that one finds in VA hospitals both issue from interest of social workers, who take an active part in the hospital program. The presence of adult men who in normal life would be working and the fact that there are funds to hire occupational and recreational therapists and vocational counselors are probably responsible for the greater interest in work programs and industrial therapy.

The problem of "secondary gain," that is, social or psychological benefit resulting indirectly from hospitalization, is important but not unique to VA hospitals. The decent living conditions maintained in these institutions and the veterans' pensions for service-connected disability make the problem acute, since partial or complete recovery—as evidenced by discharge and rehabilitation—may result in the reduction or loss of the pension. Also, patients from lower socioeconomic classes may be returning to situations that are far less comfortable than those found in the hospital. For these reasons, special efforts appear to be required to sustain the patients' motivations for returning to the community.

For a number of reasons—more funds, more professional personnel, more research—VA hospitals have been rather receptive to new trends and new ideas and their programs suggest a greater willingness to experiment. The increasing homogeneity of the patient population in terms of age and chronicity and the improved competitive position of state institutions for recruiting and retaining professionals of high quality are problems that VA hospitals are beginning to face, and their future form and functioning will depend in no small part on how these problems are resolved.

The Small Private Mental Hospital

The small private mental hospitals, especially those with national reputations, are usually thought of as at the opposite pole from the average state mental hospital with regard to the quality of personnel and the intensiveness of treatment. In general, hospitals of this type are active treatment centers with rapid rates of patient turnover. Staff-to-patient ratios are much higher than in state hospitals, and this is particularly true of those professional groups on the staff that require specialized training, such as psychiatrists and registered nurses.[4]

In addition to the obvious differences in socioeconomic status between persons who go for treatment to private hospitals and those who enter publicly-supported institutions, there are other important differences. For example, in every age group, women outnumber men as admissions to private hospitals whereas the reverse is true for state hospitals. There are also certain striking differences in diagnostic categories, for example, a much greater proportion of private hospital patients are diagnosed as psycho-neurotic rather than psychotic, and non-schizophrenic disorders (particularly depression) predominate among the psychoses. Some private hospitals, of course, screen out certain groups of patients, such as chronic schizophrenic or agitated manic patients, or specialize in certain groups, such as alcoholics.

Patients are usually referred to these institutions by their private physicians—general practitioners, psychiatrists, or other specialists—in contrast to the state hospitals where the courts, social agencies, and the police predominate in referrals. (Hollingshead and Redlich, 1958, Chap. 6.) If the hospital draws on the local population, the private physician may have attending privileges, he will be kept informed of the course of treatment and his patient's progress, and the patient will be returned to his care. Thus, as compared to the procedures of admission and release in state hospitals, so disturbing to both the patient and the institution, the paths in and out of private hospitals follow the lines of organized treatment, namely, the hospital-physician system. The dependence of the hospital on community physicians means that the quality and the type of psychiatry practiced in it is consistent with what they will accept for their patients. Since financial difficulties are endemic, this may further limit experimentation with new forms of treatment.

For all these reasons the primary modes of treatment vary greatly from one hospital to another. With rare exceptions the physical medical model prevails; and other professional groups are viewed as ancillary to the physicians. As in the general hospital, the nurse-physician axis dominates in the organization and the program of treatment. Within this general orientation, emphasis may be placed on some form of psychotherapy, on electric shock, or on drugs.

The Psychiatric Section of the General Hospital

Adequate historical data are lacking, but it is apparent that these hospitals in recent years have increased in importance as treatment institutions for the mentally ill, both in terms of the numbers of general hospitals now accepting such patients and the numbers of psychiatric admissions to them.[5] It is generally assumed that their importance will continue to increase. The recent tendency to include general hospital care for psychiatric illness in standard health insurance plans, in particular, "major medical" policies, is likely to promote the development and the use of such facilities.

Although some sections are housed in separate buildings and some units in large city hospitals contain as many as three to four hundred beds, the typical psychiatric unit consists of one or two small wards in a wing or part of a floor of the hospital. As its separation from the general hospital increases, administratively or geographically, it becomes more and more like a small private hospital. It is geared primarily to the active treatment of acute disorders and has a high rate of turnover with few patients remaining for longer than a few weeks at a time. Sometimes the patients discharged are discharged directly to a state mental hospital for continued treatment. The psychiatric unit shares with the general hospital itself the property of serving the local community and its practitioners.

As with the private mental hospital, the medical team of physician and nurse is the pivot of organization and treatment. The whole system is geared to the rapid turnover of patients. These conditions, so different from those found in state and VA hospitals, have not been such as to promote or stimulate interest in the newer social therapies.

The brief descriptions in this chapter have been aimed at acquainting the reader with some significant features of the four modal types of psychiatric hospitals, which together treat almost all persons hospitalized for mental illness. We have suggested that these hospitals differ from each other in vital ways, such as the size and composition of their patient populations, the quality, training, and orientation of their staffs, and the nature of their relationships to their communities. These differences affect the interest in certain types of treatment programs and the possibilities of introducing them. In particular, they may hinder or facilitate the development of programs that emphasize increasing the number and kinds of relationships undertaken with patients.

Many of the trends and programs that we shall discuss involve attempts to increase the range and type of staff-patient interaction. It is important to recognize that some of the new developments in care and treatment come from the teaching and research hospitals, some of which are small psychiatric institutes while many are sections of general hospitals. Although they usually are connected with departments of psychiatry of university medical schools, many receive substantial public support from municipal, state, or federal funds. Their importance is considerably greater than might be judged from the small numbers of patients they treat.

Their special role may be largely due to the fact that, while the majority of psychiatrists trained since 1945 have entered private practice, many who have chosen a career in hospital psychiatry have been trained in these teaching hospitals, and their attitudes, theories, and orientation toward practice have been formed there. In addition, because of their training and research functions, these hospitals are infused with a spirit of inquiry and experimentation. Innovations in patient care are much more likely to emerge in these settings than in others. These new programs then spread to other institutions through published reports or are carried by the graduating psychiatrists who take their ideas with them to their new jobs.

Chapter 9

Individualizing Care and Treatment

Probably most, if not all practitioners would accept Bruno Bettel-heim's objectives: "We try as far as humanly possible, to gear all efforts to the specific requirements of each child, to the peculiarities presented by his individual disturbance and emerging personality. We try to meet . . . his needs of the particular moment, situation, and personal relation" (1955, p. 3). Although psychiatrists see the individualizing of care as a desirable policy, it poses a number of problems.

An essential principle of good medical practice in the hospital treatment of the mentally ill is that the physician know his patient and the nature of his illness. This is particularly important in the psychoses, where variations in symptoms and responses to treatment may be found among patients with the same diagnosis. But to carry this principle into practice involves overcoming obstacles in the current organization and functioning of our state hospitals.

There is, for one thing, the split between public and private medicine. The vast majority of our mental patients are in public institutions, where many of the values that govern physician-patient relationships in private practice are not appropriate. The patient, for example, is not free to choose his own physician; responsibility for treatment may be spread among several rather than concentrated in one physician; and the physician is an employee of the institution as well as the patient's therapist. In addition, if the patient was in treatment prior to admission, his private practitioner ordinarily loses responsibility for him as soon as he enters the public hospital.

Perhaps a more important obstacle to providing individualized care is that our institutions for mental patients are "total institutions," whose characteristic is "the handling of many human needs

by the bureaucratic organization of whole blocks of people" (Goffman, 1958, p. 45). The total institution is all-encompassing: it
attempts to manage and regulate all of the activities of its members. Naturally, the work of the staff is easiest if all patients are
treated alike; but ordinarily patients are divided into a few categories—such as chronic or acute, psychotic or nonpsychotic, disturbed or quiet, bedridden or ambulatory—and grouped and
managed on the basis of these categories. Too often patients are
dealt with as if they lacked individual identities; they become
anonymous without special features or personal histories and are
treated impersonally and by general routines. In many institutions their vast plants and populations and their small staffs and
prescribed functions of custody and control make the disposition
to the uniform treatment of patients well nigh inevitable.

The efforts to individualize care aim at counteracting these
tendencies. The increase in the power and the frequency of attacks on de-individualizing institutional practices seems to be related to rising professional standards and expectations. And the
hope of improving the situation is more realistic in view of increases in funds and personnel. In other words, the first signs of
progress raised hopes and aspirations for the future and led to more
dissatisfaction with things as they are.

Individualized care is not in itself a specific treatment in the
same way as are drugs or electric shock. Rather, in care, treatment,
and management, responsiveness to the patient's unique needs and
desires is made an essential part of all relationships. The organic-
somatic modes of treatment may be used as one form of individualized treatment on a large scale, since drugs or shock can be
varied from patient to patient and prescriptions can be changed
rapidly with changes in the patient's state. However, it cannot be
assumed that these are specific treatments for specific mental illnesses. Unfortunately, most available forms of treatment are not
specific in this sense. Indeed, they are often no more than random
or routine procedures undertaken in the absence of anything
better suited to the particular patient.

Responsiveness to a unique pattern of needs does not mean that
each patient is always dealt with differently from all other patients

—while patients differ, they are also alike in many respects, sharing many general human needs as well as specific symptoms of illness. Individualization does mean that the decisions for treatment are based on an assessment of the patient's specific needs and not on his needs in general. Since time and circumstance change specific needs, the individualized treatment plan must undergo review and revision in relation to the patient's progress.

Individualization of care requires that the needs of patients should be looked at singly and in detail with the person and his particular needs at the center of focus; this does not mean that treatment must be individualized in all areas of the patient's life, but rather in those areas that are *salient* for his illness. In any case, full-fledged individualization requires institutional arrangements that are rarely found in our mental hospitals.

Forms of Individualizing Care

Programs of individualization fall into two broad classes. The first consists of changes in the administrative and ecological organization of the hospital so as to eliminate some of the features of the custodial and "total" institution. The second consists of the procedures and techniques introduced as specific ways of individualizing care and treatment.

PRECONDITIONS FOR INDIVIDUALIZATION

The sheer mathematics of staff-patient ratios in large mental hospitals makes it impossible for the professional staff to spend much time with other than a select few patients. Most patients rarely talk with a physician as often as once a month, and, when they do, he probably has little knowledge of the patients' specific needs. Many patients rarely have as much as five minutes' conversation a week with nursing service personnel.

Physicians and nurses often have to occupy themselves with "high level" administrative matters and with the development of routines, procedures, and standards. The head of a typical psychiatric service may be responsible for between five hundred and one thousand patients—an impossible assignment of responsibility if the individual patient is to be dealt with in a therapeutically meaningful way. Decisions about a patient are made from a distance and are based not on a first-hand familiarity with the patient's needs but on an abstract image of the patient combined with a preoccupation with the institution's needs and problems. A number of observers and practitioners argue that there must be some fundamental changes in administrative patterning and expectation for there to be any progress toward therapeutic goals.

We shall discuss four measures that can be applied to alter the mass and custodial features of mental hospitals: reducing the size of the hospital; eliminating homogeneous wards and services; establishing direct contact between the patient and his responsible physician; and providing more depth and range in the relationships between patients and personnel.

Reducing the Size of the Hospital. Attacks on the vast size of our large state hospitals are neither new nor rare: for many years their hugeness has been condemned as untherapeutic and obsolete. Sometimes their size has been defended as necessary, economical, or efficient, but rarely as desirable therapeutically. Yet it is in these massive institutions that the overwhelming majority of our resident psychiatric population is housed. As a matter of fact, many of the newer hospitals are as large as their predecessors, and many of the new facilities and buildings have been erected not on new sites but as additions to existing institutions, making them still larger.

The larger hospitals will not simply vanish, and, while they exist, they will continue to be used. Faced with this obdurate fact, some superintendents have tried to divide their large institutions into smaller, relatively autonomous units; that is, they make four or five hospitals out of one. This is not the same as the traditional division of the hospital into a number of services—male and female, acute and chronic, and so forth. Rather, ideally, each unit is made into a complete hospital with a full range of facilities, all types of patients, full control over admission and discharge practices and policies, and complete authority over its own programs of treatment and forms of ward organization. A similar development in the field of industrial organization has been given the name "decentralization."

Breaking the hospital into smaller units is expected to increase staff-to-staff as well as staff-to-patient interaction. Personnel should be able to reach the patient more easily and become acquainted with him and his needs. In addition, the increased intimacy among staff personnel is assumed to foster a higher level of morale and group cohesiveness, making it possible for each subhospital to develop its own identity and a corresponding *esprit de corps*. This, it is believed, will lead to more individualized and more personalized relationships with patients—adding further to the initial effects.

Decentralization is a compromise: the subhospitals are still linked together—territorially, legally, and administratively at the upper levels, and often functionally through the joint use of certain facilities that it would be extravagant to duplicate. This degree of connectedness leads to dilemmas that would presumably not arise if the hospitals were completely separate and autonomous. Primarily, these involve the coordination of policies and competition for resources. What is to be done, for example, if the administrator of one of the units wishes to run his unit as an open hospital but the other administrators do not want it for their own units. If autonomy in such decisions is to be preserved, then there must be institutional means for managing and resolving the conflicts it engenders. Another example: if one subhospital has a much higher rate of release than the others, should its proportion of total admissions be increased or should it be permitted to progress naturally toward relatively smaller size and a consequently better staff-to-patient ratio?

Eliminating Homogeneous Wards and Services. Most mental hospitals maintain two main organizations: one devoted to the treatment of newly admitted patients in acute phases of illness; the other to chronic patients. The general flow of patients is from the acute to the chronic service; the reverse is rare. On the chronic service an atmosphere of hopelessness prevails, patients are forgotten, and their lives revolve around the institution, not the outside world.

Practitioners have long recognized the unfortunate consequence of the chronic-acute division of the hospital, not only for the neglected chronic patients but for the atmosphere and programs of the hospital as a whole. The stereotyped view of the patients as hopelessly ill and not quite human tends to spread beyond the chronic wards and pervades the entire hospital. To avoid the consequent social and psychological crippling of patients, some hospitals have tried to eliminate the division into chronic and acute services.

It is hoped that the presence together of patients in various stages of recovery, with various types and degrees of disturbance, and the continual flow of patients out of the ward as well as into it would encourage personnel to be sensitive to the possibilities of positive change in the patients. Further, the elimination of the stagnant atmosphere of the chronic unit would provide an opportunity for many patients who are prisoners of their past histories to escape from illness-maintaining stereotypes.

The attack on the chronic-acute distinction is only the most prominent example of a more general movement toward heterogeneity of wards and services. Patients are frequently segregated according to sex, age, legal status, prognosis, and risk to others or self, but this may not conduce to their welfare. Often architectural holdovers from the past prevent as much mixing of patients as practitioners desire, for, unless there are private rooms or bays for small groups, it is difficult to have mixed wards of men and women. The rationale for general heterogeneity, as that for mixing the chronic and acute, is to combat the tendencies to respond to all patients according to group stereotypes and to facilitate self-fulfilling prophecies in which one's expectations bring about the condition anticipated. It is assumed heterogeneous wards will reduce the probability that such stereotypes and expectations will become stabilized and that, since these wards more closely approximate the outside world, they will promote the patient's eventual adjustment to it.

Eliminating homogeneous wards and services involves the necessity for resisting the persistent pressure of personnel to assign to each of the wards a distinct patient population. This pressure develops for the same reasons that lay behind the original distinctions. First, homogeneous wards make for easier housekeeping and administration. Women's requirements differ from men's regarding clothing and personal toilet facilities; adolescents and young adults differ from senile patients as to space and recreational requirements. If mixing patients is to increase their chances for receiving individualized care, then personnel must develop more flexible routines and must have access to a wider range of facilities and services. Second, there is often the feeling among the patients as well as personnel that the former prefer to be with others like themselves. If the entire hospital has six adolescent boys, the argument runs, wouldn't it be better for them if they were all on the same ward? Many of the "better" patients do not want to be on the same wards with the very sick or acutely disturbed. As a matter of fact, we know little about the adverse effects of the sicker patients—if they are adverse—but we usually assume that the "better" patients will have favorable effects on the others.

But, as it happens, patients do tend to form groups along lines of common interests or traits, different from the organization's rules and classifications. If the tendency to restore homogeneity is to be resisted, living units will have to be large enough to allow for "pockets of homogeneity" within a unit that is heterogeneous. The desideratum is that these pockets do not persist in an untherapeutic stable form and that none become so dominant and all-encompassing as to lead to a new stereotyping of the unit.

On the other hand, there are practitioners who believe that one way to begin individualizing care is to develop separate facilities for different age and diagnostic categories of patients. Thus, some institutions are being built to house, for example, geriatric patients or alcoholics, it being assumed that they have peculiar needs that can best be met when they are together. However, it is an open question whether all this is primarily for administrative convenience and ease of handling or designed to meet the individual needs of particular patients.

Establishing Direct Contact between the Patient and His Responsible Physician. In a state hospital the psychiatrist is usually responsible for an entire service consisting of a number of wards, but, with hundreds of patients in his charge, it is impossible for him to know them in any intimate or detailed way. Usually he has no administrative help beyond a secretary, and sometimes not even that. The legal questions surrounding the admission, detention, and release of patients necessitate a great deal of paperwork to which he must attend; indeed, he is forced into more and more administrative work that removes him still further from his patients. In consequence, he has to depend on intermediaries for information in drawing up his plans of treatment, since his own brief contacts usually occur in contexts where he can gain little knowledge of the patients for himself. So he must rely on ward personnel to transmit accurate information. But they may have motives other than the simple wish to present a valid picture to the psychiatrist of a patient's status and needs. Further, the patient would have to learn to communicate about himself in a manner easily and readily understood and transmitted to the psychiatrist; obviously an expectation difficult, if not impossible, to fulfill.

This problem persists because of the shortage of hospital psychiatrists. No effort whatever to bring physician and patient into closer contact can be successful if there is a ratio of four hundred patients to one psychiatrist. On the other hand, even in hospitals with a more adequate number of psychiatrists or psychiatric residents, the difficulty in establishing direct contact between physician and patient is perpetuated by traditional styles of coverage and assignment. The problems of dealing with intermediaries is compounded by the fact that there are so many nurses and attendants with whom the physician must interact and that the ward subcultures vary among themselves, so that the information he receives about patients may reflect these personnel and ward differences rather than differences among patients.

In order to bring the psychiatrist back to observing, assessing, and planning directly for individual patients, some practitioners urge that psychiatrists or psychiatric residents become ward leaders or managers: the ward is to become the unit of administrative responsibility with planning of treatment for all patients to be carried out by the psychiatrist attached to it. This is often com-

bined with the form previously described, that of developing heterogeneous wards. Under these circumstances the psychiatrist
would be in much closer contact with ward personnel as well as
with patients. In general, this gives rise to a new and more active
supervisory role.

As a ward manager he may function not only in a clinical capacity with patients but also in organizing ward activities and in encouraging nursing personnel to develop individualized relationships with patients. Through becoming responsible for a more
manageable administrative unit, the physician should be able to
see his patients' illnesses more specifically and fully. In addition,
his presence and his evident interest in individualizing care may
serve as a model for personnel.

While from certain points of view all this has obvious advantages, there is a great deal of resistance to it, even in institutions
where the numbers of available psychiatrists might easily allow for
it. To understand the reason for this resistance, one must recall
that the absence of the doctor from the scene has permitted a ward
culture to develop that is dominated by nursing service personnel.
They have been in actual charge of the patients' daily lives, and
the physician's new functions would interfere with this established pattern. Furthermore, they have taken their intermediary
function very seriously, perceiving themselves as protecting the
doctor from exploitation by patients. For example, in one hospital, when we asked ward personnel what would happen if the
doctor's office was on the ward, the response was: "He'd never
get his work done. The patients would be bothering him all the
time." The active presence of the doctor, of course, eliminates this
protective function. Supervisory nurses and ward personnel often
interpret the return of the doctor to the ward as a sign that they
have failed in some way and as a threat to the existing system of
relationships among themselves and with patients. And, of course,
the move closer to the ward is also a threat to the physician, since
it does remove the buffers between him and the patients.

Finally, this development seems to assume that physicians, because of their medical training, are equipped to manage the complex systems of social relationships that constitute the ward. Suc-

cessful administration of these units requires competence in social and group dynamics as well as in individual dynamics, and so additional training becomes necessary. The increased contact may increase disagreements between the physician and the nursing service personnel, disagreements which can no longer be ignored or pushed into the background but must be lived with day-by-day. Often the nursing supervisory staff is still oriented toward custodial-control values, and ward personnel and patients are caught in the conflict between supervisors and the ward physician who comes to his task oriented toward the individualization of patients. Thus, additional training also may be required for the supervisory staff, too, so that they and their subordinates can become active and willing agents of individualization.

Facilitating the Range of Relationships between Patients and Personnel. Ordinarily, the care and treatment of a hospitalized patient is divided among a number of different specialties and departments, each responsible for helping him at different times, in different places, and in different ways. Even where there is a comprehensive plan of treatment, there is seldom adequate co-ordination, and the patient is subjected to a disjointed and fragmented pattern of help. In addition, this traditional division of labor makes it difficult for personnel to focus on individuals as "whole" persons and so interferes with the possibility of individualizing care.

An attempt at reorganization to deal with this problem in a small residential treatment center for children (Henry, 1957) is described as "simple undifferentiated subordination," which means that the task of treating the patient is not divided up among a number of different specialties but that the total care of the patient is the responsibility of a single "counselor." The latter is given intensive supervision by the director of the institution and is assigned to individual patients and not to a ward or a specific treatment or activity. The institution is so organized as to reduce the distance between patients and staff and to facilitate direct, continuous, and varied relationships and interaction between particular workers and particular patients.

Whereas the exact number of patients that a counselor may

work with effectively is not known, it cannot be large, and there simply are not enough personnel in state hospitals to permit extensive "simple, undifferentiated" relationships. However, programs now in operation in many hospitals, but on a much reduced scale, foster similar types of relationships in assigning someone to a patient for a particular period of time or a specified sequence of activities. Often in a crisis the patient is given a "general helper." For example, another patient may be assigned to help a new one through the stress of admission and initial adjustment to the hospital; a student nurse may take a patient as a "project" and stay with him during her entire tour of duty; a volunteer may be assigned to particular patients rather than to a particular hospital service; a nurse may "special" a patient during acute depression or disturbance; or an attendant may be assigned to interact with six patients as his special group. All these rather special and limited activities provide more depth, range, and continuity to relationships between patients and personnel than is usual.

These and other programs designed to individualize care by increasing the depth and range of personnel-patient relationships differ from other developments described in this section in their direct emphasis on the nature of the relationship itself. In the forms described earlier—reducing hospital size, creating heterogeneous wards, decreasing distance between patient and physician —the relationship entered into with the patient is not defined by the administrative change itself. But the form discussed here requires, as a defining feature, a high level of direct involvement with patients. While problems that result from administrative demands to increase the intensity of involvement with patients arise fairly frequently in all programs of individualization, they are particularly common here. In general, it is easier for attendants, who are relatively untrained and often inadequately motivated for the proper psychiatric treatment of patients, to restrict the range and intensity of their contacts with patients, for, while increased involvement with patients can be potentially more rewarding and satisfying than the more restricted and impersonal relations that are now prevalent, it is likely at first to precipitate anxiety, frustration, and discouragement. Working closely with mental patients is hard work, the more closely the harder. The prerequisites of maintaining these intense contacts on a continuing basis are institutional arrangements to give continuous support and direct supervision to the personnel.

SPECIFIC PROCEDURES

In this section we shall discuss some specific techniques and procedures of individualizing care in hospital programs in three broad groups: those with a primary focus on the patient—aimed at encouraging him to express himself as an individual; those seeking to increase the staff's responsiveness to the patient's needs; and, finally, those centered on the relationship with the patient and bringing out the specifically therapeutic qualities of individualized relationships.

Fostering the Expression of the Patient's Individuality. Recent studies of the social structure and culture of the state mental hospital reveal that the hospital provides less opportunity for the development and expression of individuality than do even the most restricted sections of outside society.[1] The patient's proper role is narrowly defined, and rigid rules govern all his personal relationships. Even his psychotic behavior must be expressed through narrowly circumscribed channels, and the hospital's response to deviance from its own norms is often swifter and as punitive as is found in the nonhospital world.

In what ways, if any, are patients being helped through being encouraged to act spontaneously? Presumably, they thereby gain satisfaction and useful insights into themselves and learn to deal constructively in their own terms with their problems.

Traditional avenues for fostering the expression of the patient's individuality are the ancillary therapies found in some form in most mental hospitals—occupational therapy, music therapy, recreational therapy, bibliotherapy, and so forth. With the explicit aim of individualizing care and treatment, the patient may be given a plastic medium and told he may make with it anything he wishes. Neither usefulness nor excellence enter in, the objective being to help him find ways of expressing himself through the medium. His productions may be used both diagnostically and therapeutically; for example, the finger-paintings, drawings, or clay figures may be used as clues to his illness and his progress. In one small private hospital these activities emphasize "creative" expression. Instead of trained occupational therapists, the institution hired a painter and a ceramicist and utilized the talents of a modern dancer and a novelist. The aim was not merely to pass time more pleasantly or to express impulses more freely but to discover unknown talents and desires and to develop deep and continuing interests in creative work.

Many programs appear based on the assumption that self-expression requires one-to-one relationships between therapists and patients or even situations where the patient works by himself. This seems unnecessarily restrictive. People can and do express themselves in groups and develop as individuals through their participation in group processes, though our knowledge of the integration of group and individual dynamics is lamentably slight. Our ignorance and the scarcity of group practitioners may in part account for the limited development of group-oriented programs to foster the expression of individuality.

We found a few instances in which patient discussion groups or work meetings are in part oriented toward individualization: one of them is called Remotivation Group Therapy. Patients meet regularly in groups of ten to twenty under the leadership of a ward attendant trained as a group leader. Using poetry as a stimulus, the patients are encouraged to talk about themselves, their interests and plans, and, in general, to exchange opinions among themselves. In other group programs the patients participate in decisions about many aspects of their lives in the hospital and even, in some instances, about their release from it. (For a discussion of patient participation in decision making see Chapter 11.)

In social groups to encourage the expression and development of individuality, group norms and processes are sometimes developed that grant the patient a considerable degree of autonomy and independence. In these situations, his opinions are actively elicited; he takes responsibility for and makes judgments about issues that affect others; he sees his own ideas accepted or challenged; he recognizes their consequences for himself and others;

and, generally, he is able to see himself as someone who counts and whose opinions on important issues are taken seriously. The general assumption is that in a supportive group atmosphere he can discover, explore, and test out his own unique qualities.

Some recurrent difficulties shared by all programs arise in the fact that they all require personnel to encourage patients in the full and free expression of their needs. Staff members are asked not only to allow the patient to "be himself," but they must actively urge him toward freer expression of his impulses, an injunction directly counter to the traditional emphasis on control. Many patients, too, may be as frightened of relative permissiveness as personnel, and, inevitably, various protective mechanisms come into play, which may subvert the original intention of "free expression." This occurs, for example, if the therapists or group leaders select for participation in the program only patients who "know how to behave properly." Another problem is that norms of group life may develop that turn out to inhibit patient free expression, and these too must be recognized and dealt with.

Increasing Personnel Responsiveness to Patients. Almost all progressive developments in modern hospital practice aim in part at sensitizing therapists and personnel to the particular needs of particular patients in particular situations. We will present several specific programs that have this as a goal and that emphasize important points in the career of the hospital patient—admission, diagnosis, treatment, and discharge.

Admission to the mental hospital is all too often a humiliating experience, reinforcing the patient's low self-esteem. In an atmosphere of impersonality and indifference, he waits for attention. He is stripped of clothes, spectacles, money, watches, wedding rings. He is put in a shower. He is given a perfunctory examination and is probably not told where he is and why and what will be done to and for him and why.

Aware of the shock and pain occasioned by these first experiences, one teaching hospital arranges for the patient to be greeted on admission by a team: the attending psychiatrist, the social worker, and the nurse or attendant of the ward to which he will be assigned. In addition to lessening the trauma of admission, the procedure has the advantage of giving the staff members a joint experience with the patient, which permits them later to work out a more comprehensive and individualized plan of treatment than is usually possible. Moreover, a team representative makes the patient's acquaintance immediately and then introduces him to other personnel and patients on the ward.

In a small private hospital, where a great deal of emphasis is placed on finding alternatives to hospitalization, admission is looked upon as a crisis that offers maximum opportunity for exerting therapeutic leverage on the patient and his family. Instead of taking the admission for granted, it is used as an exploratory opportunity to see if hospitalization is really necessary.

In each instance, the attempt to individualize care consists of finding out about the patient's unique problems, respecting his need to be oriented, trying to allay his anxiety about the admission, and showing the patient that the hospital personnel recognize how important the admission experience is to him.

The diagnostic process may in itself be a form of individualization, for it implies that different mental illnesses require different forms of treatment. Unfortunately, conventional state hospital diagnostic practice tends to underemphasize the fact that systems of psychiatric nosology are only approximate descriptions and that most concrete cases present "mixed" pictures. In practice, diagnosis tends to change from understanding the patient to "fitting" the patient into the right slot, that is, it is made a substitute for rather than an aid to a full understanding of the patient. In addition, standard practice in the state mental hospitals assigns the task of preparing a preliminary diagnosis to the most inexperienced members of the staff.

The procedures of diagnostic staff conferences vary from hospital to hospital. Their primary object is a final diagnosis that corresponds to one of the official categories and can be recorded in the patient's folder in the language of scientific psychiatry. In some instances, the clinical director makes the final decision, sometimes minority opinions are recorded, and in one instance we observed a democratic vote being taken among those present, the plurality decision being the final diagnosis. Often the diagnostic conference is the arena for working out staff hostilities and struggles for power rather than a forum for exchanging information and reaching a deeper and more comprehensive understanding of the patient.

Proposals for improving the diagnostic process to allow for greater individualization usually require the utilization of a wider and more varied range of information and a dynamic assessment of the patient's functioning, not the static categories of descriptive psychiatry. As to the first, the "new" information often concerns the patient's daily life in the hospital or his total life situation in the outside world. Collecting and interpreting these additional kinds of information require that in addition to the psychiatrist, others become more involved than previously, since the psychiatrist normally has neither the necessary time nor the special competence for this. Thus, social workers, nurses, ward attendants, and ancillary therapists take on a more active role that is likely to have secondary favorable effects on their own efforts at individualization. As to the second improvement, to the extent that dynamic formulations, in contrast to static diagnoses, require continuous assessment and review of the patient's status and progress, the treatment emphasis moves sharply in the direction of individualized planning.

The assumption underlying diagnostic activity is that there are specific treatments and approaches to the patient that are more appropriate for certain illnesses than others. This is particularly evident in the use of the "interaction prescription" as a way of individualizing care and treatment. As the term implies, it is a definition of the way in which personnel should interact with patients, especially what are the proper attitudes to convey to him. The basic tools are management devices through which the patient is to be encouraged or discouraged from expressing certain feelings and behaviors. He is approached through one of a set of fundamental attitudes that vary in firmness, kindliness, activity, and so forth.

Whereas in the interaction prescription, personnel direct their attention to the underlying psychodynamics of the individual case, in a residential treatment center for children, where importance is also attached to individualized treatment, the focus is on the dynamics of the immediate situation. In "life space therapy" personnel move directly into a crisis or problem situation and try, on the spot, to discuss and work through with the patient the dynamics of his immediate difficulties. The personnel thereby become sensitively attuned to situational cues that produce marked differences in the patient's behavior, and, by noting changes in his responses, they are able to evaluate his current emotional state as well as his progress and to respond accordingly.

Until very recently little attention was given to the social and psychological dynamics of leaving the hospital. In the large majority of instances neither the patient, the hospital staff, nor significant persons outside are given advance notice of a patient's release. Often the process is quite impersonal: the patient is simply informed of the physician's decision—a decision based frequently on a brief contact during the rapid tour of the wards.

Various attempts have been made to prepare the patient and his family in advance for the homecoming. One attempt to individualize discharge is through the use of psychodrama: patients about to be discharged are prepared for some of the roles they will have to perform by acting them out and living through them in a group situation. Individualization is achieved by selecting those predicaments and problems that are salient for particular patients and helping them cope with them through the simulated situations.

All of the attempts to individualize care discussed in this section are concerned with increasing the sensitivity of personnel to the expression of patient needs so that they can respond in a more differentiated way. The interaction prescription requires translating diagnoses and evaluations into specific approaches so that the treatment the patient receives accords with its objectives. The prescribed treatments require certain qualities and characteristics of the interpersonal and ward relationships, and some ward personnel may find it difficult to "produce" the specified feelings and attitudes at the time and place required and with the designated patient.

Some modes of individualization encourage nursing personnel

to be spontaneous with patients and to use their judgment and intuition—as in life space therapy. But then a problem arises in the wide range of choices in treating patients and in the assignment of responsibility for the decision to the person closest to the situation. Where there is a general injunction, as in the interaction prescription, to be "kind but firm," then the nurse or attendant does not have the responsibility of choosing among alternatives without knowing the probable consequences of each. When standard and definite ways of dealing with patients are removed, personnel are thrown more on their own resources and this commonly increases insecurity and anxiety. The probability of overinvolvement with patients also arises, a pervasive problem in all treatment but especially acute in these programs.

The burdens of choice and of involvement are heavy ones. The success of programs for individualizing care seems to depend on the concomitant individualization of administrative and supervisory relationships with personnel. Staff needs and capacities vary in the same way as those of patients. The conditions of work must be made flexible enough to provide personnel with appropriate reward, support, and satisfaction so that the extra demands do not overwhelm them.

Maximizing the Therapeutic Functions of Individualized Relationships. The most complex and demanding forms of individualizing treatment are the various psychotherapies—both group and individual. These may be distinguished from other programs we have discussed in that the emphasis is primarily on the relationships developed among the patients as group members or between the patients and the therapist. Therapy consists in exploring the personal significance of these relationships and in helping the patient to enter into and manage them with less anxiety, conflict, and discomfort than hitherto, the specific methods varying between the various schools of psychotherapy.

Although individual psychotherapy has become less rare in recent years in the large state hospitals, the number of trained persons who are currently available or likely to become so for this intensive work is totally inadequate to the needs. It is common for the psychiatrist or other therapist to have less than ten minutes a week for each of the patients for whom he is formally responsible. This, combined with prevalent notions of "proper" psychotherapy leads to the restriction of this form of treatment to an extremely limited and highly selected group of patients. If individual psychotherapy is to have real impact on the large population of mental patients, ways must be found to apply its principles and techniques on a large scale.

Solutions usually involve introducing greater flexibility into the traditional arrangements for individual psychotherapy. The easiest solution of all is to reduce the amount of time spent with the patient. Thus, in one institution the therapists have experimented with fifteen-minute sessions instead of the usual fifty minutes, or sessions may be scheduled weekly or biweekly instead of daily. Another solution is to allow less well-trained individuals to engage in psychotherapy with certain types of patients under specified conditions. In other words, it is assumed that the experienced psychiatrist, "over-trained" for certain cases, should be reserved for those requiring his high level of competence. Of course, therapists might be trained to specialize in certain kinds of cases to permit much greater efficiency in treatment. All these proposals tend to dilute the traditional pattern of individual psychotherapy while preserving some of its principles.

Group psychotherapy has a long history in mental hospitals and appears in as many different forms as does individual psychotherapy. Nevertheless, it is not usually thought of as a method of individualizing patient care and treatment; more often it is viewed as a poor substitute for individual treatment occasioned by the press of numbers. In one large state hospital, however, group situations are being used explicitly to individualize patient care. The patients on a ward are divided into groups of six, each with a specific nurse or attendant as a leader. In essence, activities are programmed for the group as a unit; there are regular group meetings, and interaction between patients within each group is actively encouraged. It is assumed that a group identity will hereby be established, that patients will enter into various relationships with others of the group, and that getting to know the patients better because of the greater intimacy and intensity of their relationships will permit personnel to individualize care to a greater extent than under the ordinary conditions of ward life.

In addition to an emphasis on the therapeutic value of particular relationships, there is additional interest in the potential value of a variety of relationships. In two small institutions observed, personnel from all levels and divisions of the hospital—in maintenance and clerical departments as well as the clinical services—are encouraged to interact with and establish relationships with patients. No attempt is made to assimilate these relationships in some standard therapeutic model; but rather they are allowed to develop according to the personal and social requirements of the situation. This is in contrast to the individual psychotherapeutic model, where the patient's interaction with others might be viewed as an unwelcome interference. An issue that has heretofore received little attention has to do with the impact of other relationships on the one relationship that has been singled out as therapeutically significant.

Discussion

Although they are diverse in form and focus, programs of individualization are all aimed essentially at establishing the patient and his needs in the dominant position in the institution. The basic intent of this trend is to make the patient's needs, rather than the staff's convenience or administrative requirements, primary in determining how the hospital functions. But some of the difficulties in carrying out this goal seem to be related to the fuzziness and vagueness of the idea of individualization.

THE DEFINITION OF INDIVIDUALIZATION

Perhaps the most important notion related to individualization is that of personalization—which, itself, refers to a number of different things. Most broadly, it refers to relationships with patients chosen for attention because of their particular personal qualities, that is, their distinctive histories and their traits as individual human beings. Often it connotes a mutuality in the relationship in which the helper shares some of his personal feelings with the patient or lets the patient get to know him as a person. Ordinarily the term is used in the sense of the intimate, close, or special relationship maintained on a one-to-one basis between therapist and patient. Psychotherapy and simple undifferentiated care—to name just two examples—make this type of individualization the cornerstone of their treatment. But this is only one kind of individualization and does not exhaust the full meaning of the term. We have thought of the objective of the programs described above as supplying the central and most general meaning of individualization, namely, treatment planned on the basis of a particular patient's needs, and maintaining and manifesting a continuing interest in an individual patient's welfare.

If the distinction is preserved between personalization (in the sense of one-to-one "special" relationship) and individualization, it frees us to think of individualizing care in a group, rather than only on a one-to-one basis. When faced with the problem of treating many patients together, the tendency is to think of this as treating patients *as* a group rather than *in* a group, and the group is seen as an obstacle to individualizing care rather than as a potential resource.

Constructed groups in hospitals may be favorable or adverse in their effect on patients in the same ways as are natural social groups. Nevertheless, current psychiatric thought upholds the necessity of participation and involvement in social groups if the individual is to develop fully as a person.[2] To the extent that this principle comes to have more influence on treatment and research, we would expect the systematic utilization of group processes to take its place as one of the powerful tools in individualization.

Another advantage in considering individualization as a process different from personalization—where it is an integral part of a group activity—is that some of the difficulties that usually accompany special or intimate pair-relations might be minimized or avoided. We have in mind the overinvolvement of the helper and the tensions and difficulties among personnel because one staff member is maintaining a personal relationship while others are not.

An issue is the tendency to think of the absence of personalized treatment as impersonal treatment or depersonalization of the patient. Hard, cold, and indifferent handling of patients does occur in the mental hospital. All the same, the opposite, or absence, of personalized treatment does not necessarily mean indifferent or uninterested treatment. It could mean that treatment is given to whoever needs it without personal reference. It seems plausible that patients may benefit from recognizing treatment as a universal right when needed, and not something given or withheld as a reward or punishment.

Another notion is that an adequate treatment plan, to be individualized, must take account of *all* of the patient's needs. This is an impossible criterion, besides which, in practice, it serves to blur the perception of patients' real needs and the effect of treatment. Treatment is based on choice—not only among modes of treatment but among the needs and problems considered the most important and the range of possible goals of treatment. To individualize treatment does not mean treating the "whole" person, for it is not that individualization is total and other approaches partial in their view of the patient but that the former permits the necessary choices of treatment—to be based more surely on the patient's needs than on irrelevant matters, such as current fads and ideologies of practice, therapists' social values, or institutional requirements.

Certain types of personalization and the conception of "treating the whole person" may lead to serious problems, as we have suggested. We are more concerned, however, with the tendency to attribute difficulties and failings to individualization than we are with the particular problems themselves. To individualize care and treatment is difficult enough; the difficulties are only compounded when individualization is not clearly distinguished from other notions.

VALUES COMPETITIVE WITH INDIVIDUALIZATION

Certain elements related to the functioning of hospitals as social organizations, hospital personnel's orientations toward work, and general attitudes toward deviance introduce values that compete with that of individualization.

In stressing the "primacy of patient needs" as the most significant aspect of individualization, we have not entered into the question of how to balance them with institutional needs and requirements. All social organizations require compromises and adjustments from their members for proper functioning, and no particular patient's needs can be given primacy in the hospital if this involves a failure to meet institutional requirements. However, this is not a problem that can be solved once and for all by a statement of abstract principle such as "the patient always comes first." The critical point is that more than one patient is always involved in institutional treatment and maximizing the satisfaction of one patient's needs may lead to either ignoring or frustrating others.

The usefulness of an emphasis on individualization is that it keeps the problem alive and current in settings where there has been a traditional neglect of patient needs in favor of tradition or administrative requirements. We are aware that the consideration of patient needs sometimes serves only as a rationalization for decisions made on other grounds.[3] Nevertheless, an emphasis on individualization permits and even invites questioning of decisions made on other grounds—regardless of their legitimacy and worth—so that patients' needs are less likely to be forgotten in the crush of institutional imperatives.

Good working conditions do not automatically correspond to good treatment conditions. For most persons whose interest in their jobs is somewhat short of dedication—and this does not mean that they are poor employees even in a mental hospital—discomfort, anxiety, tension, and concentrated attentiveness to the patients' demands that accompany psychiatric work are not generally considered characteristics of a good working environment. Programs of individualization may intensify some problems and diminish others. Many hospital routines reflect more concern with the needs and the characteristics of the working force than of the patients. For example, the scheduling of meals and the amount of time allowed for them is set so as to permit personnel to time their housekeeping activities in accordance with the changes in shifts; but it also means that patients may have to eat when they are not hungry or to rush through their meals. To make their needs primary, by rescheduling meal hours, would make things more inconvenient for the staff. When rescheduling is done, personnel are asked to take seriously the fact that the mental hospital is different from other work situations in that its therapeutic goals are meant to take precedence over working conditions.

An analogous problem for the psychiatric and other professionals in the hospital has to do with what has been called their professional identities. The division of labor in a mental hospital is elaborate; work roles have become specialized and well established. But certain of the specific programs require the redefinition of some of the hospital jobs and consequent shifts in professional identities and perspectives, for example, a greater interest in, respect for, and concern about the patient, or a different view toward him, or more egalitarian collaboration of different levels of staff. Also, regardless of the specific content of the old or the new roles, individualization requires that comprehensive and self-consistent plans of treatment be developed in a system with a highly specialized division of labor. This demands effective planning and coordination. Beyond this, it is unclear as to whether and how this approach can fit into a system of specialized roles in treatment with various persons dealing with different aspects of the patient and pursuing different goals. (We have described simple, undifferentiated subordination as a program that assumes the incompatibility of specialized roles and individualized treatment.)

In addition to specific work attitudes and occupational perspectives, there are general values that employees and professionals carry with them. Most important from our point of view are their attitudes on deviance. At best, they may be ambivalent; at worst they may believe that "wrongdoers" should be punished. When we assert the primacy of patient needs, we are asking for a level of tolerance that to many may be difficult to achieve. Consequently, adequate training and supervision are a necessary, though not always a sufficient, condition for personnel to be able to function effectively in programs where individualization is of central importance.

This discussion is not intended to discourage practitioners from engaging in individualized programs for patient care. We have been concerned, rather, with pointing out some types of problems that are sometimes associated with this approach. It is hoped that such a clarification as this may be an impetus rather than an impediment to experimentation with processes and structures that foster the individualization of care.

Chapter 10

Breaking Down the Barriers between
Hospital and Community

The summary of a symposium of hospital administrators concludes: "Regardless of the problems and the difficulties involved in removing the barriers between hospital and community, the opinion was expressed that this is the most exciting innovation in psychiatry today." [1]

Other symposia and articles as well as our own observations and discussion with various experts all reinforce the impression that among those in the field this opinion is widespread. Historically relationships between mental hospitals and their communities have been far from ideal, but that there is a particular problem in the form of barriers between the hospital and the community seems to be a relatively recent idea.

Like all social organizations, mental hospitals have certain functions that are more or less clearly understood by their own members and by persons in the community. Commonly recognized boundaries of responsibility permit organizations to function with a minimum of conflict, confusion, and inefficiency. Usually, however, functional boundaries—among all types of social organizations and between them and the community—are not regarded as barriers interfering with necessary interaction. Therefore, when a particular boundary that was seen traditionally as serving a useful purpose—as that between the mental hospital and the community—comes to be viewed as undesirable, we may assume some fundamental changes in either the hospital or the community or in their relationships with each other have occurred.

It is to the absence of good relations between hospital and community that many practitioners refer when they speak of a barrier between them. They often phrase the problem as a lack of under-standing on the part of the persons in the community of the hospital's requirements for carrying out its program successfully. Practitioners also point to a number of specific aspects of the relationships between the hospital and the community that they believe both reflect and contribute to this general lack of under-standing. Among the holdovers from the past that are judged to be the most serious barriers between the hospital and the commu-nity are the following: (1) negative attitudes of persons in the community: the stigma attached to mental illness, fears and appre-hensions about mental patients, stereotypes of the mental hospital, and little confidence in the possibility of successful treatment; (2) the sharp differences between the sociocultural system of the hos-pital and that of the outside community; and (3) the relative lack of interaction between the hospital and community in the sense of the nonparticipation of each in the affairs and activities of the others.

As a result of recent changes in the hospital's goals, each of these traditional aspects of the relationship between the hospital and community is now perceived as a barrier whereas previously they were either accepted as appropriate or were not seen as particu-larly relevant to the hospital's functions. In other words, these characteristics of hospital–community relationships—the negative attitudes, the hospital's isolation—are consistent with the custodial and repressive goals of an earlier model of the mental hospital. They do not fit the new objectives.

Forms of Breaking Down the Barriers

CHANGING NEGATIVE ATTITUDES
TOWARD MENTAL ILLNESS, PATIENTS, AND HOSPITALS

The Open Door. The prevalent attitude toward mental illness and mental patients in our society is substantially unfavorable. It appears due in large part to the fear and anxiety aroused by the most serious manifestations of emotional disturbance, the severe psychoses. The public tends to see the psychotic as incurable and

capable of unpredictable aggressive or sexual behavior. This view
seems to extend to the less serious mental illnesses, and, unfortunately, the pervasiveness of stigma seems rooted deeply enough
to resist conventional attempts at changing it.[2]

Hospital administrators, of course, are particularly concerned
with the way persons in their local communities perceive and
respond to their patients and hospitals. The existence of stigma
makes them especially apprehensive about the community's response to new programs offering more freedom to patients, which,
a number of them told us, often delays or prevents their introduction.

Fear and anxiety also strongly color the public's image of the
mental hospital itself. The forbidding appearance of many of our
large state hospitals, especially their coldness and impersonality as
organizations, and the deprivation of the patient's adult rights all
enter into the grim picture. To this is added the belief that hospitalization for psychiatric treatment will result in permanent
institutionalization.[3] As a barrier between the hospital and the
community, stigma is a formidable deterrent to the new goals of
facilitating hospital admissions. Stigma plays a role, too, in the
widespread reluctance to refer persons or for persons to submit
themselves for hospital treatment until their illness has become
particularly severe and, to some extent, in the community's reluctant acceptance of released patients.

Below, we shall explore the impact on the social organization
of hospitals of programs and developments for reducing or eliminating stigma as a barrier between the hospital and the community. Connections between the barrier itself and current features
of hospital organization, while somewhat indirect, do apparently
exist. For example, the general difficulty in recruiting and maintaining highly qualified and well-motivated persons for psychiatric hospital staff appears in large part to be a function of the
low esteem and the associated low level of rewards for the jobs—
which is in turn related to the unfavorable attitudes. Also, the
general rejection and indifference to the patient and the hospital
may have permitted the development of the familiar quasi-feudal

social structure that is so prominent and change-resistant a characteristic of our large psychiatric institutions.

The traditional large state mental hospital is the focal point of much of the negative beliefs and attitudes about psychiatric institutions, and so many measures to change them involve modifying one or another characteristic of the hospitals themselves or of developing new and quite different facilities.

That the state mental hospital is often seen to resemble a prison more than a hospital is a function both of the public's belief that the patients themselves are dangerous—and therefore require imprisonment—and of the system of repressive control over the lives of the patients. The locked ward and the key are primary symbols of the traditional hospital. A most interesting attempt in recent years to alter the image of the hospital is the introduction of the "open door" policy or the "open hospital," and one observer notes that, among other benefits, this "eliminates the stigma which is still attached to mental disease and mental hospitals." [4]

There is a fair amount of variation among the hospitals we visited as to how open they are and to some extent as to how open they plan to become. It has apparently been not too difficult for a number of hospitals fairly quickly to reach a point where between one third and one half of their patients are on open wards (usually defined as wards that are unlocked for at least eight hours each day, where special permission is not generally required for patients to leave and re-enter).

In one 2,000-bed state mental hospital visited by us, the open door policy is the major principle of hospital administration and practice. At the time of our visit, only three out of forty-one wards were closed, and over ninety percent of the resident patients was quartered on the open wards. This remarkable degree of openness had been reached in less than three years; before that there were only two wards open and less than ten percent of the patients with "honor" cards for ground privileges. Our informants reported that during the transition period there were no major serious incidents involving patients and no opposition from the community. Personnel at all levels, concerned and apprehensive during the initial stages, now praise the policy, attribute to it major credit for an improved atmosphere, and take pride in their open hospital as an advanced treatment institution.

The policy has been in effect for too short a time for anyone to assess adequately its impact on stigma. However, all evidence that has come to our attention, while not proof, tends to support the hypothesis that unlocking the doors creates a more favorable attitude toward the institution and promotes both the entry of patients in the hospital and their leaving it. In the open hospital we have just described, the percentage of voluntary admissions has risen from twenty-five to fifty percent of the total, and there has been a doubling in the number of patients placed on convalescent care or in family care over the three-year period.[5]

The process of "opening" a hospital is complex, involving a number of interesting questions. For example, should bad risks be shifted from a ward that is to be opened? Apparently, such a move may relieve the staff's anxiety in the earliest stages but may not be necessary after that. Or, should the pace at which wards are opened be fast or slow? And should they be opened according to a predetermined schedule? (After the initial period, the pace may become quite rapid; we have no information about the effects of a schedule.)

Many students of hospital psychiatry have come to recognize that an important feature of the hospital is that it is a social system as well as a treatment facility, that is, in addition to dispensing specific treatments to patients, the various groups of persons there behave toward each other according to an intricate system of formal and informal social traditions and rules. The hospital might be called a miniature society. As members of it, individuals in the hospital regard proposals for change with apprehension and suspicion since change may disrupt established ways and require new modes of adjustment. Because of the complex and multiple ways in which persons and groups interact with each other, even a minor change in practice may reverberate throughout the whole system. It is not surprising that students of the culture and social organization of mental hospitals report strong and persistent opposition to change in organization or operation.[6]

Since the introduction of an open door policy constitutes a major change, one would expect resistance on the part of personnel, and serious difficulties in maintaining it once introduced. The little evidence we have been able to accumulate on hospitals that have pursued this new policy, through our own observations and the reports of others, indicates that the actual resistance varies greatly from one hospital to another and often—as in the case we described above—has been much less than predicted. What accounts for the variation? More specifically, what are the characteristics of hospitals where an open door policy can be carried through successfully? Many, it is true, have encountered serious difficulties, and we do not wish to leave the impression that the policy is easy to introduce.

Our general assumption is that the success of an institutional change, in other instances as well as this, largely depends on the extent and the nature of the redefinitions of their role that the change requires of persons in the social organization. That is, what important expectations and responses must change for whom and toward whom? Are the new roles more, or less, comfortable and satisfying than the old?

The open door policy requires changes particularly in the role relationships of ward personnel with patients, for the primary change is to strip away as much as possible of the protective custodial functions of the attendant and the nurse. It is no longer necessary to make sure the ward door is locked properly, nor to count patients, nor check on the presence of visitors, nor assess the possibility of elopement for different patients, nor perform any of the other standard time-and-energy-consuming activities that implement these functions. These changes appear to make the job easier, and the new policy might be welcomed on this ground alone. At least two other conditions, however, enter into determining how personnel respond. First, as they are relieved of their duty and obligation to "guard" the patient and protect the community, they must simultaneously be relieved of their accountability and responsibility for the patients' actions. When patients can no longer be kept under relatively constant surveillance—a pattern of control terminated by an open door policy—

it is impossible for personnel to control their actions. Administrative policies that require personnel to retain their traditional responsibility for patients' behavior are incompatible with the realities of the open hospital and usher in problems that are usually expressed as resistance to the innovation.

Even though this sounds obvious enough, one important psychological residue of traditional hospital culture is the skepticism of personnel regarding the support they will receive from superiors in the event of incidents and crises. For this reason, a most important ingredient of change must be establishing trust. Personnel in lower echelons must overcome their suspicion and skepticism and begin to believe the assurances of their superiors, and the development of this belief will rest on the actual performance of their superiors, as time goes on.

We suspect that the time required to open a hospital and the difficulty encountered are functions of how long it takes to establish this trust. Our impression is that one of the most important factors in the development of trust is the quality of leadership exercised both at the highest levels within the institution and in outside agencies with legal authority over its operation. Briefly, each person in the hospital can confidently accept the new definitions of his responsibilities only insofar as his superior feels a similar confidence, and this depends on the exercise of effective leadership at all levels.

Shifting responsibility for the patient's behavior to higher echelons frees ward personnel in a legal or formal sense from their obligations as guards; however, they are not yet psychologically free. Moral and social identification with the community would not permit them, regardless of administrative edict or psychiatric theory, to open the doors and let the "mad" loose on the unsuspecting community. Therefore, as the second most important precondition for an open door policy, the ward personnel must redefine the patient. The patient must now be seen as less dangerous and more predictable, in short, as less "crazy."

Whereas a radical redefinition of the patient and of mental illness would seem to require extraordinary efforts, an unrelated and fortuitous event in psychiatric treatment has permitted the change to the open door to be able to take place with remarkable ease: the advent of tranquilizing drugs. Whatever the final evaluation of their efficacy, they undoubtedly bring about a tremendous reduction in violence, agitation, irritability, and noise and, consequently, contribute to the redefinition of patient: "They're different patients now. We could never have opened the wards if they were like they used to be."

Of course, there are wards which have been opened without the extensive use of drugs. For our purposes it is unnecessary to know whether the use of tranquilizers actually precedes the redefinition of the patient or whether, once it is clear that wards can be opened without serious incident, their use is offered as a reason why the doors have not been opened before. In any case, the tranquilizers—and we believe other forms of psychiatric treatment might do so too—permit this new image of the patient to emerge. This, in addition to freeing personnel externally from their former heavy responsibility, allows them to participate in the open-door policy without intensifying the anxiety aroused by any change.

The open-door policy is an important attempt to lessen the mental hospital's resemblance to a prison. Practitioners hope, as we have pointed out, that, with other benefits, the open hospital will improve the public's attitude toward the hospital and hospitalization with the result that it will be easier to enter and leave it.

The Psychiatric In-patient Unit in the General Hospital. In some ways, the psychiatric section of the general hospital is an even more radical attempt to change traditional popular views of hospitalization for mental illness. Because it is modeled on a treatment institution for physical illness and seems to have little in common with the custodial mental hospital, practitioners hope that as these facilities grow more common they will help to change popular attitudes.

Sponsors of the movement assume that there will be little transfer to the new treatment facilities of existing poor attitudes, and, therefore, in the words of one commentator: "When the patient can be admitted to the general hospital of his own community on a voluntary basis, he and his family are much more likely to seek help at the first indications of illness" (Gayle, 1956). Furthermore, it is hoped that the approving attitudes toward general hospitals and medicine will extend to the treatment of mental illness.

Although two psychiatric units of general hospitals had been established before the end of the eighteenth century (with Philadelphia General Hospital in 1732 and the Society of the New York Hospital in 1799), they did not operate as integral parts of the hospital. The unit established by Dr. J. M. Mosher at the Albany (N.Y.) Hospital in 1902 is usually taken as the prototype of the modern psychiatric section. (Gayle, 1957; Cameron, 1957.) The growth in the number of these facilities has been particularly rapid in the last decades. While they contain an extremely small proportion of all resident psychiatric patients, in recent years they accounted for a steadily increasing percentage of all psychiatric admissions.

The most important characteristic of the psychiatric section is that it is a part of a general hospital. Because of this, its special requirements as a psychiatric facility tend in practice to be subordinated, so that it resembles the general hospital in its operation, policies, and forms of organization.

Assimilation to the model of the general hospital is particularly critical since, as a social organization, the general hospital has been developed primarily for and is geared to the interests and the procedures of the physician in private practice. The core tradition, of course, is that others in the healing professions are literally ancillary to the physician and their main job is to ensure that his orders for his patients are carried out. When this reaches into the psychiatric section, the unit's special requirements, especially with regard to relations among different professional groups and the "team" approach, are denied recognition. Attempts to resolve difficulties often follow the form of forcing the section more and more into the model of the general hospital.

When his work is dominated by the perspectives of traditional medicine, in which psychiatry has a lower status than the other specialties, the psychiatrist finds himself under pressures to demonstrate that he is a "true" physician. The specific consequences will depend on the constellation of forces, but two possibilities may be mentioned. First, it seems probable that organic forms of treatment will be preferred over recent developments in the psychological and social therapies. (We exclude from this generalization psychiatric sections that are part of teaching hospitals.) The former modalities conform better to what the psychiatrist's colleagues expect of a physician; they are more easily understood by the ancillary specialties; and they are accepted more easily by his patients who expect to be treated in accordance with general hospital practice.

Although there are handicaps in this, a potential gain is implied for psychiatry as well, as some psychiatrists stress, namely, that the pressure to act more like a medical doctor may provide a realistic basis for the training of "comprehensive" physicians. At the present time, psychiatrist-internists, who represent one type of comprehensive physician, are very few. The increased integration of hospital services and the concomitant view of the patient as a "whole" person that emerges from the re-incorporation of psychiatry into medicine may serve to foster this type of specialist.[7] The effect is likely to be mutual. We may anticipate a feedback of psychiatry upon general medicine, with psychiatrists called upon for consultation more and more by their medical colleagues.

The trend to include psychiatric sections in general hospitals still is so new that its effects on the stigma of mental illness and on the entry into and exit of patients from treatment are not known. It is clear, however, that quite a different population of patients enters the general hospital from that entering the state mental hospital, the former resembling more closely those treated in private mental hospitals. There is, for example, a relatively greater proportion of women, of psychoneurotic reactions, and of depressive psychoses than one finds in the admissions to the state hospitals.

One possible danger must be noted. Those who most closely resemble the public's image of the unpredictable, aggressive, psychotic patient continue to be channeled to the large state hospitals. Rather than changing the public's attitude, this may entrench the conviction of hopelessness about mental disease and reinforce the basic rejection of the seriously ill patient. When psychiatric sections accept all patients for treatment, there will be less difference between them and the state hospitals and less support for the public's unsympathetic attitude toward mental illness.[8]

It is also relevant to the public's attitude that hospitalization in a general hospital for mental illness permits patients and their relatives to conceal from others (and sometimes from themselves) the fact that they are undergoing psychiatric treatment: being in the hospital can so easily be accounted for on other grounds. However, the concealment is unlikely to weaken the stigma attached to psychiatric illness and treatment since it is perfectly consistent with it.

A recent development that may have considerable influence on the future use of these facilities is that of including a period of psychiatric hospitalization in standard and major medical group health insurance plans. The use of psychiatric sections in general hospitals will undoubtedly be increased thereby. Moreover, by making the financial burden easier, this extension of insurance coverage may bring patients into hospital treatment at an earlier point in their illness.

It is evident that the consequences of a major change in the pattern of in-patient treatment are complex and varied. Neither the short-run or long-run effects of these developments on the community's attitudes or on the use of psychiatric facilities can yet be ascertained. But it does appear that the most important consequences are likely to flow from the fact that the open hospital and the psychiatric section are not simply new treatments but new forms of social organization. The major locus of organizational change in the transformation of a custodial institution into an open hospital is in the ward itself and the role relationships of ward patients and personnel. In psychiatric sections, on the other hand, the most important consequences for patient care and treatment probably will come from the new relationships appearing between psychiatrists and their medical colleagues both inside and outside the hospital.

DECREASING THE SOCIAL AND CULTURAL DIFFERENCES
BETWEEN THE HOSPITAL AND COMMUNITY

The mental hospital is a completely different world from the outside community. Many observers have noted that the patient role in a "total institution" [9] requires behavior that often is inappropriate and sometimes even contradictory to the requirements of the normal adult world. This also holds true of the staff: their roles require them to live and work in a relatively autocratic structure, to shoulder responsibility for the safety and welfare of others in a situation often dominated by crisis, and to assume an authority over other adults that is far different in quality and intensity than what is found in other roles in our society. Historically, the indifference, fear, and hostility of the community have probably served to reinforce and magnify the differences between the hospital and the outside world.

At the present time, the conspicuous sociocultural differences have effects of their own. One of the most serious consequences of this particular barrier is what has been termed the "desocialization" or "disculturation" of patients. That is, the patient comes to adjust to the hospital culture and becomes incapable of adjusting to the community culture. As was observed at a mental hospital symposium:

There are thousands of people who have lived ten to fifteen years or up to a quarter of a century or more in mental hospitals where the laws, customs, living conditions, architecture, and economy in no way resemble those of the world outside. . . . Disculturation occurs when a person learns values and attitudes which unsuit him for the culture from which he came or to which he is going. Our mental hospitals are currently crammed with those suffering from secondary desocialization [Osmond, 1958].

Recognizing that long-term hospitalization is as serious a hindrance to rehabilitation of chronic patients as are the residual effects of the disease process itself, practitioners have become increasingly concerned with reducing the marked differences between life in the hospital and outside it, that is, with reducing the process of disculturation. The measures they have adopted have in common an emphasis on maintaining or re-establishing contact between the patient and the normal adult world of everyday life. This may be simply by the creation of a more homelike atmosphere on the ward through the use of decorative fixtures and standard furniture, or by involving the patient in situations or activities that are more normal than those usually found in the hospital, such as afternoon social gatherings for men and women.

Planned attempts at resocialization through alterations of the patient's customary role vary as to whether the new features are simply added to the traditional role or whether some fundamental change is wrought in the role itself. The latter programs share an assumption that the most significant sociocultural differences between the hospital and the community lie in the withdrawal from the patient of the normal rights and obligations of adults. All of the programs attempt in some measure to give responsibility back to the patient.

Programs that permit patients to work on jobs under conditions that approximate those in the outside world is one form used to give responsibility to the patient. We are not referring here to the usual forms of hospital work assigned to patients, such as work in the laundry or the cafeteria. Rather, we mean jobs in normal settings with usual standards of performance and work for which patients receive appropriate rewards and privileges.

The member-employee program that has developed in a number of VA hospitals is a good example of this. The major general objective of hospital treatment is the reintegration of the patient into the community at his optimal level of functioning. The more specific objective of the member-employee program is to aid him in the transition from the hospital to the community. The major premise is that money is a direct rehabilitation incentive for mental patients. It is assumed that an incentive-reward system typical of the larger society is necessary for successful rehabilitation. Further, patients must live in a more normal social environment where they can relearn the power of money in satisfying personal goals. The essentials of the program are that patients are discharged from the hospital and reappointed as employees; they then live in a dormitory setting apart from other patients, work side by side with "real" employees, obey rules and regulations governing employee behavior, receive a salary for their work, and may use their salary according to their own inclinations. In general, while on the job, member-employees are subject to the same pressures as other employees.[10]

In this program there is more concern about the barrier to the patient's return to the community than about his entrance into the hospital. On the other hand, we have already noted the possibility that a significant source of resistance to hospitalization may arise from the apprehension people have about whether they would be able to get out once they allowed themselves to be hospitalized. Thus, by helping to change the image of the hospital so as to diminish this particular anxiety, programs such as the member-employee one may facilitate a patient's entry into treatment as well as his exit from it.

A principal feature of the program is the fact that the position of member-employee is seen as a privilege that is granted to patients only after they have demonstrated their ability to perform successfully in other less demanding work situations. Thus, the roles of the large majority of patients within the institution remain intact.

Again, since the primary components of the typical patient role are unchanged, this program appears to meet with relatively little generalized or intense opposition. Various problems arise with regard to evaluating patient improvement when there are differences between the patient's performance in the program and his progress in therapy. In addition, there are jurisdictional disputes among the several professional groups regarding their respective responsibilities for the patient. The member-employee's status remains ambiguous, and this produces a certain amount of tension and confusion in his relations with "real" employees. We are not attempting to discount these various problems, but they do not appear to be as severe as those that arise from types of programs that attempt other significant and fundamental changes in the patient's role.

Within the hospital, the patient's life is to a large extent subject to arbitrary and external rules imposed by various authorities.

Many observers believe that this pervasive feature of hospitals has a special relevance for the problem of patient desocialization, and several programs aimed at reversing the process attempt to bring a degree of control over his life back to the patient himself. An attempt to change one characteristic (that is, the patient's social dependency and powerlessness in the hospital) is a program of self-government. Many hospitals have given patients this minimal freedom to make decisions about certain restricted activities. However, few have fostered a radical redefinition of his role by giving the patient the power of decision in important areas of his life. We shall describe one such attempt below.

On one hospital ward of patients hospitalized for from one to ten years, the staff had taken the radical step of transferring to them the power to decide whether or not a patient could be released from the hospital on either permanent or temporary terms. These patients function as if they were the physician's "release" staff and act on patients' requests for such things as weekend passes, trial visits, or discharge from the hospital. It should be completely clear that the patients are not making recommendations but actual decisions. Their collective decision—each issue being decided by a democratic vote of those present—is entered into the ward record book and is as binding as any physician's order.

The ward meetings are chaired by either the psychiatrist, the social worker, or the clinical psychologist who together compose the ward treatment team. The patients in meetings behave quite responsibly and are sensitive to the meaning of requests made by different patients. In one of the meetings observed, for example, they tried through discussing it to induce a patient to change her request for discharge to a request for trial visit. In another instance, they decided that the patient might leave for a weekend visit only if someone came to the hospital to pick her up. They behaved in an even more subtle way toward a patient who intimated that she had been tricked into coming into the hospital: they largely ignored her comments and so prevented her from asking directly for a release, a request they undoubtedly would have rejected.

The group leader, a staff member of the ward treatment team, did not direct the meeting but at the same time did not abdicate leadership. She acted as a guide and a resource, and through appropriate questions and comments helped to clarify various requests and decisions. However, the leader has only one vote in the final decisions.

Introduction of this program in democratic decision-making posed serious difficulties for the staff. In some it confirmed the fear that the patients had taken over the hospital. To others it was a basic violation of the physician's ultimate authority and responsibility. The problems have not been solved, and in the particular instance under discussion the staff of other wards avoid or make a scapegoat of the active promoters of the program. On the other hand, even those who are opposed recognize that there have been no catastrophic results and that the patients seem to have been able to do as creditable a job of making these decisions as is done in the usual release staff conferences.

Of the types of resocialization programs we have been discussing, those that permit the patient to participate in decisions about his life, such as the radical experiment just described, have the widest consequences and implications for the hospital's organization. One would expect the strongest opposition to their introduction and operation, for they constitute a fundamental shift of authority. For this reason perhaps the most severe problems of loss of authority are those created for groups in the hospital whose power rests on the traditional hierarchy and who cannot base their claims on other criteria, such as competence or training—as, for example, the psychiatric aides and attendants, in contrast to the physicians and the nurses.

A problem difficult to avoid in the above situation is that of employees coming to identify themselves more and more as members of the normal community. That is, rather than seeing themselves as a part of the treatment team working on a new program to benefit patients, the loss of authority places them in opposition to the "crazy" patients; they then seek support and security from their commonality with the normal community rather than with the hospital professions and are disposed to interpret each new expansion of rights for the patient as a threat to themselves or an infringement on their own rights.

Ordinarily neither mental hospital personnel nor patients participate in an active way in the affairs and life of the outside community, and, conversely, those of the community do not participate actively in the hospital's programs. In the absence of wholesome interaction, fears and misconceptions persist and continue to obstruct new forms of patient treatment. However, unless persons in the community have some sympathetic understanding of mental illness and the hospital's problems there is likely to be little desire for more interaction. Some practitioners believe specific programs that increase the interaction across the hospital-community boundary will help to break the cycle.

Usually the problems resulting from the present situation are stated from the point of view of the hospital. For example, if there is a scarcity of institutional resources (personnel and money) to supply anything beyond minimum requirements for the patients' needs, programs staffed by community volunteers may help the hospital to meet these needs more adequately. Or, with regard to desocialization, the presence of individuals from the community serving in various capacities throughout the hospital may do more than hospital personnel can do themselves to keep active the symbolic tie between the patient and the world outside.

In recent years it has come to be recognized that the hospital also has a contribution to make to the community and that an increased level of interaction might make the institution a more effective force in community mental health programs. For example, the hospital might function more actively as a source of information and advice about general psychiatric problems to individual professionals and organizations providing help. Although the benefits of increased interaction can and often do flow both ways, the specific programs we shall discuss tend to emphasize one or other direction.

Volunteer programs are among the most important ways

through which the community is brought into the hospital in order to benefit the patient.[11] Some are large programs with active lists of hundreds of persons and many community organizations willing to provide volunteer activities throughout the hospital. They may be under the general supervision of the social service department or organized by persons in occupational or recreational therapy, or they may have their own organization somewhat independent of the hospital groupings. More important perhaps than the service with which they are connected are the different ways in which volunteers are utilized. In some programs the content of volunteers' activity is defined largely by the needs of the hospital, that is, the volunteer is simply extra manpower doing what aides or even ancillary specialists might do if these latter were available. In others, the volunteer is encouraged to develop a new kind of activity as his own special and different contribution to the treatment of patients.

Programs in which the volunteer is encouraged to establish a personal relationship with a particular patient appear to be more effective, according to practitioners who have seen them in operation, than programs in which the volunteer is used simply as an extra hand in standard hospital activities or helps to organize recreational and social functions. Of course, the more traditional uses of volunteers provide considerable benefits to the patients in the form of a more pleasant atmosphere and in the increased possibility of informal and friendly interaction with people from the outside community. On the other hand, it appears that the impact of these programs may be markedly increased when volunteers are encouraged and supported to relate to patients in terms of their distinctive position as an outside friend who is interested in him and his welfare. In this way, the volunteer is a bridge between the patient and the world outside. Programs that emphasize the importance of personal relationships with patients appear to require some level of professional supervision. For this reason, they tend to be organized by the hospital's social service department.[12]

Regardless of the particular emphasis of a program or the amount and quality of supervision given to volunteers, their relationships with ward personnel are of great importance in determining the possible effectiveness of their work. Volunteers can contact and benefit patients only with the active help of the aides and the nurses. If the outside visitors tend to overstimulate the patients, or disrupt ward routines, or activate certain pathological currents, the aides and the nurses must deal with the problems and therefore may be hostile to the volunteers and resistant to expanding these programs. The response of ward personnel largely depends on whether the help they receive tends to outweigh the problems created by the volunteers.

Personal relationships with patients sometimes lead to deeper involvements than most volunteers are equipped or prepared to handle. Supervisory time is limited, and, if volunteers are given priority in this respect over ward personnel—who are in more constant need—this may be an additional source of ill feeling on the latter's part. By and large, volunteers cannot get the necessary support and reassurance and are sometimes disturbed and upset by the patients. This may result in withdrawal from the program or the restriction of activities to certain patients. On the whole, group recreational programs are less taxing emotionally, the volunteers support each other, and less supervisory time is needed.

An active and viable volunteer program is a good index of a hospital's willingness to bring the community into the hospital. The spontaneity of the volunteer is an antidote to institutional routines. In addition, the presence of these outsiders may encourage more professional and responsible attitudes and behavior among ward personnel. With all this, the possibility of a profound impact on patients and hospital-community relations appears to be a function of the ways in which volunteers are integrated within the over-all treatment program. Where the volunteer becomes a full-fledged member of the psychiatric team with his own distinctive role, one may expect the usual difficulties that attend the introduction of any new role to the still stumbling and unsteady team. Some practitioners believe that anything less than this, however much easier it may be, may also be less useful in advancing the hospital toward its major objectives.

Although they are not usually considered part of hospital programs, visitors often function in the same way as volunteers with regard to the objectives of maintaining the patients' connections with the outside world and lessening the desocialization effects of hospitalization. By and large, regulations and restrictions make it difficult for visitors to see and be with patients. Recently some hospitals have relaxed their rules and now permit visitors any day of the week, at any time of the day, and for as long as they would like to stay. Preliminary reports indicate that expected extra problems for personnel have not materialized and that visiting is itself a less tense situation since there is no need to cram everything into the two or three hours per week that were previously allotted. These efforts to stimulate visiting and the volunteer programs we have been discussing involve bringing persons from the community into the hospital for the benefit of patients. Among other types of programs with similar objectives are those in which the patient leaves the hospital in order to participate in outside activities. Many standard programs in mental hospitals are of this form, such as excursions to baseball games, movies, and so forth. However, their extensive use within the specific context of trying to prevent desocialization rather than just to give patients something to do seems to be a more recent development.

The meaning and the consequences of these programs vary considerably depending on a number of variables, such as, for example, whether outside volunteers are used as escorts or whether members of the hospital staff accompany the patients. It may be noted that, although volunteers readily come into the hospital to work, they apparently are not so ready to take patients out of the hospital with them on excursions or for participation in community activities. In part for this reason, some hospitals report that it has been difficult to develop extensive programs where volunteers play an active role in re-introducing the patient to the normal routines of the outside world through such activities as taking a patient home for dinner or bringing him as a guest to meetings and social affairs of community organizations. The degree of active participation that is required of the patient is also an important factor. For example, is he simply a spectator, as at a ball game, or does he have to interact directly with other people, as he might at a church supper.

If volunteers are used as escorts, there is likely to be little direct impact on the social organization of the hospital itself. Problems will generally revolve around questions of scheduling or the degree of interference in ward routines. On the other hand, if staff members accompany patients, then this may alter their role to an appreciable degree. They are no longer guards but escorts, and they now represent the hospital. In some respects the job change in bringing them out into the world may make the situation more interesting or more pleasant for hospital personnel. On the other hand, the change may also make their jobs more difficult since the structural and environmental supports of the hospital are no longer present and the new situation may be less satisfying to old institutional hands.

Usually volunteer programs are tacked on to a traditional hospital structure. Sometimes, however, this orientation comes to dominate the over-all perspective of the institution, in which case the potential effects on the social organization of the hospital and its relationship to the community are considerable. In extreme cases, as in one small private hospital we visited, every effort may be bent toward preventing the hospital from becoming an independent entity fully separated from the community, and great value is placed on maintaining an intimate functional interdependence between the hospital and the community. As an example of this, certain recreational programs are not undertaken on the hospital grounds so that patients and staff will be forced to go into the community for their play or exercise. The resulting interdependence between the hospital and the community and the associated increase in interaction are believed to help prevent the desocialization of patients.

When we turn to programs that emphasize direct benefits to the community, we usually find that the services reflect the specific psychiatric function of the hospital and are directed toward community mental health problems. But in a few instances more general services are provided. For example, the hospital's beauty parlor or its laundry may be used by residents of the community. In one private hospital, extra building space is rented to community service agencies and the gymnasium is used for practice and games by the high school basketball team. All this is quite rare, however, and, on the whole, when the community makes use of the hospital it is as a general psychiatric resource.

There is great variety among existing programs of this kind. Some are broad mental hygiene programs and may include such things as lectures by hospital psychiatrists to formal and informal community groups on principles of mental health. Or the hospital may offer specialized forms of psychiatric consultation to social agencies, courts, schools, and so forth. Departments of psychiatry in teaching hospitals have been particularly active in this. For example, one department we visited not only served all of the inpatient facilities (private, state, and VA) but staffed most of the out-patient clinics; it consulted actively with courts, agencies, and public health organizations and gave formal psychiatric instruction and consultation to other medical specialists and nonmedical community professionals. (Conversely, one also finds that hospitals occasionally make systematic use of certain specialized community resources, such as the departments of vocational rehabilitation or the visiting nurse association.)

Activities that broaden the perspective of hospital personnel might be expected to affect their work with patients and the hospital's organization itself. This possibility and the general increase in the community's understanding and support of the hospital's programs may bring it about that programs for the benefit of the community end in benefiting the patients.

In any case, all these developments have the effect of opening the hospital more and more to public view. Volunteers, for example, may begin to ask embarrassing questions, newspaper reporters to doubt the official news handouts, public forums may inquire into hospital policies.

The hospital and the mental patient in the end would be brought into the foreground of public consciousness, and the community may enter into more responsible participation in the general problem of helping the mentally ill.

Discussion

Some practitioners judge a program to break down barriers between hospital and community by its bearing on the wider context of the community's psychiatric needs and resources; others by its effect on the definition of patient. To anticipate correctly the long-run consequences of a given program, we must know which of the two desiderata is being emphasized.

In many discussions of barriers separating hospital and community it is difficult to determine whether the referent is the barrier between the state mental hospital and private practitioners, between the psychiatric profession and the lay public, or between patients and non-patients. Naturally, the differences among various barriers and the different possibilities that accompany their removal must be made clear before an evaluation can be made of any given program. In most hospitals new developments of the type we have described in this chapter are introduced and evaluated largely in terms of their relevance for and contribution to the hospital's traditional objectives of the care and treatment of hospitalized patients. It is rare that programs to break down barriers are viewed almost entirely as expressions of a fundamental shift in the hospital's focus from inside the institution to the outside community, and examples in this country are difficult to find. An English hospital, however—one of several—exhibits a variant of this new orientation, the Mapperly Hospital at Nottingham (Mac-Millan, 1958). Here the hospital has in effect been given formal responsibility for the mental health of the city's population and is the administrative center of a comprehensive psychiatric program that includes a variety of out-patient facilities as well as the in-patient service. Here a number of the barriers we have been discussing between institution and community are being attacked simultaneously. In large part, this seems to be a function of the inclusiveness of the hospital's responsibility and of the high level of administrative integration of facilities. The flow of patients between the various psychiatric facilities takes place unimpeded by red tape and jurisdictional problems. One important gain to the patients is that in-service hospitalization has become a much less significant part of treatment. Thus, MacMillan (1958) notes: "Admission to hospitals is not always the correct answer. . . . Now, our mental health service is based on the domiciliary community work and on the out-patient service with short-term admission to hospitals as required for treatment or rehabilitation."

Two characteristics of American psychiatric practice bear directly on the ease with which hospitals may undertake comprehensive community psychiatry. These are the split between private and public psychiatry and the existence of independent facilities, each with its own coverage and responsibility. Any major change in the functions of one facility has immediate effects on others, and an expansion of the hospital's functions might be resisted by the other facilities as an undesirable intrusion on their traditional preserves.

It is unlikely that the administrative pattern developed at Mapperly Hospital will be exactly duplicated in this country. Programs of hospital-based community psychiatry in the United States will probably be less comprehensive, although something similar may develop in regions where there are few private practitioners and other psychiatric facilities. However, practitioners often refer to the English system as a model and discuss existing and proposed programs without taking notice of differences between the two countries. For example, it is evident from our observations that a hospital may multiply the number of its services and orient its efforts in terms of community psychiatry and yet reach only a small and socially restricted section of the local population. That is, there may be an increase in the intensiveness of coverage given to its traditional clientele but very little extension to new persons or community groups. For example, a state hospital may introduce a day hospital, a child guidance center, or a half-way house, each of which will permit more flexible programming of treatment, but the hospital may still be serving only the same group of people. The same is true of the expanded programs of private psychiatric hospitals and psychiatric sections of general hospitals.

What is the hospital's community? Sometimes it is viewed as the geographic region; sometimes the patients' relatives, or the community's professionals; and sometimes the community is seen as an amorphous and undifferentiated mass or a homogeneous and unitary social system. This obscures some difficult problems in the re-integration into the community of the psychiatric hospital and the attendant expansion of its functions. Full understanding of the implications of barrier-removal requires detailed specification of the particular section of the community to be involved—be it a socio-economic class, an ethnic group, or an age category—and of its relation to the particular facility and the other psychiatric resources. For example, a private psychiatric hospital that extends itself into the community through a variety of programs can hardly be considered as engaged in comprehensive community psychiatry, regardless of the merits of the programs, as long as it continues to channel particularly difficult or potentially chronic patients to the state mental hospital.

Thus, paradoxically, efforts to remove the barriers may have the effect of reinforcing the differential use of psychiatric facilities. (Hollingshead and Redlich, 1958.) These and other unanticipated effects may accompany the programs if practitioners remain unaware of and are unconcerned with some of the differences in emphasis and context that we have been discussing.

With regard to our second issue, the significance of being defined as a mental patient, many practitioners assume that it would be beneficial to remove or lessen the distinction between patienthood and non-patienthood. The objective is particularly associated with the developments that permit a "quasi-patient" status, such as in day or night hospitals, or with procedures that facilitate entry and exit.

The distinction between being and not being a patient is not always clearly separated from the more general notions of barriers between the hospital and the community. Sometimes, for example, it is assumed that facilitating entry and exit from the hospital makes an inmate less of a patient. However, it is one thing for a hospital to facilitate various forms of movement in and out of the hospital, and another for the patient not to know when he is an in-patient and when he is not. In the first instance, the hospital is attempting to prevent certain negative consequences apparently due to the traditional "patient role," with its rigid isolation from normal community life. In the second instance, the hospital is attempting to prevent the development of *any* in-patient role whatever and in this way may hinder the recognition by the person of his illness and his situation—a recognition believed by some practitioners to be a prerequisite for therapeutic progress. Confusion in the rationale and processes of entry and

exit make it difficult to determine the exact significance to patients of giving less importance to hospitalization or to assess the
comparative importance and relevance of the components of a
comprehensive program in psychiatry. For example, MacMillan
(1958) notes the advantages of an integrated and comprehensive
program: continuity and flexibility of care, treatment without
damage to the patient's self-respect, maintenance of personal links
between the patient and his family and community, and the fuller
acceptance by the community of the hospital. Since it is unlikely,
for reasons we have previously noted, that an integrated mental
health service on this model will develop in this country, we
would not expect all of these benefits. Therefore, it is of critical
importance to isolate and understand the operation of the elements of such programs so as to avoid arbitrarily selecting a particular feature in the belief that it will produce the full range
of desired ends.

The distinction between the roles of patient and non-patient
has a direct counterpart in the functional boundaries between the
hospital and other psychiatric facilities. The attack on the prison-
like atmosphere of the hospital sometimes turns into a general
attack on the hospital as a special treatment institution. Little is
known about the limits to which hospital organization may be
pressed in seeking more adequate systems of patient care and
treatment; future forms may bear little resemblance to current
ones. Nevertheless, it appears as fruitful to explore organizations
where in-patient facilities have distinct functions within interdependent systems as to move toward the elimination of these institutions and the loss of what may well be their special and necessary work.

One prevalent hypothesis deserves comment: that the reduction
in barriers separating hospital and community will lead to the
democratization of the hospital's social organization. In other
words, that the walls between occupational groups in it will become less rigid as its relationship with the community becomes
more open, direct, and intimate. However, the psychiatric section
in general hospitals demonstrates that the reduction of barriers
separating it from the community is not a necessary and sufficient

condition for the reduction of barriers between groups of personnel. In general, it appears that many different types of social organization in hospitals might all be equally compatible with the elimination of barriers to the community. Even where a changed relationship between the hospital and community supports progressive changes in the hospital's social structure, we would expect the influence to be diffuse and gradual, kept slow by conflicts between the old and the new. For social organizations do not change easily. Individuals whose relationships constitute the system form attachment to the old forms and apprehension about the new and are not universally eager for change.

The deprivation of rights and the enforced hospitalization associated with commitment procedures (and the qualifying conditions that circumscribe the use and meaning of voluntary admissions) make a mockery of half-hearted and narrow attempts to give the patient "freedom." He is either free or he isn't. He and the staff both know this. If programs to reduce the separation of hospital and community are to result in profound changes in the relationships between the two, they will have to be accompanied in many states by legal changes to preserve the civil and the human rights of the patient. This, in turn, will require further changes in hospital organization and procedures.

In closing, we should like to re-emphasize the potential importance to patients of the reduced significance of hospitalization as part of their program of treatment. Yet we do not understand in detail its import for patients and programs of psychiatric care. In discussing the trend to break down the barriers between the hospital and community, it is easy to become involved in the details of specific programs and to forget that their essential significance is in increasing the therapeutic effectiveness of mental hospitals and facilitating the recovery of the patients. We trust that our discussion of issues and problems has not obscured this central point.

Chapter 11

Developing a Therapeutic Milieu

The "therapeutic milieu" has become a popular concept recently in social psychiatry, but its meanings vary. One meaning is common, namely, that persons, events, and elements in the patient's environment in the mental hospital can be utilized for his welfare, a conception which has accompanied the shift from a custodial to a humanitarian orientation (Greenblatt, *et al.*, 1955; Gilbert and Levinson, 1957). Recognizing that environmental changes sometimes produce marked changes in patients' behavior, some of those in the mental hospital field explored ways of deliberately altering specific aspects of the patient's environment or, in some cases, changing the entire social organization.[1] More often, however, only certain aspects of the social organization and only a part of the hospital are used. Thus, in some hospitals, promoting certain attitudes in the personnel or sponsoring patient government or simply opening doors to wards is seen as creating a therapeutic milieu.

Some of the assumptions and conceptions underlying the idea of a therapeutic milieu flow from the changing conceptions of the etiology of mental illness. Once psychiatric illness came to be viewed as a function, in part, of faulty personal relations in early life, there followed, at least theoretically, the possibility of deliberately manipulating the relationships in the patient's environment as a therapeutic tool. This conception was extended to the more general idea of milieu therapy, which has been defined as "procedures directed toward modification of the environmental part of the patient-environment process with a view to facilitating more satisfactory patterns of interaction—that is, transactions or relationships—in this process" (Rioch and Stanton, 1953). This definition includes psychotherapy as part of the patient's milieu, together with the attitudes of the personnel administering drugs, electric currents, and so on, though not the actual procedures involved.

An early source of ideas about therapeutic milieus came out of work with institutionalized children. In Vienna, Aichhorn applied psychoanalytic ideas in his institution for treating delinquents, a line of development continued by Redl and Bettelheim. Anna Freud and Dorothy Burlingham, impressed by the adverse effects of institutionalization on orphan children during the war years, reasoned that if the institutions were more like families they would foster healthier psychological development.[2]

Ernst Simmel in his sanatorium near Berlin stands out for having recognized that patients generalize transference phenomena to persons playing the same or similar role as the therapist, and even to the institution as a whole. This suggested to him the extension of therapeutic potential from the therapist to those others to whom transference is directed (Simmel, 1929 and 1937).

An early precursor of the therapeutic-milieu procedure was moral treatment, wherein patients were treated humanely and kindly. Just as today's practitioners disagree as to whether milieu therapy should be a focal or ancillary technique, so did the proponents of moral treatment. The principal innovations today are the more complex rationales and theories according to which different elements of the milieu may be used for therapeutic purposes.

M. S. Schwartz (1957) identifies three orientations as implicit in the idea of therapeutic milieu, all of which must be used together in some combination if the milieu is to be therapeutic. The first orientation relates to the social structure of the institution as a whole. The context and atmosphere in which personnel and patients interact is bound to affect patients in overt and covert ways. Professionals speak of a therapeutic social structure as democratic, treatment-oriented, or flexible. The second orientation refers to the specific forms of interaction or interpersonal relations that are engaged in, facilitated, or hindered. Some consider a milieu to be therapeutic if personnel try to understand patients and respond to them personally; if they are kind, sympathetic, friendly, and respectful to patients; if they are interested in them and try to meet their needs. The third refers to specific effects upon patients which the personnel try to achieve. Thus, some believe a milieu to be therapeutic when it enables the patient to accept the idea that he is ill, to develop insight into the reasons for his illness, to correct his distortions of reality, and to derive greater satisfaction from his relations with himself and others.

These three orientations are abstractions from what some people think of as a therapeutic milieu. Superintendents and other hospital personnel may refer to a milieu as therapeutic if there is one or another of these orientations. The comprehensiveness of approach in a particular therapeutic milieu is dependent on whether it is regarded as a focal or ancillary technique. In many hospitals the therapeutic milieu approach is employed as an adjunct to other therapies, physical or psychological. Some personnel regard particular aspects of it as suited to certain kinds of patients, while still others think of it simply as a way of providing a pleasant background for treatment.

The therapeutic community is a form of the therapeutic milieu that aims at the organization and utilization of the total environment. In it are included all three orientations mentioned above, providing patients with a constellation of therapeutic elements. It is hailed by psychiatric leaders as "one of the most exciting developments of the past two decades in the management of psychotics, psychopaths, juvenile delinquents and other mentally ill patients" (Silverman and Silverman, 1958). The most recent form, which was developed in England, has been adopted in one version or another by many state, county, military, and VA hospitals in the United States. Professionals in the field do not agree on a precise definition of a therapeutic community, but proponents of this approach do share the belief that even the seriously ill have a remaining core of sanity, with which treatment begins, and that a mental patient can be treated effectively and safely as a dignified human being.

There are other forms of, and attempts to, develop a therapeutic milieu that are not quite as prominent as the therapeutic community approach. Variations in conceptions and forms will be considerably affected by characteristics of the institution itself: by whether it is a VA hospital, a state institution, or a private hospital; by whether it has many or few patients or the staff-patient ratio is high or low; by what kinds of patients are admitted; by whether the institution has a long history of a custodial orientation or is a new one with a reformist base, and so on. Moreover, all these circumstances will affect the ease with which additional therapeutic milieu elements are introduced.

Forms of the Therapeutic Milieu

There is a wide variation among hospital personnel in the specific concepts and objectives seen as pursuing the therapeutic milieu approach. Measures introduced to implement the approach vary from those that serve to "humanize" the hospital situation, to those specifically used as treatment methods for a segment of the institution, to those that try to deal with the institution as a whole.

The nature of therapeutic milieu varies from institution to institution, depending on where the emphasis is placed. In one, it might be on the therapeutic community (Jones, 1953; R. N. Rapoport, et al., 1960), where, in addition to specific measures, a good community experience per se is thought to be directly therapeutic, and the process of adaptation, it is believed, will enable the patient to learn techniques that will be helpful in living on the outside. In another, it might be on developing one ward into a therapeutic milieu, in which patients are given more responsibility for the conduct of their own and hospital affairs.

PROVIDING A "THERAPEUTIC ATMOSPHERE" AND THERAPEUTIC ATTITUDES

The referent of the term "therapeutic atmosphere" is vague and difficult to specify. The atmosphere of a ward or a hospital seems to refer to the emotional climate or ethos, which is regarded as having an influence on patients. Attitudes, qualities of relationships, types of formal structures of wards and of hospitals, and physical settings—all are regarded as constituents of the therapeutic atmosphere. Despite difficulties in definition and specification, many practitioners believe that the therapeutic atmosphere is "the most important single factor in the efficacy of the treatment given in the mental hospital" (World Health Organization, 1953, p. 17, para. 4.1.1). Practitioners believe that the preservation of patients' sense of individuality and the assumption that they are trustworthy until their behavior proves the contrary contribute to this atmosphere. To create and maintain it patients are to be treated as capable of responsibility and initiative and provided with planned, purposeful activity.

The belief that a hospital atmosphere can be therapeutic is associated with a general optimism about patient responsiveness to treatment; in fact, optimism is itself thought to contribute to the therapeutic atmosphere; but there is no evidence that this therapeutic atmosphere is "the most important single factor in the efficacy of treatment," and all that can be said is that those who have put these ideas into practice believe them beneficial.

The actual activities organized depend on such things as the hospital's size and the freedom of its administrators to institute programs. However, measures may be categorized depending upon whether they are directly aimed at (a) patients, (b) personnel, or (c) the physical setup of the hospital or ward.

Patients. Some hospitals explicitly use certain general, nonspecific measures that are regarded as "good" for all patients; for example, a continuous and stable social structure in which they are given a certain degree of general acceptance, some education, and some opportunity to discharge their energies in nondestructive activities (Rioch and Stanton, 1953). Here the personnel impress upon the patient that he is still a person, even though sick, and encourage him to exercise initiative. The educational efforts, too, are designed to lead him to new ways of thinking and relating to people; for example, the patient who comes from a broken home and feels disliked and rejected is helped to develop a sense of belonging through living in such an accepting environment. Merely seeing how other patients and personnel behave with each other may help him to change his attitudes.

Nonspecific activities and attitudes such as these can be and are used in large hospitals with unfavorable staff-patient ratios. Indeed in many large VA hospitals and in a few state hospitals the therapeutic atmosphere or milieu is usually used as background or an ancillary technique of treatment, while major emphasis is placed on specific treatment procedures prescribed by the doctors.

In some hospitals, or wards in them, the therapeutic atmosphere is provided specifically for certain types of patients. For example, some practitioners maintain that schizophrenics should be treated in an atmosphere of firm and consistent discipline and made to participate in certain activities—rather than be treated permissively, as elsewhere proposed—the object being to help them learn how to behave appropriately after discharge.[3] Thus, in one hospital we visited, if a patient who is supposed to go to industrial therapy should refuse, his name is posted on the bulletin board as a defaulter. In this way he is exposed to continuous pressure to conform to the norms of the ward.

In still another use of particular approaches toward individual patients, the personnel may decide among themselves or be instructed to deal with the patient affectionately or permissively or in a withholding manner on the assumption that that is what he needs to improve. (For discussion of the use of the interaction prescription, see pp. 126–28.)

Personnel. It is widely held that a happy staff, working as a team to help the patient get better, contributes to the therapeutic climate. Although there is no conclusive evidence to show that this is actually true, there are at least indications that a divided staff may have adverse effects. (Stanton and Schwartz, 1954, Chap. 15.)

Various measures may be activated to improve staff morale. Communication channels between patients and staff groups and among the various staff groups may be opened up; the importance of team work may be emphasized, with each profession regarded as important in the over-all therapeutic effort.

Physical Conditions. Not only are good surroundings seen as directly therapeutic; but it is felt that the hospital should not be an unpleasant place that is depressing or punishing. Thus, more and more hospitals of all sizes, whether or not they emphasize the therapeutic milieu per se, try to provide cheerful wards, pleasant buildings, wholesome food, and various recreational facilities.

Yet it seems that where the therapeutic atmosphere is most stressed, a minimal standard of physical conditions is taken for granted, and more attention is given to the social relationships and other aspects of the social environment. Thus, in some hospitals, it is thought more important for patients and staff to work together "making something" than for pleasant physical conditions just to be provided. (See p. 180 for a discussion of the importance of the physical environment.)

Consequences and Implications. Providing a therapeutic atmosphere tends to break down the widespread belief that the mental hospital is a place where dreadful things happen to people. And thereby another objective discussed above is achieved at the same time: breaking down the barriers between the hospital and the community. For when visitors see patients treated like human beings rather than as something less than that, it encourages contact. Relatives are less reluctant to visit in the pleasanter atmosphere, and people in the community grow more willing to help patients in the hospital. All this may lead individuals to use the hospital more readily when ill; and, once in the hospital, persons in their home community are more likely to maintain continual contact with them. All this should work to prevent the desocialization that hampers the patient's readaptation after discharge. Such consequences, again, would fulfill some of the objectives of the therapeutic milieu: the prevention of "hospitalitis" and the increase of patients' self-esteem.

Little systematic research has been done on the effects of these procedures on patients' therapeutic progress; however, hospital superintendents and other personnel feel that they are beneficial for patients. At the very least, certain unpleasantnesses associated with the mental hospital need no longer occur: patients are not stripped of their self-esteem, they are not made to feel subhuman, and they are not given the impression that there is no hope for them. However, in different hospitals and wards, different measures are credited with being effective for the same kind of patient, and it may well be that the important thing is not the measures themselves but the manner in which they are undertaken.

It is important to observe the differential consequences of measures taken for providing a therapeutic atmosphere. For instance, one patient may react to increased freedom with increased violence, another with increased self-control. Therefore, one should understand how a given patient responds to the milieu that he is already in before specifically prescribing for him as a certain type of patient. Moreover, the same person may react differently at different stages of his illness or of his stay in the hospital. If this is so, therapeutic planning should not be static but should flow from the progress of the patient and his varying responses over time. The most appropriate attitude may well be one of exploration and experimentation.

As to the personnel, when they have been included in the planning and development of the therapeutic atmosphere, their enthusiasm and morale is likely to be high. Where the innovations are imposed from above, however, the lower-ranking staff may resist the ideas as unrealistic and a threat to their authority over the patients.

BROADENING THE BASE OF
THERAPEUTIC RELEVANCE

We use the phrase, "broadening the base of therapeutic relevance" to refer to an attempt by some practitioners to use the therapeutic potential of all persons, relationships, and events in the patient's environment. This, a relatively recent trend, deviates from the more conventional notion that only the doctor and what *he* does is of therapeutic relevance to the patient.

In part, the appreciation of a therapeutic potential everywhere and with everyone in the patient's milieu developed as a matter of economy in response to the shortage of highly skilled hospital personnel. Consequently, every opportunity was taken to use the therapeutic potential of attendants, ward domestics, patients, and various others who work in the hospital. Moreover, some professionals view all the social relationships possible to the patient in

the hospital as of potential therapeutic significance and try systematically to include them all in the program of treatment.

Various relationships and events are seldom seen as equal in
significance, though this is sometimes believed; however, what is
common is the attribution of therapeutic relevance to various
people and events in the hospital or ward system. The ward nurse,
the psychiatric technician, maintenance personnel, other patients,
or even outsiders—all may affect the patient's therapeutic progress. Underlying this conception is the belief that the essentially
human aspects of these relationships—the contact with other persons who show warmth, concern, and interest—have beneficial
effects on the patient. The quality and quantity of these relationships, while important in themselves, may also limit or enhance
the therapist-patient relationship. These ideas, when put into execution, lead to many changes in the hospital's administration and
professional services, for they amount to an attack upon the rigid
staff hierarchy and division of labor and the passivity of patients.

In broadening the base of therapeutic relevance many aspects
of the social structure of the hospital or ward require changing,
and change becomes their conspicuous and constant characteristic.
Sometimes it is assumed that certain kinds of structural stability
reinforce the patient's illness and change itself is beneficial. Old
things in the hospital are looked at in new ways. The various
professional groups take on new functions and relinquish old
ones, and some functions and activities, while they may not be
changed, now come to be defined as therapeutically relevant.
Thus, for example, recreational activities formerly regarded as
merely diverting may now be considered an integral part of therapy. With this may go a tendency to increase the range of what
is identified as the treatment unit. Treatment is now focused on
as many aspects of the patient as possible, on a wide range of his
relationships and no longer exclusively on physiological disease
or psychological conflict.

What questions and dilemmas must be faced, as a consequence
of trying to introduce a therapeutic milieu?

First, hospital personnel and administrators now must decide
the most appropriate division of labor among professionals and

between personnel and patients in the therapeutic endeavor. How much specialization should there be? Who should and can give treatment? How should responsibility for therapeutic activity be divided? Who should make various administrative and therapeutic decisions affecting the patient's care and treatment and his stay in the hospital? So far, these questions have been answered differently in different hospitals and situations. The changes made in broadening the base of therapeutic relevance have not yet resulted in much institutionalization of new functions and activities; for instance, they have not yet been incorporated in training programs for nurses and doctors. The new functions or changed meanings are variously distributed in hospitals and not yet claimed as the property of any particular profession, except locally. For instance, in a VA hospital, the question whether or not a nurse could run group therapy sessions depended on whether she had time for them and not on the propriety of her doing so. In contrast, in a nearby state hospital, the idea of nurses conducting group therapy was unheard of.

Change within a hospital may itself be disorganizing unless it proceeds in a stable context. Thus, one problem is to avoid disorganization when one is counteracting apathy. Others are to introduce and maintain an innovation so that it makes a significant therapeutic difference and to pace the transition from one stage to the next.

In reading the literature on the therapeutic milieu and hearing its proponents discuss it, we get the impression that the new ways of organizing activities are much less specialized and compartmentalized than formerly. In the conventional mental hospital, the division of labor is highly specialized, tasks are specifically allotted, and there is little overlap in the work of doctors, nurses, and aides. The current changes are along at least three dimensions, all associated with the extension of therapeutic functions beyond the psychiatrist to others in the hospital.

The first dimension is the definition of *who* is therapeutically significant for patients. In the conventional hospital system there is a pyramidal structure at whose top are the few physicians who are seen as the main therapeutic agents. Those closest to the patients, namely, the aides, are regarded as of least therapeutic relevance. In general, the scope of therapeutic relevance is narrow and restricted. But hospitals that provide therapeutic milieus think of more and more persons as able to do significant things for patients, and this may include the patient population as well as several grades of personnel. The newly included categories participate in the hospital careers of patients in different ways, of course. One large state hospital, for example, takes the stand that patients who have been in the hospital for a long time are of potential therapeutic significance to each other. These so-called chronic patients share in deciding some important administrative issues that affect their treatment. In one small hospital all persons, whether professional, semiprofessional, on the maintenance staff, or domestics, are regarded as eligible to form helpful relationships with patients. Sometimes the professional personnel are able to reach a patient only through someone on the maintenance staff, and after that they work with him in more conventional ways.

The question may now be raised as to where and with whom should this extension stop? On the basis of what criteria? For a given patient, how can one differentiate the therapeutically relevant relationships from the others and how can one weigh their relative importance?

The second dimension relates to what activities and functions of patients and personnel are to be regarded as therapeutically significant? In some hospitals, as mentioned before, occupational crafts now may be prescribed for specific therapeutic purposes. Some VA hospitals, being particularly concerned with the therapeutic potential of work, subject selected patients to various degrees of stress until they are able to accept the pressures to be expected in regular employment.

In some hospitals, in the name of therapy, patients are urged to lead a more active everyday life, to participate in ward and other meetings, and, in general, to avoid just sitting about all day, the passive recipients of environmental stimuli.

What are the essentially therapeutic activities? Opinions differ. It may be that the nature of the activity is not as important as the manner and context in which it is undertaken. The question may be less one of finding the "right" activity for a patient and more one of understanding the uses to which activities can be put.

Some activities, unlike occupational crafts, involve more abstract functions, as, for example, participation in making decisions about the patient's treatment career. In some milieu-oriented hospitals, participation in decisions and the extension of decision-making to include lower echelons of staff as well as patients are considered therapeutic for the patient.

Formerly only psychiatrists and clinical psychologists assumed the leadership in group therapy sessions with patients, but, in various hospitals now, other professional categories may do so. We have referred to one VA hospital where nurses run therapeutic groups, but at a nearby state hospital it was the social workers, and, in both, these particular professionals initiated the change with the consent of the directing psychiatrist.

Psychiatrists' functions are affected, too: other personnel now perform some functions similar to theirs. In consequence, the psychiatrists are not the omnipotent figures they once were. In addition, some psychiatrists are adding more "ordinary" workaday things to their functions. For instance, they play a part in the patients' friendship groups; they participate in committees that decide how patients should spend their leisure time. All these functions were formerly left to the nursing staff on the ward, but, as soon as they appeared important to the patients' total milieu, the psychiatrist saw them as relevant to his function, too.

The third dimension is: How are therapeutic functions broadened? Does the extension of therapeutic relevance to others in the hospital system lead to an increase in team work? Are the extended functions divided among different personnel in the hospital? Or do different personnel more often work together in the interests of a patient? It seems that this joint participation is one of the most common ways in which the extension of therapeutic functions and relevance is organized. The team of professional workers—psychiatrists, nurses, social workers, occupational therapists, and so on—together may make various decisions about the patients' treatment in the hospital, and, when at various stages, the plans are reviewed, patients may take part and assume some responsibility for putting them into effect.

The responsibility for developing plans of treatment and seeing that they are carried into effect ordinarily rests with the psychiatrists. But in milieu-oriented hospitals this is often done by *all* the personnel concerned with a given patient, who meet together, the psychiatrist being simply one of the group, and arrive at consensus about the treatment for him. They may decide that the special functions formerly regarded as prerogatives of one professional group in the hospital should be delegated to another. For instance, in one hospital visited, anyone who can "reach" a patient is encouraged to do so; once the relationship is established, the psychiatrist may take over if it seems necessary. On the other hand, even where personnel together make and carry out their plans for patients, there may remain a clear specialization of functions. Thus, if a very regressed patient needs to be clothed and fed as a way of forming a relationship, these duties are usually given to the ward aide.

Where interchangeability of function occurs, it would seem that there will always be a diminution in specialization between various roles; the boundaries about who can do what become less clear and this helps flatten the hierarchy. Such interchangeability may present hospital administrators with dilemmas in the use of different professional skills as against the over-all "human approach." Where there is an overlapping of skills, that is, where psychiatrists, nurses, and psychologists can all do group therapy, the problem arises: Who should do it under what circumstances? Where skill and training are not regarded as so highly relevant from a therapeutic point of view, more stress may be placed on anyone and everyone's human potentials. The overlapping in "humanness" may create administrative problems, for no matter what role the individual fills, he is believed to have something to contribute to *some* patient's recovery. Who then will decide, and how will they decide, which persons can be most therapeutic for which patients?

Consequences and Implications. These trends raise the basic issue: What is therapy and who can do it? "Treatment" may come to be seen as something not very specific, available in many different ways and from many different sources. As little is known about the effectiveness of these different courses, experiments may be made with many of them in the hope of maximizing help for patients.

As the scope, context, and modes of therapeutic relevance are broadened, practitioners face the additional problem of using laymen in helping the mentally ill. The extension of therapeutic relevance, including the tendency noted above toward interchangeability of function prevalent in some hospitals, may indicate only a particular stage, the preface to a reshuffling of the more conventional roles and role relationships. After a certain period of interchangeability, different lines of specialization and boundaries between roles may emerge. The present attempts to blur these boundaries simply may be part of a movement away from the old division of labor in hospitals and not seen necessarily as contributing to therapeutic effectiveness. In fact, there is some evidence for this in at least one private hospital we visited. This hospital went through the stage of less differentiation and has now turned to defining the functions of different roles very clearly, and, though everyone in the system is seen as therapeutically significant, the specific areas in which they operate therapeutically have been circumscribed.

When hospital administrators assume that a wide range of people and transactions may be therapeutically effective for patients, they are faced with the problems of gaining acceptance for the resulting change in roles. To the extent that staff involvement in therapy increases, the administrator could find himself with a new resources problem. Whereas maximizing therapeutic potential in the patient's milieu is regarded as a partial answer to the problem of limited skilled resources, carried to an extreme it may lead to a new economic problem. When everyone is busily engaged in "giving treatment," who will do the more routine tasks? If everyone is giving treatment, the problem also arises of integrating them all and of providing patients with some ordinary relationships as a "rest" from treatment.

Another problem relates to motivating personnel to become more involved in many aspects of the patient's hospital life. Some people in the hospital may not want to be so closely involved with patients. Also, increased involvement may result in increased disturbance on the part of some staff members. How can one insure that they will be helped with such disturbance? If they can be motivated to participate in the desired way, a further resource problem arises as to who should supervise, help, and train them on the job. And, where will the funds and personnel come from?

The vested interests in the present division of labor are likely to present obstacles to the further extension of therapeutic functions. A problem that merits serious study is the anxiety attendant upon, and the resistance to, role alterations.

INCREASING PATIENT PARTICIPATION

The many ways in which patients' participation is increased may be grouped in three categories: (a) participation in their own care and treatment; (b) participation in the administration of the hospital; and (c) participation in the therapy of other patients.

Patients' Participation in Their Own Care and Treatment. At the simplest level this may take the form of providing patients with many and varied things to do to keep them from becoming excessively passive. In conventional hospitals, to have apathetic patients to sit about all day with little to do, simply aggravated their feelings of worthlessness and their deficiencies in ordinary social interactions.

Participation to counteract these tendencies may be graded according to the patient's condition. For example, if he is comparatively withdrawn or disorganized, increasing his participation may mean merely getting him to do something constructive outside himself, such as painting. As he improves, attempts may be made to encourage him in more complex interaction with people in the hospital and ultimately with people in the outside world. The staff see this active participation by patients in planning and executing their own activities as having important therapeutic effects, in particular facilitating their ability to relate to others.

Some hospital authorities feel that as well as being encouraged to have an active day, the patients ought to be urged to enter into activities regarded more specifically as therapy, such as ward meetings and other sessions in which they can discuss their problems on their own initiative, if possible, and play a part in their solution. For example, in one hospital an attempted suicide was discussed with patients in a ward meeting. The general discussion by patients and staff of circumstances leading to the wish to harm oneself helped the suicidal patient to gain insight into his attempt; at the same time, other patients with suicidal impulses found they could discuss ways of controlling them.[4] The outcome, it is hoped, will be a new sense of responsibility for their own actions that will promote their social recovery.

Patients' Participation in the Administration of the Hospital. In general, patient government is concerned with formulating and transmitting patients' opinions about the administration as it affects them and with organizing their activities. Seldom are patients empowered to make important decisions, but they may be invited to express an opinion on simple things, such as whether the ward should or should not be decorated, and on other, not so simple matters, such as admission procedures, visiting hours, privileges, and, discharge policies. Sometimes the opinion-forming body and the body concerned with the organization of activities for patients may be separated. For example, at one small private hospital, staff and patients sit together in a committee concerned with formulating patients' opinion and relaying it to higher administrative echelons, with staff acting mainly to discover the nature of patients' opinions. This committee has no power to make administrative decisions. In a few instances, patients are empowered actually to make decisions about significant aspects of hospital operations.

Patient Participation in the Therapy of Other Patients. Patients are now encouraged in some hospitals to do things in small groups in order to enhance the feeling of belonging and to bring about more intimate personal relationships. In some situations patients are encouraged to discuss the behavior and psychodynamics of other patients so as to develop insight in fellow patients. Usually such attempts are under the supervision of trained professionals. In addition, patients may also be called upon to provide support to others who are working through their problems, perhaps by giving them friendly encouragement to talk in groups, or helping the violent to control outbursts, or guiding the regressed to share in ward activities.

Consequences. This trend aims at increasing patients' self-esteem and at enabling them to carry on constructive activity in ordinary life situations. Although there are no systematic studies of the direct therapeutic gains from the patients' participation in their own therapy and the directing of their daily lives, leaders of these programs feel confident that, for one thing, their self-esteem is enhanced. However, it is a question how far this can be carried and what are the limits of self-help. Problems of skill (relevant also to various professional groups) arise when, as, for instance, in some therapeutic communities, patients are encouraged to make interpretations to each other. Unskillful interpretations may be harmful; the patients may start competing along a new line—as to who is the best interpretive therapist. And learning interpretive techniques may not be useful in living outside the hospital. Within the hospital, too, participation in each other's therapy may involve patients in activities they are not capable of maintaining or which are more harmful than helpful. This, however, can be controlled by adequate supervision, and it may be that in the end the gains outweigh the disadvantages.

Another consequence of increased patient participation is that the social distance between patient and staff, especially the physician, is lessened. The patient is treated less as a child or inferior being and more as someone potentially capable of running his own life in the world of ordinary people as represented by the staff. This works against infantilizing and desocializing influences and may more readily prepare the patient for adult social roles in society. On the other hand, since reduction of the barriers between patients and staff might threaten both, it seems important to ask how far it can and should go.

The measures we have discussed may well facilitate the hospital

care of patients from some points of view, but, for them to yield
the maximum of therapeutic gain, adequate skilled supervision
must be available, and here a new shortage may arise. Then the
administrator will have to decide whether the benefits are worth
the increased expense they entail.

MANAGING THE ECOLOGICAL-ORGANIZATIONAL CHARACTERISTICS OF THE WARD OR HOSPITAL

Many people who are concerned with the provision of a therapeutic milieu for patients feel that physical aspects in patients'
environment should be taken into account and managed. The
recent concern for the location, size, and layout of wards, workshops, and other significant locales in which the mental hospital
patient makes his life are illustrative of this trend. To the extent
that it is thought beneficial for hospital life to resemble life outside, the hospital is made into a version of the society, and activities therein become a rehearsal for normal life. Many who
subscribe to this view pay attention to physical form, and the
preferred model of the hospital may be that of a small village
community with quasi-homes, quasi-factories, and so on, rather
than that of a small skyscraper.

The distinctive aspects of this newer ecological-organizational
orientation may be illustrated by organization of the ward. Wards
vary according to size, patient composition, security provisions,
and function. The ward, the "home base" for the patient, usually
provides for the "familistic functions of eating, sleeping, and development of informal, spontaneous, and diffuse relationships"
(Williams, 1957). Milieu-oriented personnel are often concerned
with manipulating the physical conditions of the ward so as to
enhance "primary group" interaction by defining and creating
wards of optimum size for the purpose. For when face-to-face contacts are stressed, numbers become decisive. So, too, whether doors
are kept locked or open may be an issue, as will also the location
of nursing stations on the ward, the arrangement of chairs in
group meetings, and whether meals are eaten on wards or in a
central dining room.

Paul Sivadon (1958) has made an explicit statement about these kinds of factors. He states:

A good therapeutic community should offer to the patient an opportunity to enter into whatever kind of group suits his condition, whether the group be large or small, homogeneous or heterogeneous. The community should also offer him an opportunity to devote himself to the kind of activity which will promote his need for expression or creation, whether this be in useful work or in play [pp. 457–58].

Sivadon feels that the therapeutic milieu should offer the patient multiple ecological-organizational possibilities. While these are difficult to foresee, he maintains that one ought, minimally, to "maintain under therapeutic control the social organization of the group," and offer the patient a range of possible social environments. Although there is no infallible method of promoting the spontaneous organization of activities, he feels certain conditions, like those of space and density, cannot be neglected.

Consequences. It is felt that limiting the size of the treatment unit facilitates an informal atmosphere, the opening of communication channels, and the clarification of different people's roles and positions in the system and enables group process and influence to act as therapeutic agents. The staff-patient ratio becomes important in influencing interaction patterns, and the optimal ratio will vary according to the kinds of patients being treated. Thus, a high ratio may be necessary to induce interaction among a group of chronic patients who have been in the hospital a very long time, whereas the newly admitted may do well with a smaller ratio. In addition, where patients are adjuncts in the therapeutic program, the ratio of staff to patient may be lowered.

It may well be that there is also a series of unintended consequences for patients that flow from a concern with these ecological-organization characteristics: staff as well as patients may be involved in the discussions and interactions about rearrangements; patient activity may increase; and focusing attention on the effect of manipulating these may itself have therapeutic consequences. What is manifest is that this interest in the ecological features, in contrast with the past, is directly concerned with the impact on patients' emotional and interpersonal lives.

General Discussion

In no other development is the impact of leadership on the quality and the form of the program felt more directly than in that of the therapeutic milieu. Several characteristics that its leaders seem to possess in a prominent degree are noted by Hamburg (1958), as follows: an intense dedication to the understanding of their patients as people and of mental illness; a respect for other human beings that pervades their relationships with both patients and staff members; a vigorous optimism coupled with a fundamental belief in progress and the perfectability of individuals; and a determination often amounting to relentlessness in the pursuit of their goals.

Hamburg further claims that the programs they initiate share certain features consistent with their personal characteristics: increased interaction, particularly between staff and patients, which is often directed to opening previously blocked channels of communication; democratic insistence on giving a greater voice in decisions to those traditionally of low status in the hospital, including the patients; emphasis on groups rather than individuals as the focus of study and action; and, finally, an associated atmosphere of movement, excitement, and reform. This similarity of personal qualities and attitudes of the leaders may produce a great similarity in the interpersonal contexts in which these milieu programs develop and in the results of these programs.

Another possible source of similarity among milieu programs appears to be a generalizing effect that often accompanies a specific effort. For, if one form or one objective is pursued, pressure develops to introduce others. Thus, an administrator concerned primarily with raising patients' self-esteem may find that, at the same time his staff has become more involved with patients and convinced they are doing something worth-while, they become thereby a greater therapeutic force. Or his major effort may be toward broadening the base of therapeutic relevance, and this may lead to increased participation of the patients themselves in their care and treatment. Again, in some self-designated therapeutic communities there is a conscious attempt to practice the whole range of forms to some degree and to aim at all the objectives, and this, of course, makes the programs alike in the end.

Programs may resemble or differ from each other in a number of general features: whether the therapeutic milieu effort, whatever its specific form, is considered focal or ancillary in the treatment of patients; whether the objectives of treatment are defined as basic personality changes or as changes in the level of role performance; whether the hospital milieu as a distinct social and cultural unit is conceived and used explicitly as a therapeutic instrument; and, finally, whether the milieu program encompasses the entire institution or only a ward or subunit.

By a focal position we mean that the milieu program is used as a major therapeutic mechanism. In one variant of it, all types of intervention in the patient's life, including organic and psychotherapies, are included. By an ancillary position, we mean that the milieu is no more than the background or adjunct of other specific therapies which are thought more important. The milieu may help or hinder therapeutic progress, but it is not regarded as the source of the main therapeutic effect on patients.

In making the distinction between intrapsychic changes and social role adjustment as objectives, practitioners recognize that they do not exist in isolation from each other; in fact, some have made serious attempts to relate the two both conceptually and in practice. However, there are marked differences in the structure and functioning of milieu programs, depending on which is emphasized.

These two, the centrality of the milieu programs and the major objectives of treatment, are theoretically independent. However, basic personality change is likely to be the primary objective in institutions where milieu programs are only ancillary. Conversely, where the milieu is the focal instrument of treatment, increased adequacy of role is likely to be the chief goal, and any psychic changes that accompany it are incidental. One striking exception, however, is the children's residential institution, for there intrapsychic changes are major objectives within programs that appear also to give importance to the milieu.

One reason that both treatment approaches are not usually

given equal emphasis is, according to some practitioners, because social milieu forms of treatment compete with psychotherapies. In some instances, milieu programs were developed as less expensive substitutes for intensive psychotherapy; in others, milieu programs are used to demonstrate new developments—as, for example, in advanced teaching and research institutions previously committed to individual psychotherapy.

To view the social milieu as the major or focal therapeutic mechanism is to think of patients in terms of an entirely new framework. For example, as more and more aspects of the patient's world and experience are taken into consideration in the treatment process, it becomes possible to use more persons, in a variety of roles, as systematic therapeutic resources. Along with this the patients' specific difficulties in social relationships and adaptation now move into the foreground of attention. As a consequence, adequate role performance becomes the goal rather than intrapsychic change.

A third variable that influences the functioning of any specific milieu program is whether patients and personnel are explicitly regarded as a social unit with certain group characteristics that have their own therapeutic possibilities, in other words, as a social system with a structure, norms, and cultural values that are relatively independent of any particular individual. What use, if any, is made of this conception to understand and to direct the therapeutic progress of patients? For example, are patients involved in cooperative activities on the assumption that functional interdependence will have certain therapeutic consequences? Is the existence of group norms that permit or foster the expression of certain forms of behavior thought helpful to patients?

Sometimes the "community" is the primary value in the milieu program, and the rest of it is seen either as specific techniques that express the general community pattern or that have very specific functions. In other settings, the therapeutic use of community processes is seen as but one technique among others that together constitute a milieu program.

Almost all the new hospital programs that we have seen are restricted to subunits or, in some cases, to single wards, and this is also true of therapeutic milieu programs. And it is quite common for the functional and administrative requirements of the institution to conflict with the requirements of new programs in one of its subparts, but it is especially so when the innovations are therapeutic milieu programs. The radical alteration of traditional roles of patient and staff that the new ideas entail may end by making the unit with the therapeutic milieu program the scapegoat of the rest of the hospital. Often at first this bolsters the *esprit de corps* of the milieu staff, which, faced with a common enemy and sharing a common fate, responds to attack by blaming their difficulties on the larger institution. This hinders a realistic assessment of the program and in the end may have damaging effects. Further, for the milieu staff, alienation poses so difficult a problem that they may end it by dissociating themselves from the program so that they can regain acceptance by their professional colleagues. Indeed, the prevalent conception of the milieu or community as a closed social subsystem as well as the relationships between it and the total institution call for careful examination.

While bearing in mind the general point that particular milieu forms vary widely, each case providing a unique constellation of circumstances and emphases, it may be instructive, nevertheless, to examine one institution in detail. Our example is an institution that differs in a number of important respects from the others, especially in that its milieu program tries to encompass the entire institution.

AN EXAMPLE OF
A COMPREHENSIVE THERAPEUTIC MILIEU

Hospital A is a small, private hospital having less than one hundred in-patients. It is an open hospital, with a high staff-to-patient ratio, and a large proportion of its staff consists of highly skilled professional psychotherapists. Most of the patients are borderline cases and not severely disturbed.

Its milieu program is particularly comprehensive and encompassing in that the entire hospital is used as an inclusive social system with a number of interdependent parts, and the totality is seen as the potentially therapeutic milieu for patients. The milieu

program and individual psychotherapy are seen as equally important and complementary. Thus neither approach is ancillary, and
both personality change and role performance are considered important. The view that the milieu is equal in therapeutic potency
to psychotherapy is associated with a theoretical position which
asserts that basic personality change may result from certain forms
of social participation as well as from individual psychotherapy;
that the types of changes that take place in individual psychotherapy and in the milieu program are often different from each
other; and that there are some fundamental changes that can take
place only through certain forms of social involvement and participation, and, therefore, the milieu is not simply a substitute for
psychotherapy but a different form of treatment with different
possibilities for personality and role changes inherent within it.

The most general and prominent characteristic of Hospital A
is an elaborate, differentiated community structure that clearly
marks out functions and roles for persons and subunits. Patients
and staff persons engage in a multiplicity of role relationships
with each other, but not all roles are equally available for all, and
distinctions are maintained between patients and staff and among
various types of staff persons themselves. In other words, while all
persons in the institution have responsibilities to each other and
the community as a whole, the several responsibilities are distinguishable from each other and depend on differences in competence, need, and formal position. The underlying orientation is
to give the patient an opportunity to participate in a variety of
positions in different areas of living—work, democratic decision-
making, and psychotherapy. It is felt that patients should participate in many areas outside the hospital and that the relationships
in all the areas together make up a person's pattern of social interaction.

The model is that of a modified representative democracy with
community roles characterized primarily by position and function
within this type of system. The community's business is conducted
through an elaborate system of committees that establish, organize, and coordinate recreational and productive activities and devise formal rules to regulate social relationships within the hos-

pital. Patients are elected as members to the committees from small subunits, and they maintain a high level of participation in the initiation and execution of the community's programs. The ultimate responsibility of the medical director for the institution's place in the larger society is explicitly recognized, but he is not included in the governmental machinery except as the final authority on specific questions, although all others have a place on the committees.

In addition to the relatively relaxed atmosphere and the non-punitive attitudes, there are special features in Hospital A that derive from the "political" concept of the community. All persons in it have equal responsibilities and rights as community citizens, for it is assumed that, regardless of emotional condition, patients can take responsibility for their daily lives. And this works toward other goals, namely, increasing the self-esteem of patients, preventing "hospitalitis," and providing corrective emotional and learning experiences.

The hospital, defined as a differentiated social system, has a counterpart in a view of personality as a system, one in which pathology may involve only certain parts or levels rather than the whole personality; thus more use is made of the intact portions of the patient's ego than is usually the case. Simultaneously the patient is also given individual psychotherapy. Each of these approaches focuses on different aspects of the patient's illness and engages different motives and strengths. Therefore, a great deal of pressure can be brought to bear against patients acting out a "sick" role in the community situation. The milieu program requires that possibilities be maximized for normal social relationships among patients. Social interactions based on assumptions that one or the other party is "sick" are thought to be untherapeutic. Apparently, the fact that certain aspects of the patient's pathology are "engaged" in the individual psychotherapeutic situation makes it more possible for patients to respond adequately to the reality demands of their daily life situation than would otherwise be the case. This is in contrast with other therapeutic milieu programs where the distinction between "healthy" and "sick" parts of the patient's personality is not made use of—a usual situation, where the milieu is the focal form of treatment. In these programs little or no emphasis is placed on individual psychotherapy, and all aspects of the patient's personality are seen as involved in his pathology, and all his relationships and activities are treated as relevant parts of his participation in the milieu program. Since all relationships and situations have similar therapeutic potential, distinctions are not made among different types of therapeutic processes and effects. Under these conditions it is possible to excuse a patient's irresponsibility to the community or his lack of participation in required activities as a function of his sickness, and he may be permitted to act out his "sick" role in the community. This is not true in Hospital A, where excuses from community participation and responsibility are granted only under special conditions for restricted periods of time and where, in order to remain in the hospital, the patient must show that he has the capacity to perform adequately as a citizen.

In Hospital A the form that we have called "broadening the base of therapeutic relevance" has special features associated with it. In particular, neither patients nor staff are engaged in using specific techniques of psychotherapy as forms of interaction with each other. In many therapeutic milieu programs all persons and events in the patient's environment are believed to effect movement toward psychological health, and this is sometimes transformed into the notion that the model for dealing with the patient should be psychotherapy. This "fantasy of life as one great psychotherapeutic hour" is discouraged in Hospital A. The fundamental conception here is that different relationships have different types of therapeutic significance and that these different types are each important.

In our discussion of Hospital A we have ignored its special problems, such as the need to deal with the continued attractiveness of the "sick" role for the patients, and we have not commented on several broad questions, such as the possibility of the wider application of such a model with its high demand for skilled personnel. It seems that, to a large extent, some of the serious problems that plague milieu efforts originate in the assumption of an inherent incompatibility between individual and group processes and goals. Attempts are made at Hospital A to avoid this problem by granting to group and individual processes equality in importance but functionally different parts in treatment. This constitutes one form of resolution of certain dilemmas in practice raised by milieu programs that tend to concentrate on either the group or the individual alone.

Chapter 12

Problems and Issues of
the In-patient System

In the last three chapters we discussed three themes with which practitioners in mental hospitals at present are occupied: individualizing care and treatment, breaking down the barriers between hospital and community, and developing a therapeutic milieu. We view these themes as important trends—though not the only significant trends—in the field of mental hospital care and treatment. We have used them to analyze new practices and programs being introduced in mental hospitals and to discuss some of the assumptions and problems involved in trying to change the mental hospital in accordance with these new ideas.

For the purpose of analysis we discussed these trends separately. In practice, however, programs that pursue one theme ordinarily employ processes that we described as characteristic of another theme, and achieving the objectives of one program sometimes requires the development of one of the other programs. For example, the amount of individualization possible in a particular hospital depends, in part, upon the nature of the hospital milieu, for some milieus facilitate, while others deter, individualization of care. Reciprocally, the ways in which care is individualized contribute to the therapeutic quality of the milieu.

Similarly, whether a milieu is therapeutic for patients is affected not only by the ways in which care is individualized but also by the hospital's relations with the "outside." Thus, the community's attitudes, wishes, and fears can enable or block the creation of a therapeutic milieu, and the kinds of barriers that exist between the hospital and community in part determine the general atmosphere and milieu in the hospital. In turn, the transac-

tions staff and patients undertake to individualize care, and the
image and reputation the hospital has in the community as a consequence of the milieu that it has created, facilitate the relaxation
or increased rigidity of the barriers between hospital and community.

We are suggesting that developing one set of means or program
for changing a mental hospital inevitably affects, and is affected
by, other programs and aspects of the hospital. For this reason,
these programs should be seen both as separate endeavors with
unique objectives and modes of procedure and as interrelated
processes.

Although we focused on these three themes, it should not be
assumed that these necessarily are the most effective ways of helping hospitalized mental patients or that the forms through which
these themes are instituted are the most effective ways of achieving stated objectives. Research has yet to be done on the conditions under which these programs help, or do not help, patients
and on the kinds of modifications that might be necessary if they
are to attain their therapeutic ends. It is hoped that such research
will help practitioners guard against the assumption that because
these programs are fashionable and invested with positive affect,
they will necessarily facilitate the improvement of patients.

In this chapter, the themes serve as points of departure for our
analysis of the conventional state mental hospital as a social system. Here we are concerned with the latent or underlying problems practitioners face as they pursue these themes and with some
basic issues and dilemmas manifest in the mental hospital. We
ask: What limitations, strains, and contradictions are inherent in
the conventional, large state mental hospital? What basic features
of these hospitals are related to the emergence of these new programs? Individually and collectively, the themes imply that the
form and structure of the large public mental hospital does not
provide the most effective instrument for achieving therapeutic
objectives. In these huge institutions that house and care for the
great majority of our hospitalized mentally ill persons, programs
initiated to individualize care, to break down the barriers between hospital and community, and to develop therapeutic mi-

lieus must confront basic problems and defects in the mental hospital social system. From our point of view, the problems are a function of both the frame of reference that guides practitioners and the social structure that directs the mental hospital's operations.

The Frame of Reference

The psychiatric version of the medical-clinical frame of reference guides the thinking and the actions of professionals in mental hospitals. Dissatisfaction with this perspective and concern with its limitations are implied in the theme "developing a therapeutic milieu," although this implication is usually neither pursued nor stated clearly by practitioners working in these programs.

From our point of view, the conventional medical-clinical point of view seems to be only partially adequate and relevant only in segmental ways to the phenomenon ordinarily labeled "mental illness." Because this phenomenon is so complex and because it involves social as well as psychological and somatic dimensions, an adequate understanding of it calls for concepts from a number of frames of reference and for an interpretive framework broader than the conventional medical-clinical perspective. Indeed, some of the practitioners' difficulties in increasing their therapeutic effectiveness may be a function of their exclusive use of the somatic and/or psychological frame of reference in diagnosing and prescribing care and treatment. This limits their understanding of phenomena that may be related to, but lie outside, the knowledge and conceptualizations that characterize their conventional frame of reference. It also limits their awareness that many solutions to their problems might lie in ways of thinking that are foreign to their perspective and in areas in which this perspective does not permit a search for solutions.

In making explicit here some of the assumptions behind the conventional medical-clinical frame of reference and the consequences for patient care of its exclusive use, we hope to shed light on the reasons for its limited adequacy, the ways in which it might be supplemented, and some of the inevitable difficulties that arise.

The frame of reference ordinarily used by practitioners is based upon two premises: (1) that individuals who exhibit the forms of disturbed or unconventional behavior called "psychotic" have an "illness" (that is, are "sick"),[1] and that the difficulty lies within them, in the disordered functioning of their physiological and/or psychological apparatus; and (2) that to "treat," "cure," or otherwise effect a favorable change in this "illness" an understanding of individual biochemistry, physiology, or psychodynamics is sufficient.

From the assumption that certain kinds of deviant or unacceptable behavior are illnesses and those who present them are "sick," it follows that they belong in mental "hospitals" which should be directed by a "medical" staff trained to deal with "pathology." Thus the first premise establishes the rationale for using a hospital as the treatment site, medical personnel as the agents of treatment, and medical-clinical procedures as the means of treatment. And these conceptions are cherished although no demonstrable organic base has been found for the disorders of the majority of the mental hospital's population: the schizophrenics, manic-depressives, psychopaths, alcoholics, and persons with character disorders. Why, then, do many if not most psychiatric personnel believe that severe emotional and mental disturbances are illnesses and the conventional medical-clinical approach the most appropriate one?

One answer is the conviction that, although no organic base has yet been found for many disorders, eventually the pathological entity will be discovered, for without doubt it exists. In insisting on explanations in terms of defective organs or body chemistry, psychiatric practitioners thereby preserve a close link with traditional medicine.

Where the psychodynamic rather than the somatic perspective is used, practitioners ordinarily maintain that extremely deviant behavior in the affective, conceptual, or action spheres is an "illness" and, again, that the medical-clinical model is appropriate and sufficient. This assumption, while it is usually made a priori, is sometimes justified by the successes of the psychotherapies (just as the justification for the somatic view is sometimes based on the successes of drugs and physical therapies). It is also argued that deviant behavior should be viewed as illness because it is potentially or actually destructive of the self and others and because it involves psychic distress or pain.

When disturbances are labeled "illness," treatment based on the physician-patient relationship will be seen as the most appropriate and efficacious. However, it is not clear why such disturbances should be interpreted as illness that need "treatment" rather than as psychosocial disabilities calling for the patient's reeducation or resocialization. Here we question the efficacy of commitment to the conventional medical-clinical orientation, exclusively. We would argue that practitioners encounter problems in the course of treating inmates because their conceptual tools and the associated practices are only partially adequate.

Another set of explanations for psychiatric adherence to the medical-clinical frame of reference is in the nature of psychiatry as a profession. Their training and the kind of practice they usually undertake lead psychiatrists to take it for granted that disturbed behavior is illness, to seek data and explanations in accord with this point of view, and to resist giving equal weight to alternative or supplementary viewpoints. Resistance stems in part from their emotional, professional, and career involvement in the frame of reference in which they are trained, from which they derive their security and status, and to which they owe their allegiance. Psychiatry does not differ from any other profession in this, but it is particularly vulnerable because its subject matter includes phenomena with social as well as biological and psychological dimensions.

The second premise is related to the first: When disturbed behavior is viewed as illness, it follows that alleviation of the difficulty will be based on an understanding of individuals or their component parts. This means that the mind, nervous system, or chemical make-up of individuals or the "person as a whole" are the units of treatment; that biochemical solutions are sought for interpersonal problems or that treatment consists of attempts to affect the psyche or emotions as if the person were an isolated entity and the doctor-patient relationship a separate experience in

a universe insulated from its social context. Such views of the unit
of treatment prevent the practitioner from appreciating, analyz-
ing, and utilizing the therapeutic possibilities of social contexts—
be they small groups or the institution as a whole. When the psychiatrist is trained to look for and deal only with inner states—
organic or psychodynamic—he is blind to the social sphere. And
if his concepts permit him to think only in individual terms, he
is unable to conceptualize in social terms and to see the relevance
of networks of interpersonal relations and the mental hospital as
a social system for his therapeutic efforts.

This is not to say that the psychiatrist in the mental hospital
avoids dealing with phenomena at the social level. He does so all
the time when managing wards, services, and entire hospitals. We
simply mean that his frame of reference does not equip him to
deal with these social phenomena in as sophisticated or therapeutically effective a manner as he deals with the somatic or the psychological. The facility he develops in handling social processes
is derived from experience or common sense; psychiatric theory
has had little to contribute to the understanding of a complex social organization. Since the psychiatric frame of reference is relevant only to the behavior of individuals, explanations of the working of the mental hospital must be couched in terms of individuals.
Thus, the psychiatrist attempts to understand the hospital's social
system as if it were an individual. He sees persons in the hospital
in their separateness, one at a time, instead of in terms of collective
structure and patterns, and he therefore deals with the psychodynamics of individuals, instead of institutional or group dynamics. As a consequence of his partial perspective, the psychiatrist is often ill-equipped to perform that part of his work in the
mental hospital that concerns itself with the management of social contexts at different levels of organization and complexity.
He cannot exploit the opportunities available in the hospital social organization, nor has he the conceptual framework that will
enable him to prevent untherapeutic effects of the administrative
machinery.

In addition, the conventional psychiatric perspective fails to
equip the psychiatrist with the conceptual tools to discover the

social means for achieving his therapeutic ends. Although he may be able to discover the needs of patients in his care and how a particular staff member might go about meeting these needs, he is ill-equipped to conceptualize or utilize the social processes and structures that will make need satisfaction possible; nor does this framework give him an awareness of, guidelines for, or knowledge about the basic social conditions that will permit and encourage, as compared to those that will prohibit or prevent, the meeting of patient needs.

Ordinarily the psychiatrist sees the meeting of patients' needs as a problem of changing individual staff members not as a function of the total mental hospital system and its parts. For example, when he wishes to inculcate "respect for patients" among subordinate staff, his psychiatric perspective leaves him with two courses. If he is organically oriented, he has no theoretical guidelines at all; he may exhort staff or appeal to conscience or sympathy. If he is psychodynamically oriented, he may suggest individual or group psychotherapy, or he may resort to individual conferences with personnel in which he uses psychodynamic knowledge and techniques. In either case, he overlooks the extent to which his objective depends upon structured patterns of concern and respect penetrating staff-staff and staff-patient relations at all levels of the hierarchy. The discovery and creation of these social conditions requires a frame of reference for conceptualizing social processes and structures as well as individual psychodynamics.

Finally, conventional etiological explanations and diagnostic processes omit any theoretically sophisticated attempt to understand the social conditions and dynamics that contribute to patients' disturbance, or to designate and classify the patients' social deficits, or to identify the social conditions and particular ingredients of the milieu that might contribute to a given patient's improvement.

These deficiencies in the traditional medical-clinical frame of reference have inspired the search for supplements, one being the view of disturbed behavior as a defect in socialization or education as well as organic or psychodynamic impairment. This leads to a conceptualization of alternative institutional contexts in which help can be given, to the use of a greater variety of personnel as helpers, to the designation of a variety of units of treatment, and to new modes of effecting help. It involves understanding the patients' various milieus, including both the immediate one on the ward and that of the hospital as a total system. With this approach, psychosocial solutions are given as much emphasis as biochemical or psychodynamic, and the sociological frame of reference becomes as much a part of the practitioner's armamentarium as are the organic and psychodynamic approaches.

Social Structural Characteristics

Explicitly or implicitly, the programs previously described are attempts to grapple with the difficulties that flow from the basic structural characteristics of mental hospitals.

HOSPITAL SIZE AND STAFF-PATIENT RATIOS

The controlling fact in the state mental hospital is the large number of patients and the small number of staff employed to care for and treat these patients. Because of patient-staff ratios, hospitals must be run as large-scale social organizations, with attendant bureaucratic procedures. Each of the themes we have discussed, but especially that of individualizing care, raises the problem of dealing with the pervasive influence of large hospital size and small staff-patient ratio. The consequences of these two characteristics permeate the entire hospital and make it inevitable that the custody-control orientation will dominate hospital operation. The staff readily and compellingly falls back on punishment, restraint, and confinement to preserve social order and set for themselves only minimum tasks that will keep patients in line.

Large hospital size and small staff-patient ratios also lead to bureaucratization and the mass handling of patients. The organization must be run by rules, regulations, and procedures that apply formally to all patients, regardless of individual need. This minimizes the possibility of staff knowing patients intimately and having significant personal relations with them. Instead, patients are handled impersonally as objects, their activities are routinized, they are neglected, and they are managed in batches according to the needs of the institution. This is conspicuously the case in institutions where the patients number between one thousand and ten thousand and where there are as many as one hundred patients on a ward managed by one or two attendants.

CONFLICTING GOALS: CUSTODY-CONTROL AND TREATMENT

Another pervasive characteristic of the large state mental hospital that hampers the individualizing of care and the developing of therapeutic milieus is the obligation to pursue two major goals simultaneously: custody-control and treatment. Custody-control emphasizes conformity, order, subordination of the patients' needs to institutional routines, and punishment for minor violations. In contrast, treatment calls for meeting patients' individual needs, organizing ward procedures for their benefit, and manifesting continuing concern that everything undertaken is directly relevant to bringing about their improvement. Naturally, these incompatible expectations produce strain and continually impede the practitioner in achieving therapeutic ends.

If conflicting goals inevitably create difficulties in the mental hospital, why are both pursued? Our society assigns this dual function to the mental hospital in large part as a consequence of its ambivalence toward mental patients. On the one hand, the mentally disturbed person is seen as a dangerous deviant, a threat to the norms, and the mental hospital is the social agent for isolating and restraining him. But he also is seen as a sick person in need of help, and the mental hospital is asked to rehabilitate him so he may resume his place in society.

One consequence of the dual mandate is a split in the staff's ideology and orientation: attendants in general represent custody and control, and the professional staff represents treatment. Attendants develop a custody-control culture (a set of institutional means and a complex of attitudes) to pursue their goal and to defend themselves against changes in the established pattern of managing and controlling patients. For not only does society expect it, but hospital authorities also ask attendants to control and store patients; and the attendants readily come to view this as their central function and expect it of themselves. As nonprofessional persons, they share the layman's dread, contempt, and disrespect for the mentally disturbed and the impulse to punish him, and, since they are minimally trained (if at all), they have no tradition or background of therapeutic attitudes and norms. Attendants, in many ways, are like the patients they handle—in socioeconomic status, education, achievement, and value-orientation. Their constant association with patients provokes anxiety, and their sociocultural similarity evokes fear of being like patients; thus attendants are easily threatened by patients. This psychological threat to the attendants as persons, unrelieved by continued and built-in support from the institution, makes it necessary for them always to be certain of their domination of patients and to anticipate the disruption of routine as a threat to the maintenance of social order. This, added to the staff-patient ratio, reinforces the need for coercive control and for subjugation of patients. Finally, from the attendant's point of view, it is much more burdensome and difficult to control patients by understanding and therapeutic handling than it is to maintain a tight rein and a static equilibrium on the ward and to cow patients and keep them safely and quietly stored away.[2]

In contrast, the professional staff is dedicated to treatment goals. However, there is a conspicuous gap between their ideology and their practice, only in part to be attributed to the power and pervasiveness of the attendant culture. The other part is related to the conditions under which professionals are forced to work and to the discouragement and disillusionment they inevitably suffer. Insufficient professional and nonprofessional staff, large numbers of patients, inadequate funds and space, lack of professional stimulation, the crushing burden of paper and other administrative work, the impossibility of playing traditional professional roles, and pressures from lower levels of staff mean that control features will take precedence over treatment functions.

THE PATIENT'S ROLE IN THE MENTAL HOSPITAL

Much in the patient's role in the state mental hospital is conducive to desocialization and/or persistent disturbed behavior: his membership in a mass, being rejected by the staff, experiencing their disgust and fear, and being made aware of his caste-like position. Practitioners introducing new mental hospital programs contend with the problems inherent in the patient's place in the mental hospital.

Even though the goal of the mental hospital is to restore patients to normal living, it is difficult for those who have spent a long time in it to resume living outside it. The patient gradually unlearns normal modes of functioning and acquires a set of attitudes and habits that unfit him for ordinary living.

Desocialization is engendered by enforced dependency and passivity. In the conventional large state mental hospital, the patient is given little or no significant responsibility and little opportunity to make important decisions; he is subjected to continuous orders from others, to regulation for minute aspects of his behavior, and to severe restrictions of movement. Then, too, having all his needs met (though at a minimal level), he has no opportunity for productive remunerative work or intimate and meaningful relationships with significant others. Thus, there is a severe disparity between the expectations of him on the outside as an independent, autonomous, and self-directing citizen and his desocialized role in the hospital; he is not motivated or helped to move toward the outside and ends by being unable to conceive of himself as living outside the hospital at all.

To be a mental patient also means to be immersed in a "sick context," in which the large proportion of persons also are disturbed. In this sense, too, the social environment is abnormal, and there is a greater probability that patients will reinforce each other's difficulties than that they will facilitate each other's improvement. Indeed, it is asking too much to expect a patient to improve in a human environment largely populated by persons whose needs are as desperate as his own and with whom he can develop little normal exchange. This is especially true when he lacks meaningful activity throughout the day and his psychosocial needs are conspicuously denied fulfillment.

The patient in the mental hospital is treated, moreover, as if being a patient were his only role: all others, for example, father, son, worker, student, or citizen, are largely suspended while he is in the hospital, and the person is completely submerged in the status of patient. This is reflected in the way the institution deals with him, in the attitudes personnel have toward him, and in the limitations placed upon him; there is virtually no opportunity for an inmate to perform roles other than that of patient. Restrictions are, in part, instituted for the convenience of staff and, in part, on the assumption that this will hasten his improvement. It is probable that the twenty-four-hour-a-day experience of being viewed and treated as a patient confirms this self-image and stimulates resigned acceptance of it. In addition, the staff sees him only in terms of his "illness" and views mental illness as "a disease of the total person." Experiencing the person only as patient tends to increase the staff's hopeless feeling about him. This, too, makes it difficult for him to leave.

In more theoretical terms, the role of patient is not adequate as a provisional and transitional one. There are no clear means of leaving it: no clearly ascertainable bridges or pathways to the outside and no well-defined institutional stages through which he passes on his way back to society. This lack of clarity about transition points makes it difficult for him (as well as staff) to see how he can "earn promotion." The patient role also is an indefinite one in the sense that there are no time boundaries to being a patient. When staff can neither specify nor explain the course of his improvement nor indicate the steps leading to his discharge, he cannot foresee the termination of his status as a patient. The vagueness associated with "getting well" may contribute to his confusion, uncertainty, and despair and so prolong his stay.

To a significant degree, mental illness entails low self-esteem, and many features of hospital experience contribute to the further lowering of it. The patient is at the bottom of the ladder; attendants view his status with contempt or disgust, stigmatize him for it, and, in general, regard him as something less than human. Even when their attitudes are not quite so harsh, there still is a caste-like line between the patient and everyone else in the hospital, and the degradation is a serious obstacle to his improvement.[3]

HOSPITAL ATMOSPHERE

The atmosphere in the conventional large state mental hospital is, in part, a product of the custodial emphasis, the disturbed population of patients and their feelings of hopelessness, patient-staff ratios, and societal expectations and attitudes. Innovations in mental institutions contend with a tone and mood that, in general, is a stumbling block to therapeutic efforts. The staff's apathy, their indifference to patients' needs, their hopelessness about the patients, and the sense of resignation and defeat that pervades staff-patient relationships inevitably lead to impersonal and indifferent relationships. And as long as this atmosphere is sustained, the patients will remain anonymous, forgotten, and neglected, and the practitioners will face an uphill battle in introducing and developing therapeutic programs. For this reason, almost all new programs directly or indirectly aim at changing hospital atmosphere so as to awaken hope in both staff and patients.

INSTITUTIONAL RIGIDITIES

Each of the three themes, and especially the individualizing of care, implicitly are concerned with the inflexibility and resistance to change inherent in the structure of the conventional large state mental hospital. The therapeutic task the hospital sets for itself requires a flexible, responsive institution, able to alter its structure and modes of operation. Openness to change is called for by the heterogeneous population, by the variety and intensity of the patients' needs, by the various stages of psychosocial development the patients have reached, and by their rates of progression or retrogression; but state mental institutions ordinarily change slowly and imperceptibly.

In the first place, slow change in mental hospitals is taken for granted. As they have grown larger and more cumbersome, change has become more difficult to effect and manage. For, with the increase in size come the bureaucratic necessities of large-scale organization with its highly developed division of labor and its emphasis on routine, rules, regulations, and the mass handling of patients.[4] Bureaucratic organization perpetuates the view that the way things at present are organized is the way they should be organized. It focuses on institutional machinery rather than on the patients' needs. Bureaucratic means of insuring the institution's perpetuation become ends in themselves. In addition, once a large state mental hospital finds an equilibrium that is relatively "trouble-free," the staff exerts pressure to maintain it.

The culture of the mental hospital attendant, emphasizing as it does custody and control, tends to prevent, resist, and counteract change. The nursing staff perceives new programs or other changes as threats to their self-interest and to the social system that serves their needs. Their power to sabotage innovations makes them a force toward institutional inertia.

Patients, too, resist change. They are not eager to become detached from surroundings to which they have grown accustomed nor to participate in experiments that disrupt their equilibrium.

Finally, the very difficulty of introducing and maintaining change in institutions discourages practitioners from "disrupting the established order"; there is always some threat of disorganization and loss of control when institutional rigidities are relaxed and familiar ways abandoned. This threat of disorganization and of the unfamiliar, with the accompanying fear of the lack of control over patients, restricts efforts to effect significant changes in the large state mental hospitals.

As a consequence of these rigidities, few are ready to respond to, and capitalize on, change in patients. In addition, fixed structures and unvarying processes in the institution may perpetuate, reinforce, and "lock in" some forms of pathology and thus contribute to keeping patients in the hospital.

These characteristics of the mental hospital are not isolated phenomena. They merge and reinforce each other to give the hospital a recognizable form and tone that presents serious impediments to effective therapeutic actions. Although the combination of these characteristics produce a nontherapeutic institution, it is the large size and an unfavorable staff-patient ratio that constitute the basic structural conditions that underlie the state mental hospital's custodial emphasis, mass handling of patients, institutional rigidities, apathetic tone, and perpetuation of an untherapeutic patient role.

The implications of our analysis for action by mental health professionals lead in two directions. One is to accept the mental hospital as the basic institutional form for helping psychotic persons and then to explore ways in which it can be radically altered to eliminate its untherapeutic features. The other is to abandon the mental hospital and to develop instead new institutions, social arrangements, and processes that will provide a better fit between the social system and patients' needs.

Part IV

The Ex-patient System

Chapter 13

The Development of Aftercare

In contrast to out-patient and in-patient care, aftercare is still in an initial stage of development. Just as the latter part of the nineteenth century saw the growth of mental hospitals and the first half of the twentieth saw the proliferation of mental hygiene clinics, so the 1950s mark the turning point in post-hospital care.

Aftercare, that is, the formal help, whether treatment or rehabilitation, given a person who has been in a mental hospital, is largely a service in name only. For the majority of ex-patients today there is little or none of it. Much of what is available is nominal, rendered in compliance with the law or the policy attending the release of patients from state mental hospitals. Yet, never before has there been so much interest in helping mental hospital patients return to the community. Old assumptions and practices are now widely questioned, and programs are being explicitly designed for particular types of ex-patients. The old and the new now exist side by side so that aftercare is a patchwork quilt of old ideas and new theories, with experimental programs implementing both.

The absence of aftercare in this country in the past was partly the result of the mental hospitals' view of themselves and their patients. Until recently, most state hospitals conceived of themselves as protectors of the community from its mentally ill, who were to be locked away. The custodial orientation was related to attitudes of hopelessness about curing patients, and it contributed, in turn, to patients' lack of improvement. With this orientation one assumed that a patient was either sick or well and that his illness was encapsulated within him. Most were not expected to recover. Recovery was believed to depend on the patient's self-recuperative powers rather than on anything done for him. In this climate of thought, there was little place for the idea that other people or the environment could bring about recovery. Nor could there be much concern about post-hospital help in a day when patients either left the hospital "cured" or not at all. When after-care was given, it tended to be modeled on parole with surveillance rather than to be regarded as treatment. Even if hospitals then had had a different conception of aftercare, there would have been little possibility of implementing it, for they had little money and few personnel; little help could be expected from community agencies which considered the ex-patient to be the state's responsibility. But, in recent years, this has gradually given way to a more hopeful view of patients' recovery and release. Three ideas in particular have influenced the trend toward providing aftercare.

First, the conception that much mental illness is a function of poor interpersonal relationships has been particularly important in furthering the belief that continued help in the post-hospital period is necessary. As the hospital staff came to the idea that the genesis and maintenance of certain disturbances resulted from disordered interpersonal relationships, they saw that it was folly to treat the patient in the hospital and then return him to the same stressful situation that led to hospitalization. They then felt that their task was to modify his unsatisfactory relationships with significant persons and to help him to find new relationships in the community. Post-hospital help was needed if patients were to maintain the gains made during hospitalization. These ideas are now part of many hospital programs and increasingly are part of programs for ex-patients sponsored by community organizations.

A second recent idea influencing aftercare has been that of distinguishing between psychodynamic processes constituting mental illness and the social crippling resulting from institutionalization itself. Some experts have even maintained that much of the disability connected with severe mental illness is extraneous to the illness and is superimposed by hospitalization in total institutions,[1] and they have been concerned with opening hospital doors and treating patients in the community. Others who insist that the emotionally handicapped person can learn to adapt to society despite his disabilities are particularly oriented toward developing rehabilitation facilities to help ex-patients perform better in various areas of life, say, at work or in the family. It follows from the distinction between mental illness and social disability that rehabilitation outside the hospital can be the corrective for patients' difficulties. At present, many are released from hospitals with the proviso that they receive aftercare.

Interest in psychiatric rehabilitation developed largely after World War II. Prior to that time, rehabilitation was designed for the most part for the physically handicapped: the few rehabilitation programs in mental hospitals during the 1930s and early 1940s aimed largely at providing activities to counteract withdrawal. Programs based on the notion of the hospitalized schizophrenic as an inadequately socialized or a desocialized person developed more recently. Present attempts to alter patients' alienation from normal social roles parallel the efforts of the British in Civil Resettlement Units to reverse the desocialization associated with the experiences of being a prisoner of war (Curle, 1947; Curle and Trist, 1947).

Psychiatric rehabilitation seems at first to have focused on helping chronic patients develop or relearn behavior appropriate for living outside a hospital. These early psychiatric rehabilitation programs were located in mental hospitals, but, when it became clear that certain behavior can be successfully learned only in the settings in which it belongs, they were moved out into various settings in the community. Today they are found in the homes of foster families, in sheltered workshops, in recreation centers, and the like as well as in hospitals.

Though many such programs have been initiated in the past ten years, "rehabilitation" still means many different things.[2] Sometimes it is used to refer to both "treatment" and help in social adjustment; sometimes, only to social reintegration in society. Regardless of what it is called, today more emphasis is placed on helping the ex-patient outside of the hospital perform more adequately in his social roles.

That persons in the community may play an important role in the fate of the hospitalized is a third conception that has influenced the present course of aftercare. It is now believed that the identification of who is sick and who should be hospitalized depends not only on the symptoms manifested but on the expectation and tolerance of deviance of the patient's family and social group.[3] This is only a step from developing a variety of environments suitable for various ex-patients. Today much work is being done with others in the ex-patient's milieu so that their expectations of him will more nearly coincide with his abilities.

Psychiatrists' interest in working with the ex-patient's environment has been stimulated by the therapeutic milieus developed in hospitals and by the professional optimism in general about manipulating environment for therapeutic ends. Administrative therapy and milieu therapy are now found in community settings such as "halfway houses" and day hospitals. Social workers have long been occupied with their clients' environment as part of casework and now are beginning to apply group work principles to groups of ex-patients. Psychologists, too, although to a lesser extent than psychiatrists and social workers, are becoming interested in working with environmental forces.

Many of the present forms of post-hospital help, it is clear, are based on practices used in other connections and adapted to suit the discharged mental patient. For example, vocational rehabilitation until recently was confined to the physically handicapped; group work seems to have been developed for recreational groups and more recently used with juvenile delinquents.

With new forms of hospital treatment and, particularly, with concerted use of drug therapy, the length of hospitalization is growing shorter. As a consequence, some of the released patients are still in need of treatment and rehabilitation. Of these, a few visit community out-patient clinics or see psychiatrists in private practice, but the majority do not seek, and are not given, help and have become the focus of a growing concern, of both the mental hospital and the community agencies (Freeman and Simmons, 1961).

Present Nature of Aftercare

Increasingly, professionals recognize that ex-patients are not a discrete population that can be characterized in any simple way but a heterogeneous group with only a single and not necessarily significant property in common: hospitalization. More practitioners are coming to believe that variables such as age, sex, education, personality constellation, social class, length of hospitalization, type of in-patient treatment, diagnosis, number and frequency of hospital admissions, length of illness prior to admission, level of pre-hospital functioning and of recovery—all should be considered in determining if aftercare is needed and what form it should take. Thus in many programs aftercare is, as far as possible, tailored to the particular ex-patient.

In general, though, aftercare programs may be classified into two types: one seems to be for ex-patients with short-term hospitalization (that is, acute cases), and the other for those with long-term hospitalization (the chronic patients). As noted earlier, it is now believed that isolation from the community and lack of opportunity to participate in their own treatment and care and to do useful work prevents many chronic patients from assuming adult social roles on release. Their rehabilitation is a slow process of learning or relearning, which to some extent must take place in the community itself. Almost all professionals consider aftercare to be a necessity for chronic patients: day hospitals, sheltered workshops, and foster homes are usually designed with them explicitly in mind.

Whereas almost all ex-patients who had been hospitalized over one year are believed in need of some follow-up, many practitioners with whom we talked questioned whether it is true of the short-term patient, particularly if it was his first admission and he has been in the hospital for ninety days or less. Some ex-patients manage well without further help, and aftercare under some conditions is even thought to be detrimental, for the following reasons.

First, aftercare may foster overdependency on the professional. Providing the ex-patient with a continued protector and helper, along with the expectation that he needs one, may encourage him in the very behavior that the practitioner hopes to decrease. Secondly, aftercare may foster "psychiatric hypochondriasis." Continued connection with formal organizations may lead the ex-patient to be overly concerned with his emotional reactions or with job or family adjustment. And his family or friends, on their side, may define him as a frail flower constantly needing to be protected and watched lest he suffer a relapse. Thirdly, aftercare may aggravate the stigma of having been a mental hospital patient and encourage him to continue to think of himself as sick.[4]

These three considerations keep professionals from recommending that *all* patients on release, indiscriminately, receive aftercare. There is, however, a strong belief that all ex-patients should have the opportunity to get it if and when they need it. What services are available in any geographic area is one of the most important determinants of what post-hospital help an ex-patient is given. In large measure, it may be more a matter of chance than of plan whether an ex-patient receives psychotherapy or social casework, help through foster-family care or through a "halfway house," a sheltered workshop service, or vocational counseling. Only in a few places are several of these services found together. Consequently, a patient may receive vocational counseling but not the supportive psychotherapy he needs, and so on.

Professionals' perspective regarding goals for different ex-patients is another important factor. If the major intent of aftercare is surveillance, then aftercare may be an extension of the hospital's custodial system, and ex-patients will be "watched" for a limited time to make sure they do not injure themselves or others. If the goal is the avoidance of rehospitalization, then they may be given drug maintenance–therapy; and if the goal is optimum functioning in work, family, and other social situations, then they may be given more extensive help. In actual practice, even while holding the same general philosophy, professionals differ in the level of performance they consider satisfactory in their ex-patients. Some strive to bring them a measure of self-satisfaction as well as efficiency in their social roles; others hope to restore them to their pre-hospital level of functioning.

The choice of goal for his ex-patients is largely a function of the professional's philosophy of treatment and the policy of his agency. One central issue is the dilemma of helping either a few ex-patients a lot or many a little. Clearly not all ex-patients needing help can be given all they require. Some compromises must be made between the number helped and the maximal goals sought.

The kind of help offered ex-patients depends on the professionals' strategy of intervention. If they believe that the psyche is the unit of care, then treatment may deal with intrapsychic problems. If they believe that disability in role performance is purely a psychodynamic problem, they are not likely to make use of rehabilitation services. If adjustment at work is seen as prerequisite to familial and social adjustment, then they will offer considerable vocational help. If they believe that psychotherapy is not as useful as "living experiences," then they will consider using facilities that guide ex-patients through certain social experiences. Or they may assume that services are less important than the attitudes and feelings of helpers and then their concern will be with the quality of the relationship between patient and helper. If they consider the patient to be helpless, then they may try to do many more things for him than if they believe he has a core of strength.

However professionals may plan aftercare, their prescriptions are ultimately subject to the views, caprices, and vetoes of ex-patients and their families, who may reject help for a variety of reasons. Though professionals may define goals, ex-patients may redefine them or define them differently. Some ex-patients accept help if they feel it is confined to keeping them out of the hospital and does not interfere with their life activities. And some view it as appropriate only to their work and are content with minimal functioning in the family or other relationships. Others may refuse treatment for intrapersonal problems on the ground that it invades their privacy or because of their unpleasant hospital experiences or their distrust of middle-class helpers. In contrast to the in-patient, the ex-patient can exercise a veto by withdrawing from help, and often there is little the professionals can do about his veto.

Finally, aftercare is hampered by conditions not readily changed: the limits of current psychiatric knowledge and skills, the limitations of mental hospitals as treatment centers, shortages in facilities and personnel, and the community's rejection of ex-patients. On the other hand, all this is offset, at least in part, by the growing movement in psychiatry toward adequate rehabilitation and treatment in the community for those not in need of continued hospitalization.

Chapter 14

Tailoring Aftercare

Individualizing care has been an important concern of practitioners in post-hospital settings as well as for those working with inpatients. Both subscribe to the belief that the program of treatment of each patient should be viewed as a unique problem. The orientation of practitioners who are introducing programs of individualized care in mental hospitals has been described in Chapter 9, and, as practitioners of aftercare share it in all its essential aspects, we need review it only briefly here.

Individualization is not in itself a specific treatment, though specific measures, such as drug therapy, may enter into a program of individualized care. Nor does alert responsiveness to the patient's unique pattern of needs mean that the "whole" patient is to be treated. Rather, individualized care means that in those areas and at salient times care is fitted to the constellation of needs characterizing a given patient. It calls for continuing re-evaluation of the patient's changing needs. But individualization of care does not mean that each patient must necessarily be handled differently: many have similar needs that can be met in similar ways. Nor does it necessarily involve personalization, which is but a type of individualization in which the relationship between patient and helper is close, intimate, or in some way special. Finally, individualized care does not require a one-to-one relationship. Indeed, the tendency to regard either a close or a one-to-one relationship as essential hinders other forms of individualization, such as handling patients in groups or dealing with them in an impersonal (though not nonpersonal, harsh, or indifferent) manner. The principle of fitting care to patients' needs is equally applicable to in-patient care and aftercare but the problems entailed are not the same.

Perhaps the greatest obstacle to individualizing care within the large state mental hospital (see Chapter 9) is the fact that these are "total institutions," characterized by mass care. Most workers in hospitals concerned with individualizing care are relatively clear about the properties of the situation they are trying to alter —depersonalization, the patient's loss of status, the handling of his everyday needs in a routine and standard manner, his lack of participation in or control over his fate in the hospital, and so forth. Most practitioners are familiar with the programs designed to do away with these shortcomings of the total institution, for they have been widely reported.

But in the case of individualizing aftercare, practitioners must start from the beginning. They are faced not with mass care but no care at all, and their task is to set up a structure within which care can be given. This may to some extent be an advantage in that from the outset they can build the kind of situation required by their conceptions of care. On the other hand, they have a job of persuading legislators, administrators, and practitioners in the community of the importance of a particular kind of program and of its right to compete with other programs for the limited local resources. Thus it should be remembered that the practitioners' attempts at individualizing aftercare represent an earlier stage of development than the corresponding work in mental institutions. Furthermore, aftercare workers are less clear about solutions than are mental hospital workers. Finally, not only are there fewer programs of individualizing aftercare, but those that exist are largely pilot projects and small experiments.

In in-patient care the focus is generally the particular disorder or a particular stage in the patient's recovery, but in aftercare it is more often his community relationships and the setting to which he has returned. Another difference is that in aftercare practitioners are oriented to a longer period of time; increasingly, they are accepting long-term commitments to ex-patients, realizing they must expect to deal with recurrent post-hospital crises. Tailoring care to facilitate an early release from the hospital has a different quality and tempo from tailoring aftercare to meet changing and life-long needs.

Aftercare may be seen from two general perspectives: (*a*) the creation of conditions that make tailoring possible or that facilitate it and (*b*) the specific programs and processes.

Creating the Preconditions

If a variety of aftercare services [1] is not available from which the practitioner may choose those appropriate to a given ex-patient, he will find individualization of care difficult to achieve. In most communities there are few if any specialized post-hospital programs, and community agencies' services often are not available to ex-patients. In aftercare, therefore, even more than in in-patient programs, a considerable amount of effort must be devoted to establishing the preconditions for individualization. In fact, most efforts at individualizing aftercare are on this level.

The preconditions roughly fall into three categories.

ESTABLISHING THE ORGANIZATIONAL FRAMEWORK

The only formal aftercare available in the past came largely from mental hospitals. Preoccupied as they were with the inadequacy of in-patient treatment and care, most institutions devoted little of their resources to aftercare. And agencies in the community did not provide it for reasons that included their fear of ex-patients, their conception of their functions, and their belief that the hospital ought to provide for ex-patients. Even though both hospitals and community agencies have altered their orientation and practice somewhat, many experts believe an effective aftercare program calls for a specific public agency charged with responsibility for its development. After all, the mental hospital's job is mainly treatment; maintaining the patient's connections with the community and promoting his social integration is secondary. When the patient returns to the community, his need for the two types of service may be in the reverse order.

That an agency separate from the hospital must assume responsibility for aftercare is only one point of view. Some experts argue that continuity of care is more likely to be maintained if the hospital administers aftercare and that, particularly in the smaller states, mental hospitals can assume responsibility for aftercare, developing special programs for ex-patients and, at the same time, stimulating local agencies to participate in them. The VA hospitals, in particular, run aftercare programs of high quality.

The fact that such a controversy exists means that aftercare is achieving explicit recognition as a legitimate social service. This is an important step, making possible the social conditions and structures that will permit the tailoring of care for ex-patients.

INCREASING RESOURCES

In many areas the great disproportion between available services and the number of ex-patients requiring them makes it impossible to meet ex-patients' needs. Much is now being done through grant-in-aid programs to bring consulting services of the state mental health staff to public and private agencies, to initiate new services, and to stimulate education and training of health officers, nurses, social workers, general practitioners, and other community workers.

Attempts to increase the number and variety of resources available to ex-patients are based partly on the recognition that ex-patients are discriminated against in comparison with other clients in the present system of community health and welfare services. Where these services are few, the ex-patient, as a devalued person and one who is thought difficult to handle and succeed with, is neglected or given a lower priority than other needy persons. Even where a great number of agencies and services exist, ex-patients are likely to receive little help.

Finally, certain types of ex-patients, those with marginal social adjustment and little motivation to seek help, those with histories of alcoholism, drug addiction, and aggressive behavior, and the elderly unemployable, who are likely to be permanently dependent, tend to be excluded from most programs.[2] This is not only because they are harder to deal with but also because the present trend is toward transitional facilities offering relatively short-term services and specialized settings. That is, the current major development in aftercare is of facilities that bridge institutional and community life. Except for foster-family programs, which have been operating for some time and have not been greatly expanded, little is available for ex-patients with marginal types of adjustment who need extended care. Yet only when there are sufficient services for all is the tailoring of ex-patient care likely to achieve momentum.

PROMOTING FLEXIBILITY IN
COMMUNITY WELFARE SERVICES

Even though some community agencies accept former mental hospital patients, their rules and operational modes often are not geared to ex-patients' specific needs. Many professionals believe that considerable alteration must be made in the inflexible and selective function of these agencies if they are to tailor the care of the ex-patient, which, by definition, requires flexibility.

Changes are called for, in particular, in regard to eligibility. Some agencies require that a mental hospital patient be in the community several weeks before he can receive welfare payments. Since patients often have no funds with which to establish themselves locally, the waiting period is a great hardship and sometimes even actually prevents their release.

Changes, too, are needed in the definition of the support the welfare agencies are empowered to provide. As Williams (1960, p. 37) points out, some allot money for warm coats but not for the winter underwear so urgently needed by persons in unheated quarters. Or, to cite another example, a state division of vocational rehabilitation may agree to provide funds for training an ex-patient for a job but not for buying him false teeth to enable him to make a suitable appearance in applying for it.

Then, too, flexibility is required in the definition of the time during which help is given. For example, it is the policy of some state vocational rehabilitation agencies to close an ex-patient's case if he continues in employment for thirty days. This obviously is not long enough to achieve a stable job adjustment, and many practitioners feel that their vocational needs could be better met by a more flexible follow-up period. Too standardized a period of follow-up hampers most programs of convalescent leave from state mental hospitals. Only the specialized aftercare facilities—day hospitals, halfway houses, ex-patient clubs, sheltered workshops, to mention only a few—dealing with a small proportion of ex-patients in need of help, explicitly recognize the importance of a flexible period of service.

Some agencies fail to seek greater flexibility for ex-patients because they use another type of client as their model. For example, where the physically handicapped are the major clientele, the extent to which ex-mental hospital patients' problems differ from them may not be appreciated.

Specific Programs and Processes

Tailoring aftercare as a practice rather than as a principle is only beginning, so that we can cite only a few examples to illustrate major trends. These trends fall into two categories.

EXPANDING THE SOCIAL SERVICES OF EX-PATIENT FACILITIES

Where the social services needed by their patients are unavailable, ex-patient facilities have sometimes provided their own social services. Thus, day hospitals develop their own sheltered workshop, hire rehabilitation counselors for vocational placement, and have their own ex-patient club. Their workers counsel relatives, arrange for psychiatric or medical care (or give it themselves), and find living quarters for their patients. Halfway houses find it necessary to take on vocational activities as well as recreational programs. Ex-patient clubs enlarge their functions to become rehabilitation centers with prevocational and vocational programs, even providing housing and finding jobs for their members. Although some experts believe that community agencies should provide services so as to maintain the ex-patients' community connections, their unavailability has led the specialized facilities to add more and more services.

EXPERIMENTING WITH NEW TYPES OF HELPING RELATIONSHIPS

Many of the conventional therapeutic procedures appear to be inappropriate for certain types of ex-patients. Recently, practi-

tioners have been experimenting with new approaches to ex-
patients whose mental illness has extended over long periods; or
who are marginally adjusted, regularly unemployed, little motivated to participate in treatment, and discouraged or pessimistic;
or in whose case a succession of therapies has yielded little permanent results. What they seek is a therapeutic relationship which
would not be as formally structured, would not rely as heavily
on the patients' verbalization of problems, and would not keep
therapist and patient as distant from each other socially as has
become the convention. Thus, they have developed for these ex-
patients a greater emphasis on recreational and social activities,
on teaching work skills and habits, and on informal and spontaneous discussion of problems, with therapy taking place "in the
open" rather than at designated times. Staff may assume an active,
directive role and, in some instances, participate as peers in the
patients' activities. This kind of therapeutic relationship is similar
to activity therapy with emotionally disturbed children.

One such program (Lesser, 1960) is run by a day center of an
out-patient mental hygiene clinic. It is staffed by a psychiatrist,
a clinical psychologist, an occupational therapist, and a social
worker, with the responsibility for major treatment dependent
upon the ex-patient's relationship with the various team members,
all of whom participate in the varied activities of the center. More
formal individual and group therapy sessions may be held when
the patient is ready for them. Although it was not exclusively for
marginally adjusted ex-patients, a similar type of activity-oriented
relationship was developed by a psychiatric nurse in a day hospital
(LeVan, 1958). With the help of occasional volunteers, she ran
a highly individualized day care program despite limited resources.
With considerable imagination she devised activities for the small
group of women referred to the day hospital, even including training in simple nursing procedures with her own equipment. Another program designed to facilitate ex-patients' vocational rehabilitation (Wheat, et al. [n.d.]) originally was structured along the
lines of intensive, interpretive group therapy and later converted
to something like an activity program, with the therapist and the
group observer acting as co-leaders. More spontaneous, less formal

patient-helper relationships also characterize many halfway houses, rehabilitation centers, and ex-patient clubs.

There are, however, few guidelines for approaching patients in spontaneous and unstructured ways. Most psychiatrists, psychologists, and psychiatric nurses have had little training in such a role and have had to guard against the constant pressure of their previous orientation toward a formal, more restricted, and better-defined therapeutic role.

The use of volunteers in rehabilitation centers and other aftercare facilities, the efforts to draw in the general practitioner, and the increasing use of public health nurses, social welfare workers, and vocational rehabilitation counselors is not only an attempt to increase services; it is also an occasion for increasing the ex-patients' ability to carry on normal relations with persons in his community.

Some of the specific programs described in Chapters 15 and 16 can be considered illustrations of individualization as well as of grading stress on ex-patients and providing continuity of aftercare.

Discussion

In this section we turn to issues connected with individualization and the effect of the practitioners' cultural biases.

A problem is created if individualization were always to be maintained as the central value of aftercare programs, as is often the case in private agencies in their pursuit of so-called quality or intensive care. They define their responsibility as serving well the few persons they have selected. But public agencies are responsible for aftercare of all patients released from public mental hospitals. Thus, giving help to all who need it is an obligation publicly-supported agencies cannot easily escape. By concentrating on coverage, they find they do not have the resources to provide intensive care for those who need it. In this way, individualized care conflicts with coverage.

Those practitioners who would always give individualization of care priority over coverage are not facing the fact that the practitioner in the public agency has to deal with *all* ex-patients who need help and does not have the choice of giving intensive help to just a few. Furthermore, they fail to recognize that extensive coverage increases the chances that a greater variety of ex-patients will be selected for the intensive help that some agencies are able to give.

The second issue in individualization also centers around two positions, though it is rarely discussed as a two-sided question. Practitioners tend to give priority either to developing specialized facilities for ex-patients or to encouraging community agencies to serve ex-patients as well as other members of the community.

The professionals who support the growth of special ex-patient facilities—halfway houses, ex-patient clubs, rehabilitation centers for ex-patients, day hospitals, and the like—believe that the ideal situation would be a spectrum of these services, among which they could choose according to their patients' needs. It is implied that agencies serving others cannot provide the care ex-patients need, either because the staffs ordinarily lack the necessary skill and understanding or because they discriminate against ex-patients. Hence arises the argument that care will be individualized *only* if special facilities with trained staff are developed for ex-patients.

While not discounting the need for some specialized arrangements, several leading practitioners believe that the emphasis should be on help through the ordinary community channels of social assistance. They assume that the main goal is the ex-patient's community adjustment and that this requires social learning and not "going deeper into the patient's psyche." And community adjustment is thought best achieved by his participation in community facilities, not by segregating him. Even if special arrangements may be needed in certain instances, every opportunity should be taken to use what is locally available; all too often the potential usefulness of existing services is neglected in favor of segregated facilities. Finally, it is argued that this is the more realistic position, since many areas of the country have neither staff nor money for special services.

The opposed positions reflect differences in opinion on how rehabilitation may best be effected. One position is that special facilities are required because it is either too difficult or inefficient for community agents to provide effective aftercare. The population of ex-patients needing help is seen as largely a psychologically incapacitated group whose members will not improve unless handled by professionals trained to treat the mentally ill. The other position is that workers in community agencies can be adequately trained in a reasonable amount of time to be of help to ex-patients; not only that the majority of ex-patients needing help can get it in community agencies but the advantages of effecting their rehabilitation in ordinary community settings outweigh the disadvantages.

Here the disagreement is not so much over the goals to be achieved as over the means by which rehabilitation of ex-patients can be effectively pursued, given the resources. Only carefully designed research can answer the question as to which are more effective or more efficient for various types of ex-patients.

Limitations are imposed by the practitioners' cultural and professional biases. We maintain that, while they have done a great deal in the way of individualizing care in certain areas, they have neglected others that might prove to be equally important. Aftercare programs take account of sex and age, degree of recovery, and nature of the pathology but have largely ignored social class and cultural background. Patients' social norms and roles are rarely analyzed before a halfway house or a day hospital is designed. Although little explicit attention is given to the matter, middle-class norms and role patterns (that is, the norms of the practitioners themselves) are used as the basis of most programs. In the few instances in which attempts are made not to impose the helpers' norms on the patients, there still is little systematic assessment of patients' norms and of concrete provisions that ought to be made in the program if these, rather than the helpers', values are to prevail. If, as now appears to be the case, the majority of mental hospital patients are lower class or lower middle class and if this continues in the future, it would seem incumbent upon practitioners who try to individualize aftercare to consider how help may be made more appropriate for this population.

Wheat, *et al.* (n.d., p. 8), noting that most techniques of treatment are designed for individuals of other than the lower class, conclude that the current concepts of psychopathology as they apply to the lower class should be reappraised and then the cultural and social forces that could be fruitfully exploited in therapy should be identified. The practitioner might, as did these researchers, experiment with the usefulness of programs oriented more to action, less to verbalization of problems. Or he might combine professional and lower-class social norms, by, for example, devising a day program with a helper from the lower class. Initially, the worker might see his job as discovering what the patients' norms are in their work and family situation and what is realistic to expect of them. As more is learned, it might be possible to structure recreational, occupational, or other activities more appropriate to the life of these ex-patients than are now provided, for the neglect of class and cultural characteristics—all of which significantly determine the reality the ex-patient must adjust to—may result in programs that are less effective than they might be.

There seems to be universal agreement that individualized care is basic to any major alteration in the ex-patient's status, yet there are only a few such programs. Generally, we may expect that individualization in aftercare can be achieved only if additional resources are available. But in emphasizing the need for resources, practitioners should not overlook the sensitivity of the helper to the ex-patient. Even where there are a number and variety of aftercare facilities, it still may be difficult to find exactly what a particular ex-patient requires. But if, in fact, it can be conveyed to the patient that he is being looked at in terms of his specific needs, the concrete gap in services might be mitigated to some extent. After all, effective aftercare depends primarily not on facilities or services but on the personnel who use them and on the way they are used to help the ex-patient find a more satisfactory existence in the community.

Chapter 15

Grading Stress

The belief that hospitalization need be only a transitory stage in the career of the mental hospital patient has inspired the search for ways of moving him out of the hospital earlier in his illness. But there is more to this than the mere exchange of one setting for another: a central problem is to get him to give up the role of patient and assume that of a member of the community. A strategy now in use is that of providing "opportunities for the graduated assumption of responsible freedom," to use the expression of Richard Williams. This process is called "grading stress." [1]

Effective ways of helping the patient return to community life have been sought partly in better methods of treating the psyche, on the assumption that this will lead to alteration in social behavior. But many practitioners also believe it necessary to work directly on social behavior itself. The two levels, personality and social behavior, are involved in the process of grading stress, by which is meant increasing the patient's social competence by moving him through a succession of situations requiring more and more complex performance. Various means are used to manage the resulting tension and to prepare him for the next step. Each step is designed to bring increased tolerance of certain stresses and more normal social behavior in that context.

In this chapter the focus is on ex-patients. But to understand the different meanings practitioners assign to the term "grading stress," it also is necessary to see how they use it in in-patient programs. It is not always clear what kind of program they have in mind when talking about grading stress. They may mean ways of classifying patients or managing them in institutions; or they may be referring to complex programs in which graduating stress is a focal treatment-rehabilitation technique at each stage in the in-patient and ex-patient career. There are at present at least four referents of the term.

1. "Grading stress" often means no more than what is implied by the common-sense notion that a child must creep before it can walk; for example, granting patients various degrees of freedom and responsibility in moving them from closed wards to semi-open units and then outside the hospital. Similarly, ground parole, town parole, weekend passes, and convalescent leave are points on a continuum of freedom along which a patient progresses. Each step acts as training for the next, and it, in turn, serves as reward for adequate performance.

But this is grading stress only in rudimentary fashion. Usually there is no systematic training for movement to the next level, and indications of change or growing ability may not be fully utilized. It seems more often to be a device for managing large numbers of patients than a technique for advancing patients from one level of performance to another. Indeed, the view that stress has been graded is developed *ex post facto*. The patient moves to the next step only after his behavior has changed. Thus much of the process is not so much graduating stresses as it is *movement from one status to another*.

2. Many hospitals and some aftercare agencies, however, do develop programs in which grading stress is specifically used to improve the patient's functioning. Often, however, its systematic use is in but a single area, such as work or recreation, and it plays a small role in other connections, such as psychiatric treatment. Yet, in that limited context, a true sequence of graded steps is designed through which he is helped to progress. He may enter the program early in hospitalization and continue in it until he leaves. When grading stress is carried out in this way, only selected tasks or interactions are graduated so that it is not a focal technique in the over-all help process.

3. Grading stress, although identified in some programs as the primary process, sometimes is introduced only near or immediately following hospital release. Here stress is graded only at one phase of hospitalization, but it is done systematically in a number of areas simultaneously. Since the severe cultural discontinuity

between hospital and community makes discharge a more or less threatening experience, many patients need carefully graded steps between hospital and community. Thus, to practitioners with this view, grading stress primarily means a technique for easing the transition to the outside and refers to the practices involved in moving a patient into a transition facility (Greenblatt, 1959).

4. In addition to the above views, grading stress may mean a focal process of help in many areas and phases of the patient's career. For example, the Vermont Project for Rehabilitation of Chronic Schizophrenic Patients (1959) developed a system of graded privileges within the hospital, graded group activities in occupational therapy and recreation, and graded employment, first in hospital industry and later in daytime employment in the community. Grading stress is continued after the patient leaves the hospital and enters the halfway house. This usage gives grading stress a different meaning from the one it has in programs described above: it becomes the orientation toward help within which treatment and rehabilitation proceed. Carried to a logical conclusion and elaborated, it could become a philosophy of rehabilitation.

In addition to differences in regard to the centrality of the process in the treatment program and the areas and phases of the patient's career in which it is applied, there is disagreement between practitioners on the type of disability for which grading stress is suitable. They have applied it to three kinds of disabilities or handicaps.

Many patients are unfit to resume community living because of handicaps resulting from long years of hospitalization—the break in community ties, the atrophy of social and occupational skills, and the discrepancy between their attitudes, values, and habits and those outside the hospital. It is currently believed that much of the desocialization through which these handicaps are acquired is not inherent in the illness. Nonetheless, the patient must be resocialized step by step for living in progressively less protected environments. The patient who comes into the hospital inadequately socialized in the first place also requires socialization if he is to bridge the gap between hospital and community. The disabilities of both groups may be quite generalized, and they may require help in many areas.

A second set of handicaps exists when, despite exposure to all available forms of treatment within the hospital and despite recovery from the acute phase of the illness, the patient still is left with symptoms, such as hallucinations, ritualistic and compulsive acts, continued depression, impaired memory, and so on. Or his manifest symptoms may be more or less abated, yet he is unable to see himself adequately or to act appropriately in certain situations. Helpers dealing with disabilities of this type are concerned with more than reduction of his symptoms: they must improve social functioning by a program fitted to his strengths and disabilities.

The third kind of disability is unusual vulnerability to ordinary incidents that may become crises, such as criticism by an employer, family fights, or the derisive comments of peers. In some, vulnerability is greatest during the first year following release. To decrease vulnerability to the stress of life outside the hospital, patients may need help in relatively specific disturbing situations only, such as, for instance, at work or in the family.

Programs may deal with all three disabilities, whether the patient is in a hospital or in an aftercare setting, though many practitioners associate grading stress only with disabilities of the first type—"hospitalitis." This is partly a result of the current emphasis on helping chronic mental hospital patients to move out of the hospital. But, as noted, in actual practice this is but one view of the process. Practitioners increasingly are convinced that patients with any type of disability need to be helped in a graded way if they are to maintain themselves outside hospitals.

Forms of Grading Stress on Ex-patients

Grading stress on ex-patients is, above all, a general method of helping them achieve a different level or type of functioning. As a consequence, its form may vary widely from program to program. It may be systematic or unsystematic, consciously or unconsciously used, focal or marginal, widely or narrowly applied, limited to certain phases of the patient's career or spread over several phases. Even though a grading-stress approach is used in work with patients, what is done may not be so labeled; in fact, although much of what we would consider grading stress is involved in casework and psychotherapy, to choose two examples, their practitioners rarely call it that.

There have been few explicit published statements of the steps in grading stress or its basic ingredients. To date, only a few who practice it systematically report what they do. One of the clearest discussions can be found in the article by Sivadon (1956) in which he describes a re-education program for regressed patients in his hospital. Building upon the work of Hermann Simon, he worked out a sequence of more than thirty stages of activity in which milieu, work, materials, and relationships are geared to the main functional structures of the patient's personality and his level of maturity. He specifies what sort of work, material, and so forth, a regressed patient should be given to reach a more mature level. Nothing of this kind has yet been worked out for ex-patients who are at higher levels of social and psychological development though still suffering from disabilities of various kinds.

Nonetheless, when we abstract certain elements of grading stress from existing programs, the following seem to be most important.

First, the patient's functioning is evaluated to determine his *current* level of behavior and to estimate his *potential* one. The latter need not be determined in any final way before the work with him begins, but some indication of it will give the worker an idea of possible goals. Grading stress always involves social norms and values, and goals are related to more normal or more socially acceptable behavior.

The second component is the working out of the steps intervening between the patient's present and potential level of functioning. This begins with calibrating some "activity" (whether it be a relationship, a task, or play) to the level of his behavior, calibration being based on some theory of the relationship between the media used and the patient's behavior. Here the basic concern is with balancing protection of the patient with exposing him to demands for functioning; the worker must protect him from overwhelming demands that might lead to retreat rather than to movement toward the goal. At the same time, he tries to bring about change by making demands the patient can meet.

Furthermore, the program works out for each patient the way in which initiation, practice, and graduation shall occur at each step in the process. Grading stress requires that he be prepared for the step and given assistance in taking it; he must have opportunities for perfecting the learning involved; and a channel to the next step must be provided so the process may begin anew.

The role of a helper is implicit. This is someone—either a professional or a trained layman—whose function is to plan and manage the procedures described above. This is not to say that some patients do not grade their own stresses; some do so both in the hospital and afterward. For example, a patient may withdraw from others on his own or avoid tasks engendering unmanageable tensions until he is ready for them. Gradually he resumes relationships and broadens his participation. But it is precisely because many are unable to grade the stress on themselves successfully that they need help. Both the social system and the patients' intrapsychic difficulties contribute to their inability. Hospitals in general are not flexible enough to grade stress in a highly individualized way. Similarly, though less obviously, the family or the work situation in the community make it difficult for the patient to participate according to his degree of toleration. Thus, many social systems operate in the same direction as the patient's intrapersonal difficulties and prevent him from graduating his own stresses. A helper is necessary to manage elements of the social system and to work with the patient's assets, so that he gradually may achieve success in performing more normally.

In all programs of graded stress, the practitioner manages, step by step, some aspect of the environment to which the patient is exposed. At least three aspects of environment may be media for grading stress: the tasks and activities he engages in, the human relationships he carries on, and the setting in which he lives, works, or plays. These three are so closely related that it probably is impossible to grade stress in only one while ignoring the others. Yet practitioners tend to emphasize one or another, and for purposes of discussion we shall consider each a separate form.

GRADING STRESS BY MANAGING TASKS
AND ACTIVITIES

The word "activities" is used here broadly to include any kind of experience or service which is part of a planned sequence aimed at the elevation of the patient's level of performance. Helping patients reach higher levels of social maturity through structured activities that make increasing demands on them has been a central method of occupational, industrial, and recreational therapy in mental hospitals. It is now used in sheltered workshops, ex-patient clubs, rehabilitation centers, and day hospitals. Workers have two problems in applying it.

The first is assessing the patient in order to determine the type and level of activity he should be offered. His age, his sex, the diagnosis, his physical fitness, his behavior, and the nature of his problems are most often considered. (See, for example, *The Objectives and Functions of Occupational Therapy* [1958].) Consideration also is given to past experiences relevant to the activity, such as his previous occupation, his past interests or hobbies, or the difficulties he had prior to hospitalization.

These considerations also enter into the selection of ex-patients for an aftercare program. The persons accepted are those with characteristics which practitioners feel are most likely to lead to success. Thus, for example, Altro Workshop in New York City (Bellak, *et al.* 1956) selects clients according to their potential to learn work habits and to follow through in a situation of competitive employment, their degree of illness, and the readiness of the family to accept referral to the workshop. It excludes those whose past histories disclose impulsive behavior, acting out, or bizarre motor behavior, those actively prone to homicide or assault, the acutely self-destructive and the manifestly hallucinating. Nor do they accept persons so mentally or physically ill or aged that it seems unreasonable to expect amelioration. In aftercare it is assumed that certain types of persons will succeed better than others and that they should have priority in access to available resources.

The other concern is to classify tasks on a continuum of com-

plexity, each level being related to differing needs or characteristics of the patients.

There are a number of dimensions of any activity. Those most
frequently taken into account in grading stress are the intricacy
of the task, the nature of the materials, the time required for
completion, the pace, and the amount and kind of interaction it
involves. Others are the dangers and the energy entailed and the
usefulness of the activity. In turn, intricacy, for example, depends
upon the number and variation of operations, whether or not
instruments are used, and the skill required. Thus, sweeping the
floor, crushing rubble, and clay modeling are considered simple
activities, for they require little manual dexterity, little contact
with others, and few or no instruments, and the pace and time can
be adjusted to the person. Basketmaking, square dancing, or operating a single-needle power sewing machine are of a higher order;
and work involving great skill, such as wrought-iron work or
games requiring close attention and capacity for following rules,
is considered even more complex.

The activity to be used as the medium for grading stress for a
particular patient may be chosen on one of several bases. It may
be selected because it provides opportunity for further personality integration, which was stabilized at an immature level.
By facilitating the working-through of unresolved conflicts, latent
energy is freed and its investment in adaptive behavior is permitted. Or it may be chosen because of the ease with which
it can be learned and the opportunity it provides for acquiring general social skills. The theory is that learning a specific
skill, such as operating a sewing machine in a sheltered workshop, permits the ex-patient to acquire the attitudes and habits
of work necessary for participating in any work setting. There is,
however, the danger that ex-patients may be assigned to activities
in which they have no interest, rationalized on the ground that
they will develop transferable skills. Finally, ex-patients may be
permitted to choose their own tasks on the assumption that free
choice will enhance motivation.

But the selection is only partly decided by the practitioner's theory; it also depends upon the available social organization. Where only a simple organization is needed, such as in many recreational activities, the selection may be made more on the basis of theory than it is where, as in the case of many work activities, a complex organization is needed or special equipment is called for.

The selecting of the task and the preparing, initiating, and gradual moving of the patient from one step to the next must be performed by someone in close contact with him. Where there are few workers, as in some day hospitals and ex-patient clubs, these things may be done by a single helper. But this need not be the case: the functions may be split between several, each having a different role. For example, the ex-patient's work supervisor or group worker, his caseworker, and his psychiatrist may be involved in different ways and to different degrees in his day-to-day learning. Or several workers might share the same grading functions. In one rehabilitation center, several workers graded the activities for each ex-patient in much the same way and also participated in the varied aspects of the work and recreation program.

Not only are there different patterns of organizing the helpers but there are several forms that the patient-helper relationship can take. The one-to-one relationship is only one form and is not a necessary condition for grading stress through activities. A helper may grade activities for a group of patients as well as for an individual. In many ex-patient clubs, for example, the helper is concerned with selecting activities for them in order to broaden their horizons, increase their social and other skills, and yet protect them from feeling too alone, conspicuous, or inadequate. The assumption is that members of the group in general are at the same level of development and, therefore, need the same activity; or that, in spite of differences in social competence, each can benefit in some way from a program oriented toward helping the group as a whole. At the same time, the helper may explore ways to provide for individuals' needs to the extent that it is possible to do so in work with the group.

USING THE PATIENT-HELPER RELATIONSHIP IN GRADING STRESS

The interpersonal relationship is used to grade stress by many different professional groups—psychiatrists doing psychotherapy, social workers engaged in casework, public health nurses following up the sick in their homes, and rehabilitation counselors working with handicapped persons—and also by nonprofessionals, such as volunteer workers and foster-family caretakers. All may use their relationship with their patient to graduate the stress he experiences and to move him closer to a given goal. Even though other aspects of the work may be more important than grading stress, it is clear that grading stress through managing the elements in the relationship is a generic process used in work with disabled persons and a resource of a number of professions.

In using his relationship with an ex-patient as a means of grading stress for him, the helper tries to respond to him and his problems in a way that will assist him generally to enlarge the scope of his activities or relationships and to act in more normal and appropriate ways. Further, the helper may aid him in clarifying his next step, in gaining the confidence to undertake a new activity, and so forth. Whatever the starting point of their relationship, in general, the helper and patient must constantly alter its nature if the latter is gradually to function more independently.

Graduating stress through the use of the interpersonal relationship involves problems of reality in the ex-patient's life—getting a job, taking medication, finding suitable living arrangements, and so on—and, at the same time, it involves the use of the helper-patient relationship as a training ground, that is, as a rehearsal for maintaining other human relationships.

The helpers cannot start at a standard beginning point, since ex-patients are at various stages in their development and have problems in different areas. Thus, they must grade stress quite differently with different patients. Part of their skill is in discovering which are the salient aspects of the relationship, when the patient is ready to move to another stage in it, and what the nature of that stage is.

The setting in which the helper-patient relationship is found often has an important effect on what is done. For example, in a transitional setting that provides the ex-patient with a certain amount of support, the helper may be free to deal more directly with his emotional problems. But, as Sheldon Messinger pointed out,[2] where facilities are lacking, the practitioner himself may have to act as a buffer for the ex-patient, an additional and essentially unconstructive role which exhausts his time and energy.

The worker who uses his relationship with the ex-patient to graduate stress for him may begin by ordering the issues the ex-patient confronts in such a way that the latter can deal constructively with them. For example, for the ex-patient who cannot handle several problems at once, the helper may see that they are considered one at a time in an appropriate order. Thus, for a patient nearing release from the hospital, the helper may determine that working at a job while living in the hospital is more promising for him than moving out of the hospital and then finding a job. Finding a job is the issue to be raised first. For another patient, the reverse may be true: the helper initiates discussion of foster-family care and later raises the problems of work. For an ex-patient living in a halfway house, work may be a more appropriate issue than suitable recreation, though for other ex-patients it may be the reverse. Psychological problems also are discussed in a graded fashion where this is indicated. Not only may the helper assist the ex-patient in looking at more of his internal conflicts but he determines which should be discussed first and which left until later.

Secondly, the helper may gradually increase his expectations of the patient regarding the assumption of responsibility. The helper may begin by taking the major responsibility for certain actions but expect the patient in time to assume a larger and larger share of responsibility for himself. For example, a nurse in a day hospital may give an ex-patient his prescribed drug each day but let him know that she expects him to gradually assume the responsibility for it himself. Later, she may give it to him in weekly supplies and check him at increasingly longer intervals. Or, a helper may serve as an intermediary between him and his significant others. In this way the helper takes the pressure off him. Later, the helper may expect the patient to deal with these persons himself.

Thirdly, the helper may grade his or her own "tolerance" of the ex-patient's behavior. At first, the helper may accept his behavior, whatever it may be. The helper may show approval of his attempts to solve his problems, may praise or encourage him and take it calmly when he appears inappropriately dressed or late for his appointment, and so on. Later, however, the helper may begin to make demands upon him, perhaps, initially one at a time; for example, that he dress properly, or get up at a proper time each day, or get a job.

Certain ex-patients need help in relationships with peers and authority figures. Some, for example, can be comfortable only in one-to-one relationships or in loosely knit groups of persons like themselves. The helper, particularly the group worker, may try to give them opportunities for new kinds of relationships with a variety of individuals. Many helpers operate on the theory that some ex-patients must be given practice in new roles and relationships in a sheltered situation (a protected setting or a therapeutic relationship) and slowly helped to venture out, for instance, to assume leadership in an ex-patient club or to work as an employee in a transitional setting, and, after that, to perform the same tasks in unprotected situations.

Stevenson and Fisher (1954), a psychiatrist and a social worker, graded stress with the objective of restoring to employment several chronically unemployed patients who were in supportive psychotherapy in an out-patient clinic. After preliminary appraisal of a patient's physical condition, reassurance and explanation about work was given, and the issue of employment was broached. Though the psychiatrist considered him ready for work, the patient usually felt he was being "pushed." After several interviews in which the obstacles to returning to work were discussed, the patient was referred to the social worker for simultaneous help with obtaining a job. She was sympathetic but firm on the issue of employment. She provided other help, referring him to jobs or to agencies for job placement, while working with his family to modify obstructive attitudes. In the succeeding phase, the psychiatrist became even firmer about employment, in some cases increasing the pressure by planning the termination of public assistance. The social worker became more "motherly," providing additional services and more frequent interviews, so that in the end she became the principal therapist. At this point, the patient usually became employed, but the relationship with the therapists continued for some time.

GRADING STRESS THROUGH THE USE OF
TRANSITIONAL SETTINGS

Graduating stress through the use of transitional settings involves drawing upon entire social systems to give the ex-patient an environment that will further his greater social competence. That is to say, the emphasis is not on providing particular tasks or relationships (though these usually are part of it) but on gearing the social organization—the norms, values, patterning of social roles, and so on—to the job of retraining.

The use of the transitional setting to move the ex-patient toward normal social life is based on the assumption that it is not sufficient just to provide graded tasks or single relationships. The setting as a whole must be organized to help him deal with stress. Many, for example, hold that preparation for independent living must be made in settings closely approximating reality and hospital settings, even in the more progressive institutions, are too unlike the outside world. Indeed, the less progressive hospitals— and these are the majority—actually retard their patients' adjustment to the outside world by socializing them in a culture that unfits them for community life. But the ordinary community may not be useful to ex-patients. It may reject them, expose their inadequacies, or ignore them.

These kinds of experiences in the community have convinced many practitioners of the need for an environment in between that of the mental hospital and the unprotected community. This may be provided in either of two ways. One is to place the patient in a community setting that already naturally possesses many of the desired characteristics as may be found in foster-family care programs and in some work programs. For example, the Eudawood

Tuberculosis Sanitarium and the Spring Grove State Hospital in Maryland collaborated in setting up the living and working conditions in the Sanitarium for patients from the State Hospital (Isaacson, 1958). There are several advantages in using a natural setting for retraining mental hospital patients. Living or working in a real life setting, the patient is exposed to normal social behavior, routines of ordinary life, and community roles. He is a member of a normal group and expected to conform to its norms. At the same time, he is given help in learning new roles. And if there are various built-in protections, he is sheltered from situations that would engender too much stress. But it is not easy to change the ex-patient's situation in such settings as he progresses, and it is often difficult to locate settings of this kind for the many ex-patients who cannot manage on their own.

These disadvantages influence some practitioners to adopt other tactics: they have *constructed* social settings with just the combination of therapeutic and real-life characteristics they presume ex-patients need; for example, sheltered workshops that require the behavior that is normal in factories: spending a full day at the shop, punching a time clock, working under the supervision of the foreman, and the like. At the same time, they have built into the transitional facility certain qualities of the therapeutic setting: attention to individual needs, availability of social work services, medical care, and so on.

Since practitioners devote more attention to constructed aftercare settings than to natural ones, one might conclude that they believe the former are best suited for this purpose. One might maintain that constructed settings are more flexible and more suited to individualized care, because they exist purely for therapeutic ends. But this is by no means substantiated, and practitioners ought not to assume it is so. Constructed settings may simply attest to practitioners' present concern with developing facilities that are one step away from the mental hospital. As ex-patients graduate from them still requiring some degree of help and protection, practitioners may turn to considering additional ways of using natural settings.

This raises the question of the way that practitioners regard transitional facilities. Some assume that the patient must pass through phases or steps in his rehabilitation before he can resettle himself independently in the community. Patients, however, pass through rehabilitation stages in different ways and so require various transitional settings and in different order. For one the order might be: the night hospital, the halfway house, an apartment of his own and help from a clinic social worker. For another: the day hospital, the sheltered workshop and the night hospital, and real work in a protected situation. Furthermore, nothing inherent in the facility makes one closer to the community than another; a setting can be used in different ways for various patients, serving as a terminal point for one, a starting place for another.

But other experts view transitional settings as all on an equal level, simply one step away from the mental hospital, the way station between it and the real world. One facility is not more protective than another; different organizations simply deal with different areas of life and different problems. As long as the ex-patient stays in an aftercare facility, whether he participates in one or in several, he is in the transitional phase, and, when he leaves, he moves into the phase of living in the community.

Still another conception of transitional settings might be called the stepladder notion: each occupies a certain rung on the ladder bringing the mental hospital patient closer to the community. Each facility tries to offer help in a particular area and to a different degree of whatever is being graded—freedom, responsibility, opportunity for new relationships, and so on. Thus, some settings are more like mental hospitals, others more like their counterparts in real life; some are appropriate to ex-patients needing a highly sheltered life, others suited to the partly independent.

Even though there are still only a few aftercare facilities, practitioners must become aware of the implications of their view of transitional settings, if they are to be planned in a logical way. For the attitude of the practitioner affects his use and his expectations of them. And when practitioners with differing views are working together, considerable confusion and difficulty in communication and in planning may arise unless they make clear what kind of transitional setting they want and what its relation to others should be.

Whatever their differences, practitioners do agree on two general attributes. The setting should provide ex-patients with more exposure to community attitudes, values, and social roles, and practice in assuming them, than is possible in the mental hospital. And, at the same time, their failures and inadequacies in the settings must not meet with the consequences that follow in the real world. In short, a transitional facility must make real-life demands while protecting the ex-patient from demands he is not ready to meet.

The literature on transitional settings does not specify further what characteristics are desirable or required. However, the following conceptions come from practitioners we interviewed.

In accordance with community norms, the ex-patients' needs and problems in various areas of life should be handled in different places, for example, sleep, play, and work should be separate from each other. As Goffman (1958) points out, in the mental hospital the barriers between these spheres are broken down, and "all aspects of life are conducted in the same place and under the same single authority." Even before Goffman suggested it, practitioners were aware that it would be more normal if an ex-patient's life functions were dealt with separately, as on the outside, and this is sometimes seen as basic to the development of a normal self-image.

Furthermore, by segregating functions, one may avoid a feature of total institutions that might prevent growth in social competence, namely, that misbehavior in one sphere is held against one in other spheres. Although practitioners may not have been aware of this problem in quite this way, some feel it important to keep an ex-patient's deficiencies in one role from blurring his adequacies in another, and that it is easier to do so if the settings are kept separate. Thus, an ex-patient may be viewed in the sheltered workshop as a competent worker who merely needs more training and self-confidence, yet in the ex-patient club he appears immature and in need of extensive, long-term help. On the other hand, some believe that for certain ex-patients it is not useful to segregate activities as completely as in normal life; ex-patient clubs attached to day hospitals, for example, may be more effective than if independent and work tasks undertaken in a halfway house may be a better way of learning the work role than working in a sheltered workshop.

Most practitioners argue that activities in the transitional setting should be as like their counterparts in the community as possible without sacrificing other values, such as attention to individual needs; that in work settings, ex-patients should be involved in real work or in socially useful activities, even if unpaid; and that recreation not only should be meaningful to those involved but should approximate recreation in the community.

In the matter of responsibility for himself, an ex-patient in a transitional setting should be in a position between that of the in-patient and one who is not a patient at all. In a mental hospital, there is a tendency, now altering somewhat, to plan for all the patient's basic needs and to deal with him as if he were a child. In a transitional setting, according to some aftercare practitioners, he should assume responsibility for his own behavior in some things (such as in getting there and going home, performing assigned tasks, and so on), and supervision, though needed, should not be the watchful guarding of the mental hospital; yet he cannot be expected to assume full responsibility for himself.

A closely related question is the degree of self-determination the ex-patient is permitted in the daily schedule, choice of activities, and plans for the future. The personal autonomy of the hospitalized is limited, even though some institutions are now allowing more freedom, inside and outside, and more opportunity to choose work or recreation. Practitioners believe that transitional settings should go even further, just short of complete self-determination; the aim being not mere freedom of choice but the educated freedom of wise and appropriate choice that is based on acceptance of realistic limits.

Finally, there is the view that the transitional setting should differ from the mental hospital and from the community in its special attitude to deviant behavior. It is not merely a question of accepting deviance more easily than the community and less so than the personnel in the mental hospital—contrary to the popular conception, deviance is often accepted in the community and heavily penalized in the mental hospital. Rather, staff and patients should have a *reeducational* orientation; that is, their objective should be to teach the nonconforming member how to behave more appropriately.

At present, there is no well-developed theory about how reeducation can be brought about. Many practitioners believe the approach must be to help the patient locate the basis of his inability to behave in approved and expected ways and find some mode of altering it. Rather than getting rid of the problem by discharging the troublesome person, as happens in industry, the helpers in the transitional setting should develop ways of coping with it. For ex-patients to learn to handle their deviant behavior, they must be more insulated from rebuke, ridicule, or derogation than they might be in an unprotected setting. Yet they are not to be looked upon as completely unable to control their impulses or to conform to rules. A transitional setting can make an important contribution to retraining by expecting the ex-patient to behave normally and to abide by the normal rules of dress, decorum, responsibility, and the like. Thus, in halfway houses, for example, this is often achieved by other members exerting pressure on the deviant member to conform.

In theory, the transitional setting, one might say, simulates real life in that more attention is paid to the patient's performance than to his psychodynamics; yet it also simulates the clinical setting in that psychodynamics are taken into account as much as possible. As to its culture, the transitional setting resembles the outside world more than the mental hospital, for example, in not focusing exclusively on the person's emotional disturbance; yet it resembles the progressive mental institution in providing benign situations for social relearning.

Although practitioners regard some characteristics of the transitional facility as indispensable to achieving their goals, we believe that these are not important in themselves but only insofar as they increase the ex-patient's ability to deal with stressful situations. Some characteristics may be eliminated and others added as more is learned about their effects.

Some practitioners assume that simply placing a person in a transitional setting will automatically grade stress. But grading stress can never occur automatically; it must be managed so that the specific requirements of a given ex-patient are met and the context of his experience altered as he changes. By virtue of its flexibility of operation or its method of handling deviant behavior, a transitional setting may make graduating stress easier for a helper than it would be in a community setting. But since ex-patients are differently affected by the same setting, there must be someone to manage it so as to bring about the desired effect. Grading stress is in effect individualizing care; it cannot be a standard process with a fixed time-span and a series of steps, uniform for all.

In practice the various forms of grading stress are likely to occur together. Their interweaving is illuminated in the following example of a helper making use of a sheltered workshop for an ex-patient. Beginning in the hospital, the social worker, vocational counselor, or both together start to plan for a given patient, evaluating his level of functioning and his readiness for the next step. The planning establishes a series of goals appropriate to him. Then he is prepared for his visits to the sheltered workshop. The first time or two he may be escorted there, but, after the introductory visits, he comes alone to be initiated into the shop itself and helped to "learn the ropes." For some patients this may mean learning how to act and talk like a worker, or to exclude from one's talk "crazy things," tolerated in hospital but not at work. It means learning attitudes required by a boss, as well as to see the man as a boss, not as a father or doctor whom he may resemble. It means fitting into the expectations of other workers whose attitudes are not like those of other patients. It means learning to meet the demands of management without violating his fellow workers' norms of production.

After successfully meeting the stresses attending his initiation, he may then be assigned to some simple repetitive operations, on a full-time or part-time basis, depending upon his emotional strength. He may be given substantial supervision and encouragement, some nods of approval and some practical assistance from fellow workers previously selected by staff to be helpful and congenial to him. He may be assigned to a section of the shop where fellow workers in general are the most mature and understanding.

Increasingly, as he succeeds in mastering simple tasks and dealing with problems such as punctual and regular attendance and problems attending normal interpersonal relationships, he may be provided progressively more complex tasks with decreased supervision, with occasional and appropriate criticisms for lapses in workmanship. Concurrent with his accommodation to the grading of stresses in the shop, he may receive help from a caseworker, adjusted to meet his changing needs.

On the basis of his cumulative successes, the patient may be graduated to a part of the shop that resembles in almost all respects the work demands and conditions he will experience in competitive employment. Finally, after continued success at the shop over an appropriate period of time, he graduates into regular employment.

Summarizing, we can see the patient move from simple to increasingly complex tasks, from highly personal and permissive supervision to that which is less so, from part-time to full-time sheltered employment, from substantial to occasional support by a caseworker, and, finally, from sheltered to regular employment. Some of the elements, such as the initial permissiveness and the highly personal relationships are not, in themselves, a requirement; they were included in the process of graduating stress in the case described above because they were appropriate to the needs of the particular patient at that point in time. For other patients, these elements might be inappropriate and even detrimental. Grading stress in the sheltered shop, as in other settings, requires continuing observation and evaluation of the patient and a fitting to him of the responsibilities and demands that he can handle.

While in practice two or all three forms of grading stress— managing tasks and activities, using the helper-patient relationship, and using transitional settings—appear together, each is a conceptually distinct approach. Theoretically, they are but different levels of organization that may be used in teaching socially and psychologically handicapped persons to achieve greater social competence. Thus, when the practitioner is concerned with managing tasks and activities, his unit is the individual: his level of energy, his motor coordination, the meaning of his objects, and so on. When he grades stress through managing interpersonal relationships, he focuses on the interpersonal level—on the ex-patient's anxiety in his relationships, on the nature of his social interaction, on the fit between personalities. And when the practitioner is concerned with grading elements of a social setting, the unit must be the social system: social roles, norms, and the interrelation of social processes. The reason practitioners have made less progress with the last-named than with the first two may be because most of them are trained to work with intrapsychic and interpersonal phenomena but not with the social system. The skills involved in grading stress through managing social settings may not be the same as those required to grade stress in the other ways, and, if practitioners wish to make headway in developing transitional settings, they must make more use of social system theory.

Discussion

Is grading stress an effective way to increase an ex-patient's social competence? Present research is only suggestive. As Meyer and Borgatta (1959a) point out, it is difficult to evaluate treatment programs, especially to devise standardized and logical methods of assessment. There still are few scientifically rigorous appraisals of aftercare and none at all that assess grading stress per se.

Meyer and Borgatta (1959a) after an arduous attempt to evaluate a sheltered workshop program for ex-patients, the Altro Health and Rehabilitation Center, conclude: "There is some but not very strong evidence that referral to Altro has a favorable impact on this type of posthospital patient" (p. 99). Another study, that by Ullmann and Berkman (1959) assessed a Veterans' Administration foster-home program and demonstrates that the time patients remained out of the hospital was significantly prolonged by placement in a family. The two studies indicate that the programs, taken as a whole, make some difference in ex-patients' ability to remain in the community. However, they do not specify graduated stress as the helpful component—nor does either establish how the patients' behavior actually changed and how other people reacted to them.

Several studies show that the environment to which the ex-patient returns makes a difference in his subsequent career. One, conducted in London by G. W. Brown, *et al.* (1958), reports that schizophrenics with long hospitalization who returned either to parents, wives, or hostels relapsed in the first year significantly more often than did those who returned to other kin (mainly siblings) or to lodgings. Even though more of the patients who were rated "not improved" on discharge went to stay with parents or in hostels, the differential rates of failure persisted at a significant level when the degree of illness was controlled. Freeman and Simmons (1958) compared the careers of patients in the Boston area (most of whom were schizophrenics) hospitalized more than 45 days who returned to conjugal families with those returning to parental families and found that, of those who performed at low levels in the community,[3] many more husbands than sons had to go back to the hospital. They concluded that parents are more tolerant of this kind of deviance than wives.

However, both these studies found that ex-patients who succeeded in staying out of the hospital and lived in their parents' homes had significantly lower adjustment scores than those in other settings. Of the two groups, the former were "sicker" at the time of hospitalization, but, in addition, the environment to which they returned was less favorable to the development of adequate forms of social behavior.

Family structure (probably related to family attitudes and expectations) is significantly related to ex-patients' performance level. Simmons and Freeman (1959) found that those with low levels of performance were commonest in households where other males could share the role normally expected of the ex-patient, that is, the adult male; and, on the other hand, high levels characterized ex-patients returning to families with high expectations, and no one else to play the role of adult male.

The work situation, itself, influences the ex-patient's level of performance: Brown, *et al.* (1958) report that, of the 41 percent of the ex-patients who worked for six or more months, 97 percent succeeded in remaining in the community; whereas, of the 43 percent who were not employed, only 46 percent succeeded in staying out of the hospital. Furthermore, more than one third of the 89 successful patients who worked for most of the year were rated by the researchers as either moderately or severely disturbed. Thus, they reached the conclusion that psychotic symptoms were not a serious obstacle to employment. Other researchers, for example, Cohen (1955), state that employment is an important preventive of relapse. A job may act as a stabilizing force, helping to prevent regression and supporting acceptable behavior in the ex-patient, who derives from it a feeling of usefulness and heightened self-esteem. Then, too, as Brown, *et al.* (1958) suggest, to some degree the value of a job may be in the enforced daily separation of the ex-patient and his family. Finally, employment and the accompanying earning power may make the ex-patient more acceptable to his family. Indeed, hospital personnel regard employment as a sign of adjustment and probably are less ready to rehospitalize a former patient if he is employed.

Both the Brown, *et al.* (1958) and the Freeman and Simmons (1958) studies support the proposition that the attitudes, expectations, and norms in the ex-patient's social environment significantly affect his behavior, and it is corroborated by a variety of studies dealing with mentally ill subjects. For example, Aronson and Polgar (1960), analyzed events leading to the psychiatric hospitalization of servicemen. They conclude that whether persons with "chronic difficulty" developed overt psychotic symptoms and were hospitalized largely was dependent upon their relationships with significant persons, particularly supervisors.

What is established by the studies in the field about the grading of stress in the post-hospital care of mental patients?

First, practitioners are on firm ground in assuming that ex-patients' performance can be influenced through the management of relationships and exposure to appropriate norms and expectations. And there is some support for the assumption that for keeping patients (especially husbands) who demonstrate low levels of interpersonal and occupational performance from returning to the hospital, the most unpropitious setting is their own family. The former assumption is maintained in most programs of graded stress; the latter is maintained by those who grade stress through the use of residential settings.

Second, these studies, especially that of Simmons and Freeman (1959), suggest that practitioners may be successful in keeping out of the hospital those patients at a low level of functioning who return to parental homes but that they may not achieve a normal adult role as long as they remain there. The most one can expect under these circumstances is to establish them in tolerant households and to maintain their current level of functioning. On the other hand, more adult patterns of living might be brought about eventually in other residential settings, although the patients may return to the hospital more often. But, even then, rehospitalization does not necessarily indicate lack of progress toward community readjustment.

It appears, then, that practitioners oriented toward keeping the patient out of hospitals and those concerned with increasing his social competence cherish different philosophies of aftercare. It may be that the latter are more concerned with improving the level of performance even if it means risking return to the mental hospital, whereas the former are more concerned with keeping him out of the hospital, even if he is able to stay out only at the price of a low, unchanging level of functioning.

Third, the studies do not suggest a one-to-one relationship between level of expectation and level of performance; that is to say, they do not state that both rise together. They only suggest that, if expectations are not beyond the ex-patient's current level of performance, he is not likely to do any better. Higher expectations are a necessary but not sufficient condition of improvement, for they do no more than open up the possibility of change. In addition, it seems necessary to gauge the expectation to the patient's probable next level of behavior. In short, what is needed is graded stress in conjunction with greater expectation.

The reason that greater expectations, alone, are not likely to alter performance may be precisely that, in part, a mentally ill person's difficulty is his failure to live up to expectations. He considers this failure only one more evidence of his inadequacy, and it nourishes his feelings of low self-esteem, self-revulsion, and hopelessness. On the other hand, exposing him to expectations that are *possible* for him, but also require of him more adequate behavior than he shows, is a way of breaking into the cycle of low expectations, low performance, guilt, and low self-esteem.

The ex-patient's increase in social competence when in transitional settings is probably not only a function of expectations appropriate to his level of performance. When one considers that mental illness itself may be his response to the normative structure, a way he handles others' expectations of him, it follows that his success in transitional settings also may be due to their neutralized norms, that is, norms less affectively loaded and sanctions less punitive than those in ordinary life. And when he fails to live up to them, the experience is less traumatic and less discouraging. In other words, the symbolic meaning of the normative structure of the family and the transitional setting may be different. If so, this difference alone might permit the ex-patient more latitude in experimenting with new forms of behavior and in acquiring more satisfying patterns of living.

It follows from all this that in managing the ex-patient's course in transitional settings, the practitioner must necessarily be concerned with the symbolic meaning of the norms in his patient's personality constellation. Much research may be needed before we learn what this means in rehabilitation.

For example, it may be that changing the norms of the parental family promotes the rehabilitation of ex-patient sons better than attempting to rehabilitate them in transitional settings. For, in the long run, it may be self-defeating to raise their performance there and then return them to their families, as long as familial expectations remain unaltered.

Finally, these studies throw light on the concept of "tolerance" of deviant behavior as it relates to helping ex-patients function more adequately. "Tolerance of deviance" is often advocated uncritically as a panacea, as though the major, if not only, deterrent to ex-patients' improvement is the common unsympathetic attitude toward the mentally ill. Aronson and Polgar (1960), however, report that the acceptance of nonconforming behavior without penalty led to "ingenious failure"—the deviant expended more effort and ingenuity to achieve failure than he needed to be successful. And Simmons and Freeman (1959) point out that mothers' "toleration" of the behavior of ex-patient sons with low levels of performance was associated with continued low performance. Thus, it appears that tolerance of deviance may encourage deviance. We need to know a great deal more about how attitudes affect this kind of deviance and the conditions under which tolerant attitudes bring about improvement in behavior before we can generalize as to the kind of attitude the practitioner or the public should hold. But clearly, the implication of the work done this far is that lack of tolerance is not the general explanation of failure of ex-patients to achieve higher levels of social competence.

If grading stress is to be systematically practiced, a number of basic issues must be faced and resolved. The following are the most urgent.

It is obvious that individualizing care is a necessary condition of grading stress. Practitioners agree that what is an appropriate way of grading stress for some ex-patients is highly inappropriate for others. But almost all programs we visited or learned about had adopted rules and practices that operate against individualized care. For example, a sheltered shop terminates almost all its cases after eight weeks; another requires its clients to spend the entire day there, whether working or idle. Some halfway houses have rules that apply uniformly to all residents, such as that they be employed or that they limit their stay to six months or less. This is not to say that there must not be any general rules but rather that, in significant areas, individualization should be more important than a general rule.

Repeatedly, the outward form of grading stress may be found

in a program but, in fact, it may not be there in substance. We cannot elaborate here on all the ways in which failure to individualize care can result in failure to grade stress. We can only note that ultimately an effective program of graded stress, with its concern for graded goals appropriate to different patients at different periods in their careers and with its emphasis on "timing" of exposure to stress, must operate on the principle of individualized care. Otherwise programs are compelled to operate on abstract principles apart from the specific and changing needs and capacities of widely diversified patients. With our present knowledge, if grading stress actually is to be done, it is necessary that each ex-patient become the focus of an unique experimental process, with gradients and timing of exposure to stress shaped by his particular needs, potentialities, and achievements.

Furthermore, if practitioners are able to design individualized programs of care, there is no substantial reason for their failure to include in these programs ex-patients who are able to function only minimally in the community. At present, in most aftercare programs run by private agencies or voluntary groups, they usually are not accepted as clients. They either live marginal existences in tolerant homes or are returned to mental hospitals where they live out their days as institutionalized cases.

But if practitioners hold that all ex-patients should be given the opportunity to learn to live in the community, if they believe that a large percentage of them can learn to function with greater competence than most do at present, they must at least experiment with grading stress for the minimally functioning ex-patient. This work may lead to long-term post-hospital programs of care. In the event that these patients show little alteration in behavior, is the work with them justified by the knowledge that might be gained from the experiments? Are such programs worth-while even though work with other ex-patients whose prognosis is better may be curtailed? Can practitioners find a way to safeguard these programs from becoming dumping grounds for the "failures" of other programs? This danger especially is real as long as case loads are large and the need for quick success is pressing. The result might not be an attack on the problem of hospital chronicity as its wholesale transfer to a new setting. The fear that long-term post-hospital settings will develop into centers of chronicity may have kept practitioners from developing them. Nevertheless, programs to explore the potentialities of grading stress for minimally functioning ex-patients are long overdue.

Perhaps most crucial is the question of how to bring ex-patients into these programs. Should they be persuaded or coerced? Various studies (Meyer and Borgatta, 1959b; Olshansky, et al., 1960; Freeman and Simmons, 1961) show that ex-patients do not voluntarily seek aftercare, even when concerted effort is made to encourage them to do so. Is this because ex-patients function adequately in the community and therefore do not need aftercare? J. A. Davis, et al. (1957, p. 39) report that, of a cohort of 126 cases, approximately one third remained out of the hospital continuously for over two years following release but that only half of them were working full-time or responsible for the care of a home. In other words, only 21 of the original 126 performed adequately at work—at least, when only one criterion of adequacy was applied. Similarly, in a study by Adler (1955) only about one third of the released male patients were regularly employed.

It would seem then that a great many ex-patients are functioning inadequately and that aftercare might help them achieve a higher level of functioning.

Freeman and Simmons (1961) suggest that, in order to insure out-patient aftercare, the patients might be obligated by law to participate in it. This, of course, is contrary to the philosophy of treatment of most private social agencies and private practitioners as well as contrary to the accepted cultural norm that persons should have the right to remain sick, disabled, or handicapped if they so choose as long as they do not endanger others.

Some practitioners believe that, if aftercare is integrated with in-patient care, the post-hospital program from the beginning will be accepted by the patient as the next step in his career. If he is prepared for this step during his hospitalization, neither legal or other types of coercion should be needed. But it is both inconsistent and unrealistic to release patients with low levels of performance from mental hospitals, which is taken to mean termination of treatment, and then to expect them, as we now do, to volunteer for further therapy, restriction of activity, and direction of their lives. In either solution, the position taken is that practitioners, representing society, have a right to attempt to bring about improvement in a social handicap. This is by no means the same thing as society's right to incarcerate in institutions those considered by its agents to be mentally ill. If it is right to restrict and direct the life of the patient recovering from mental illness for the purpose of altering his behavior, then is it not also right in the case of other handicapped persons—the chronically ill, the physically disabled, and so forth? Practitioners may choose this course, but they should do so in full knowledge of what they are doing.

Meyer and Borgatta (1955b, pp. 44–45) refer to this "dilemma between a voluntaristic philosophy of treatment and failure to reach a target population" as "one of the most crucial problems of the social work field as a whole." More than that, it is a major problem in the field of the care of the mentally ill.

A final issue is that of the adequate coverage and integration of the areas in which ex-patients may need graduated stress.

Lack of coverage of various areas of the ex-patient's life in which he needs help and lack of integration of different kinds of programs are two of the most serious deficiencies of present attempts at grading stress. Thus, one can find day hospitals or sheltered workshops where grading stress is carefully carried out in the work area—attention is even given to the ex-patient's intrapsychic difficulties—but no provision is made for grading the stresses attached to his living arrangements, even when they interfere with his progress at work. Similarly, even foster-family programs and halfway houses of high caliber, while giving detailed attention to grading the stresses in the transition from hospital to community pay little systematic attention to stresses associated with work or recreation. The same can be said of other kinds of programs.

There is, in fact, to our knowledge, no program in this country that adequately covers the areas in which ex-patients have difficulty and grades the various spheres simultaneously in an interrelated way. However vast the effort, such a program must be developed and its results assessed if the effectiveness of grading stress is to be adequately tested.

Though such an undertaking may appear difficult, it is important to note that a model for such a venture exists in the "transitional communities" for returned prisoners of war developed in England near the end of World War II (Curle, 1947; Curle and Trist, 1947). In many ways the task of transforming POWs into independent citizens is similar to increasing the social competence of ex-patients. The POWs were alienated from society and showed symptoms of desocialization: apathy, fear, hostility toward society, and dependence on the Army. The Civil Resettlement Units (CRU) were set up to "act as bridges between the Army and civilian life by providing a 'community' in which there was considerable intercommunication between these two spheres—a community designed along specifically psychological lines as a transitional society" (Curle, 1947, p. 42).

Many of the techniques described in this chapter as ways of graduating stress for ex-patients were found in this program: the use of sheltered workshops offering the POW opportunity to gain confidence in manual skill as well as in his ability to complete a task through the use of personal initiative; the secure introduction to "problems and social fields from which otherwise his participation might have been withheld by his anxiety, his guilt, or his hostility"; weekend leaves to reintegrate Army and home life gradually and in small doses; units run on the principle of voluntary democratic participation, with morale based on self-discipline; and use of unit members to assist in the resettlement of new arrivals. The similarities between these features and those in transitional settings for mental patients is striking.

There were differences however. Recognizing that readjustment is a two-way process, the CRU's made greater use of representatives of community organizations (trade union officials, factory workers, industrial executives, local civic authorities) and of volunteers. And the community was expected to share the responsibility for "integrating CRU into the total home society" (Curle, 1947, p. 65). Moreover, systematic attention was paid to developing the most promising social structure and culture for achieving their objectives. Since it was assumed the POW's problem lay in the social area, specifically in his inability to live in society, they understood that in large part the success of their endeavor was dependent upon developing an appropriate social structure. It was also assumed that this inability could be reduced through retraining. Therefore, an educational rather than a medical approach was adopted.

The issues discussed above are more than theoretical issues. They also are practical issues affecting the possibility of the practitioner putting his philosophy into practice. Thus, one who believes he can develop an adequate program for grading stress, without individualizing care or without considering the difficulties involved in the recruitment of ex-patients into aftercare, to name two problems, may find he has a program in name only.

Chapter 16

Providing Continuity of Care

The idea of continuity of care for ex-patients seems to have grown out of attempts to improve arrangements for post-hospital help. The term "continuity of care" sometimes is used synonymously with "aftercare" or "follow-up help" to indicate that some provision is made for mental patients after they leave the hospital. Tyhurst (1956) had in mind another meaning when he stated that it is an ideal now realized only for the private patient able to pay for full psychiatric care and that usually "the whole treatment plan is discontinuous. There is no relationship between the referral situation, the in-patient treatment, and the post-discharge environment." Here continuity of care refers to the planning of a patient's treatment so that the help given at any point is part of a total program. This is the more conventional use of the term and the one we use in this chapter.

In either sense of the term, continuity of care may be said to exist if the practitioner plans current help for the patient in connection with that previously given. Sometimes the patient experiences it as a continuation of previous services, but this is not a necessary criterion. In some circumstances, in order to provide for his needs of the moment, the service given must differ from past help. But if it fits into a general plan of treatment, care may be said to be characterized by continuity.

A number of programs for in-patients, out-patients, and ex-patients have continuity of care as a goal, though phases of treatment are administered by separate agencies. It is rare for a single program to encompass all phases of a mental hospital patient's career, and few, if any, combine services to mental hospital patients with help to out-patients who are never hospitalized. In other countries, particularly in England, to integrate all phases of care is a primary objective. The program of Mapperley Hospital at Nottingham (MacMillan, 1956) mentioned in Chapter 10 is an illustration of a highly integrated, well developed, all inclusive program of continuity of care. In this country, programs providing this type of continuity of care are a thing of the future. However, because they believe our conventional separation of inpatient, out-patient, and ex-patient care leads to discontinuity of care, some practitioners are trying to replace the present system with coordinated care programs.

As an idea rather than a general practice, continuity of care of mental hospital patients is by no means new. For many years, social workers, especially, have believed that hospital treatment would be more effective if patient and family were visited prior to hospitalization; if the relationship established then were maintained until the patient was settled back in the community; if the patient's treatment and the social work with family and patient were related; and if hospital and post-hospital help were connected. While here and there some attempt was made to continue a patient's treatment and rehabilitation after he left the hospital, little was done in an extensive way.

In seems that for continuity of care to be thought of as a necessary element and systematically practiced in a treatment program, certain ideas had to be present, but these did not enter into psychiatric thinking until a short time ago. For continuity of care rests on the assumptions that mental illnesses represent different degrees of disability and that many persons so handicapped are able to live in the community and can remain there if appropriate help is available.

As long as professionals held that patients must be cured before they can be released from hospitals and that cure is a fixed point that can be attained in the hospital, continuity of care was irrelevant. Those who needed care received it in the hospital; those on the outside were considered not to need continued treatment because they were cured. But many practitioners now believe that the process of recovery may extend over a long time and that some ex-patients will need long-term help after leaving the hospital. Others hold that cure is achieved only occasionally and under special circumstances and that recurrent crises are common among ex-patients, for which they need intermittent help from professionals. Whatever view is held, a change has occurred in the way in which the majority of mental hospital patients are seen. For one thing, tranquillizers have made it possible for practitioners to accept the idea that chronically ill patients can live outside the mental hospital if continued treatment is provided.

Furthermore, the concept of continuity of care has assumed such great importance in practitioners' thinking because they are coming more and more to believe that the mental hospital is not the only, or even the most effective, context for the treatment of the seriously emotionally disturbed. In fact, even hospital superintendents now point out the potential damage that can be inflicted on the hospital patient who might be better treated in the community. And finally many practitioners believe that to complete the treatment and rehabilitation started in the hospital, the patient, first, must live in the community and, second, must continue his treatment.

The current belief that rehospitalization can be prevented in many cases has promoted programs of continuity of care. Today, while practitioners think rehospitalization is a therapeutically useful maneuver in certain circumstances, in others they fear that it may be damaging or, at least, unnecessary. They argue, however, that the ex-patient must have post-hospital help when, unable to cope with stressful situations, he responds with psychotic or psychoneurotic upsets, and that it is not the inevitable reactivation of the disease but the absence of help during crises that necessitates his return to the hospital.

These ideas, coming together at one period in psychiatric history, have led to what may well mark a new conception of the most desirable organization of services for the emotionally disturbed. If we realize how few programs are systematically practicing continuity of care, the conception appears unimportant, but, if we also realize that almost all leading practitioners in aftercare believe that it is one of the ideas that *ought* to be put into practice, we may expect the rapid development and spread of such programs. Thus, even though the programs are few, it is important to find out how continuity of care is currently executed and what are the barriers to its realization.

Forms of Continuity of Care

However great practitioners' interest in continuity of care, it can be achieved only through appropriate organizational arrangements. But at present there are many, perhaps insurmountable, barriers.

Among requirements for continuity in patient care, foremost is the linking together of the agencies and/or the helpers working with the patient during the phases of his illness. To link helpers in the hospital and community is obviously needed, but it is equally necessary to bring together all those working with a patient within a single organization. Linking ranges from an informal connection to an explicit arrangement between persons helping a patient at different times, the former occurring usually in small organizations or communities where professionals know each other intimately. The explicit formal arrangement characterizes organizations or communities whose size calls for the exchange of patients' records, memoranda, conferences between workers, and the like. Linking does not necessarily mean coordination of agencies, only that helpers from different settings or programs work out a plan for a given patient. In some instances there may be a concerted effort to get the staffs of two agencies to hold a common view of the ex-patient's problems and to work together toward the same goal. In other instances contacts between workers are routine, in still others contacts are discontinuous and sporadic.

Of course, a precondition of continuity of care is the willingness of the patient to continue to be helped. Programs differ regarding the option given the ex-patient to accept or reject aftercare, with compulsory aftercare programs at one extreme and voluntary participation in aftercare at the other. However entrance to aftercare is arranged, most programs share common convictions about the patient's transition from in-patient to ex-patient status; for example, it should be gradual rather than abrupt, reassuring rather than anxiety-provoking. But they differ as to whether patient or staff is expected to take the initiative in arranging for aftercare and whether and how the patient is prepared for aftercare prior to release.

Most practitioners believe that continuity of care requires appropriate timing of aftercare contacts. Such timing cannot be standardized and must vary according to the ex-patient's need. One construction of this view is that no time should elapse between release and admission to aftercare because all ex-patients need immediate support. Delay in initiating contact with ex-patients results in discontinuity, even though help is finally given and is consistent with previous service, because it means the institution's requirements rather than the patient's determined the timing.

Finally, continuity of care requires the previous phases of the patient's mental hospital career be taken into account in the planning of further help. Yet this also is difficult to implement in practice. What usually happens is that only the latter part of the patient's hospital experience, and only a small segment of that, is thought relevant to aftercare. Just how much of the patient's experience is pertinent to a particular kind of aftercare, and how might one use the information about previous and current experiences? Professionals with different orientations see different events as relevant; moreover, it is often difficult to obtain information about what happened to a patient in the past.

In summary, the arrangements for continuity of care made by practitioners usually involve five elements: links between all the patient's helpers, gaining the patient's cooperation in entering aftercare, providing for the transition between settings or types of care, appropriate timing of contacts, and relating aspects of the patient's previous experience to the further care planned for him. All these are involved in different degrees in each of the forms of continuity of care outlined below.

CONTINUATION OF A RELATIONSHIP

Some practitioners believe that continuity of care can best be achieved if one helper maintains a relationship with a patient during the various phases of his treatment and care in various institutional or community settings. In this way he may have a corrective emotional experience, a model for identification, an opportunity to correct distortions, and a chance to verbalize his problems to someone who knows him intimately to gain a better understanding of them. Aside from the specific therapeutic possibilities in a continuing relationship, a helper who knows the patient well can act as a pilot and a source of support in various settings, helping him deal more effectively with his own experience.

The physician who maintains responsibility for his patient throughout all the treatment phases is one example of continuity of a helping relationship. Here it is implied that the disability of the ex-patient is an illness and his aftercare is largely a medical problem requiring direct contact between him and a physician. But, while continuity in the physician-patient relationship has long been a principle of general medicine, its extension to psychiatric disorders has been limited by the split between out-patient and in-patient psychiatric care, each of which is managed by its own medical personnel. Now, the growing number of psychiatric sections in general hospitals and the extension in some localities of medical insurance to psychiatric illness increase the likelihood that the private psychiatrist will treat his patients during both their out-patient and in-patient phases. Moreover, continuity of care by general practitioners has been encouraged by hospitals and furthered by the widespread use of drug maintenance therapy, the proper administration of which requires continued medical supervision. Finally, the trend toward using the physician is further demonstrated in the attempts to have mental hospital psychiatrists (usually psychiatric residents) continue their relationships with released patients in out-patient clinics. An even greater degree of continuity is established when the hospital psychiatrist also sees the patient in a pre-admission clinic before hospitalization.

Alongside the trend toward increasing physicians' participation in aftercare is that of increasing the variety of professionals who maintain continuing relationships with patients. Here, the conception is that many ex-patients do not need medical treatment and that factors such as the patient's personality structure, his specific social needs, and the personnel resources in his community should determine which type of service he is offered. Thus, in certain instances, social work hospital staff continue to see the ex-patient. In other instances, community helpers, such as public health nurses, social workers, or vocational rehabilitation counselors, continue in the post-hospital period a relationship developed prior to the patient's hospitalization or his release. The rationale for making one of these workers the key helper is that aftercare is primarily a problem of rehabilitation and as such is a social not a medical problem, and that workers trained in the use of community services should provide the patient with the continuing relationship.

Continuity of a relationship with a helper is believed to have distinct advantages. Of all the forms of continuity of care, it is least affected by the patient's entrance into or discharge from an institution. Thus, there will be fewer gaps in help because of the limitations of a particular institution; continuation is not contingent upon a succession of administrative arrangements; and the problem of linking helpers in separate agencies is eliminated. If a satisfying relationship with a helper developed in another context is continued in aftercare, he is more likely to feel positive about aftercare and less likely to feel distrustful of and resistant to it.

A disadvantage in a patient's having just one helper is that the patient's chances of being without any help at all because of unavailability or departure of the helper are greater than if he had several. Furthermore, he is denied the benefit of relationships with different types of persons in a variety of professional roles. Finally, if he has several helpers, his chances are greater of finding one with whom there is a particularly good therapeutic fit.

CONTINUITY OF SERVICES

Continuity of service means that help continues even though the helper may change; not the particular relationship but the type of relationship is important. It is attempted in two ways: either the mental hospital administers aftercare as a continuation of in-patient care; or, through a collaborative arrangement with a hospital, a community agency provides post-hospital help related to that received by the patient in the hospital.

Foster-family care (Hollier and Harrison, 1956; Fisher and Hirsch, 1957) is an example of a hospital-managed aftercare program with a high degree of continuity. Though the patient transfers from the ward's social worker to a family-care worker, change of helpers does not mean interruption in service or in kind of service. Since she is thoroughly familiar with the program, the first worker prepares the patient for entering family care and the second can quickly become familiar with his hospital experiences and problems through hospital records and his first worker. Continuity of service follows because the helpers have the same professional training and use the same techniques of help, participate in the same program and in the same institution, and so share a common set of understandings, philosophy of aftercare, and specific practices.

Continuity of service seems more difficult to provide when aftercare is administered not by the mental hospital, but, for example, by a community aftercare clinic which provides the ex-patient's therapy or casework. It is hard for helpers in different organizations to achieve a working relationship. Prerelease planning and the development of a relationship between patient and aftercare worker before discharge tend to be neglected. That this is not solely owing to geographic distance is demonstrated by the fact that a few community agencies have found ways to provide continuity in service. The Altro Health and Rehabilitation Services, Inc., in New York City (Bellak and Black, 1960) helped establish a rehabilitation team at Rockland State Hospital (Orangeburg, N.Y.) to stimulate the planning of rehabilitation early in the patient's hospitalization and to prepare him for aftercare at the sheltered workshop. A joint project between Jewish Family Service, Inc., in New York City and Hillside Hospital at Glen Oaks, N.Y., (Marcus and Gilchrist, 1959), in the course of demonstrating that a family agency can offer an important service to ex-patients, worked out at the same time a plan for continuity of casework service. The family agency's worker participated in the predischarge conference and, when possible, interviewed the family and patient prior to discharge, establishing a relationship with the patient she continued after his release from the hospital.

Although continuity of service seems easier if the mental hospital handles aftercare, some experts believe that in many instances this is neither possible nor desirable. The geographic distance between home and hospital may be so great that adequate aftercare can be given only by an agency in the ex-patient's own community. Thus, in many of the larger states, if the present trend continues, community agencies aftercare clinics are and will continue to be the main source of aftercare. Then, too, some feel that the ex-patient's reintegration into the community will be furthered if aftercare is handled by a community agency rather than by a mental hospital. Many ex-patients, particularly those hospitalized involuntarily, are antagonistic to the hospital and its workers and fear that continued help from them will increase their chance of rehospitalization. Some practitioners believe the stigma of help is lessened if it comes from a community agency and not from a mental hospital. And the change of workers as well as the transfer to a different agency may impress on the ex-patient the changes occurring in himself. Since community agencies represent the greatest potential resouce for augmenting aftercare services, it is important to work out a plan for using their staff to give continuity of care.

CONTINUITY OF PROGRAM

While most practitioners think of continuity of care as the continuation of a specific helping relationship or service, some would include continuation of a program for the patient under this rubric. What is continued is not a given treatment, service, nor relationship but the plan developed for the patient while he was in the hospital. Thus, even though the post-hospital help may differ from the hospital's and he may have a new helper, continuity may be built in by coherence of the plan of treatment.

This is the aim when a vocational rehabilitation counselor from a state department of vocational rehabilitation is assigned to a mental hospital to help plan and carry out a patient's work rehabilitation. But this does not, of course, necessarily mean that continuity in care will, in fact, occur. Continuity depends on many other conditions, in this instance on the hospital's interest in developing aftercare plans, on the seriousness with which it regards the vocational rehabilitation counselors' recommendation, and on the resources at hand. The counselors assigned to mental hospitals sometimes complain that the institution is not interested in their services and does not know how to use them and that their own agency places limitation on their planning for patients' needs. Almost always, too, there is the complaint that the paucity of community resources makes it impossible to carry out aftercare plans. Yet, despite difficulties, many hospitals now make effective use of vocational rehabilitation counselors.

Another arrangement to insure continuity is the providing of aftercare by community agency workers, for example, those of a health department (Peeples, 1956) or those of a social welfare department (Winston, 1958), in cooperation with mental hospitals. In some instances, the worker is given a brief orientation at the hospital though his day-to-day work is in the community. When the patient is about to be released from the hospital, the agency is notified, and a summary of his record and the recommendations for aftercare are given the worker who is to assume responsibility for him. The worker may visit the family and prepare them for his return, then continue to follow-up patient and family for a period of time in order to implement the hospital's recommendations. While it has the advantage of the geographic proximity of helper and ex-patient, such an arrangement creates many problems. Since ex-patients are only one of a community agency's responsibilities, it may not have much investment in helping persons with the type of difficult problems they present nor the time required to deal with these problems. Often agency workers complain that the hospital does not give them adequate information, that they do not receive referral early enough, or that they receive insufficient consultation from medical staff.

Here, too, despite many community workers' lack of training in handling ex-patients, some experts believe there are advantages in having a community agency rather than a mental hospital or special ex-patient organization provide aftercare. Ex-patients are impressed when a community agency takes an interest in them and gives them services similar to those received by other people. Here again, some practitioners emphasize that, if continuity of care is to occur attention will have to be paid to developing cooperation between hospital and community agencies.

RELATIONSHIP WITH AN ORGANIZATION

Finally, some professionals visualize continuity of care as being effected through an ex-patient's continuing relationship with one organization. The focus here is more on the consistency of post-hospital services over a long period of time than on the continuity between hospital and post-hospital care.

When a professional says that continuity of care can be achieved by the ex-patient's maintaining a relationship with an organization, he does not mean that the ex-patient necessarily is in continuous contact with a helper. One ex-patient will contact the agency infrequently; he primarily needs the knowledge that he can turn for help to an organization that knows him. Another needs periodic contacts of greater frequency. Still another requires permanent and continual help. In each instance, continuity of care is being given if the help at any point takes into account what has been done in the past. Continuity of care can be achieved if the ex-patient renews his contact with a given organization when he needs help. Though the patient sees different helpers and is given a variety of treatments and services over a period of years, the organization, itself, may approach his particular needs in an integrated way. Here, coherence and consistency make for continuity of care.

Permanent and continual help is a most difficult commitment for an organization, since it requires so much of the staff's time. In this country, of the few programs of this type, the most notable is foster-family care. In one such program, the chronic patient is placed in a suitable home with the understanding that the social worker will visit him and the foster parents each week, indefinitely; as a matter of fact, workers believe that this commitment is a prerequisite to keeping him in the community.

Some drug maintenance programs operate on the assumption that the chronic patient requires indefinite continuation of medication (Kris, 1957). Proper administration of drugs presumes knowledge of his previous reactions, and he must be seen regularly if complications are to be prevented and the drug properly controlled.

There is some support for the idea that continuous care may not be necessary. Certain ex-patients can be helped to remain in the community if they are checked on an infrequent but regular schedule, the usefulness of which lies, in part, in its demonstrating that some organization is really interested in them and that, if necessary, they can come to it for help. In the Follow-up Clinic of the Allan Memorial Institute of Psychiatry in Montreal, Canada, former patients who live some distance away are "written to automatically three months after discharge and at six and twelve months if they reply. This serves to give them a good deal of support and often helps to re-establish them in treatment as this becomes necessary" (Boag, 1957).

In some places, continuing help is given ex-patients through widely-spaced visits of public health nurses who not only assist them in immediate problems but keep the door open to further help. As noted earlier, many practitioners believe the public health nurse is the most appropriate community worker to give follow-up care. She generally is accepted as qualified to help families with all kinds of problems, from prenatal care to innoculation against communicable disease, and her strategic position allows her to refer patients and families to community agencies for services she cannot give. Again, though the particular nurse may change, the agency's records make it possible for any of her colleagues to determine what has been done for the family in the past and what might best be done at present.

Finally, a variety of organizations offering aftercare—mental hospitals, clinics, halfway houses, social rehabilitation centers, and day hospitals—assure their clients that, following the period of active service, they are welcome to visit at any time.

One halfway house (Vermont Project for Rehabilitation of Chronic Schizophrenic Patients, 1959) encourages its ex-patients to keep the connection alive and to return for consultation and for meetings of the ex-patients' club. This open-door policy is a common way of keeping in touch with those who need continuing though not necessarily frequent contact.

Continuity of care in any of these four forms [1] is conspicuously rare in the aftercare of mental hospital patients. Where it is practiced, however, some programs combine several forms; for example, a foster-family-care worker continues a service begun in the hospital, gives the patient new services, and helps him maintain a continuing relationship with an organization.

Discussion

The usefulness of aftercare is all too often reduced by an unnecessary fragmentation and unrelatedness of services given at different times. Past services should be meaningfully related to present ones, and all must add up to a well-planned total pattern. This conception might be considered utopian in view of the small proportion of ex-patients actually receiving aftercare. But leading students of the subject put it forth as neither impractical nor idealistic in the hope of influencing the future organization of inpatient and ex-patient care. The conviction is growing that only a program providing continuity of care can maximize the services of the limited number of available professionals. The basic difficulties in achieving continuity in care are due precisely to the shortage of professional personnel, the lack of funds for aftercare, and the great geographic distances often separating ex-patient and mental health facility. While these are limitations, continuity of care would be still difficult, even if considerably more money and personnel were available.

AROUSING PROFESSIONALS' INTEREST IN
GIVING AFTERCARE

A major obstacle to continuity of care is professional indifference to aftercare in general, a state of mind imputed to community agency workers by rehabilitation-oriented staffs in mental hospitals and to mental hospital staffs by workers in the community. Mental hospital staff who believe that the final stages of patients' rehabilitation must occur in the community complain that agency workers repudiate responsibility for ex-patients on the ground that they need long-term help, are too "sick" for them to handle, or require the specialized help of a mental hospital or aftercare clinic. A few agencies do give short-term help but to a limited number of ex-patients. The mental hospital practitioner realizes that agencies' reluctance is based on fear of the patients' becoming permanently dependent upon them and of long-term commitments that would tie up their staff with a small number of clients. These are questionable assumptions, for aftercare does not necessarily call for long-term help nor large amounts of professional time, nor involvement in insoluble problems. Such assumptions about aftercare are based on the model of interminable psychotherapy—years of a highly trained professional's time devoted to one patient whose gains are never solidified. Indifference to aftercare, however, is not limited to community agencies: general practitioners in large part have hesitated to give post-hospital care despite concerted attempts to enlist their aid (Ruilman, 1960).

It is interesting that precisely the same charge is made against mental hospital personnel by workers in community programs, who report that they are expected to handle ex-patients capable only of marginal social adjustment with little or no help from mental hospitals. They complain that hospital workers are so involved in treatment and so oriented toward illness that they do not have time for planning rehabilitation and make little attempt to work with the community agency staff before the patient leaves the hospital. Particularly when the patient is in the hospital on a voluntary rather than committed basis, hospital personnel may not even refer him for what aftercare is available. Cooper (1957) observes that a central problem for aftercare clinic staff is created by referral to the clinic at the time of release or only shortly before it, instead of long in advance.

We found that it is not unusual for community agency personnel and mental hospital staff to deprecate each other's interest in aftercare, and in ex-patients, as well as to question each other's competence to give aftercare and willingness to work with other organizations. Whatever the justification, mutual distrust increases the separation between the work of hospital and community agencies and hampers both in taking the first step toward cooperation. Yet, even if they held more favorable opinions of each other and were committed to working together, continuity of care would be difficult to effect. For the required organizational arrangements cannot easily be developed if the professionals continue to uphold current institutional and professional prerogatives.

THE JEALOUSLY GUARDED
INSTITUTIONAL DIVISION OF LABOR

A professional in almost any organization can document the numerous ways in which its rules and organizational boundaries make interorganizational work difficult. The division of labor between personnel in mental hospitals and in community agencies is especially powerful in preventing the staff of the one from working with the other to develop continuity of care. For example, though maintenance of one helping relationship is considered by some leaders to be the preferred form of continuity, this is precisely the form most difficult to arrange for psychiatric patients. The private psychiatrist can serve as the patient's hospital physician only if the patient is hospitalized in a psychiatric ward of a general hospital, and then only if the psychiatrist has hospital privileges. It is well-nigh impossible for the private psychiatrist to continue his patient's treatment if the latter is hospitalized in a public mental hospital. Similarly, few community agencies can arrange for workers to maintain contact with clients who are hospitalized. The reverse is true when the patient leaves the state mental hospital. For his hospital physician to continue to treat him on the outside, the hospital must have its own aftercare clinic and make explicit arrangements for the given physician to work there. Continuity undertaken by a nonmedical staff member is no more feasible. In some hospitals, staff are specifically enjoined from continuing relationships with discharged patients.

Even where the organization's rules permit the professional to work outside its traditional boundaries in order to provide continuity in patients' care, the attitudes of other professionals intervene. Thus, in one instance, attempts by public health nurses to work with mental hospital patients before release were frustrated by the unwillingness of hospital staff to give them information or to confer with them about patients. Several years of groundwork were necessary before a working relationship between the nurses and hospital personnel was established.

DIFFERING GOALS, VALUES, AND SOLUTIONS

When one or a combination of workers in one organization attempt to coordinate efforts with workers in another on behalf of a patient, various difficulties arise ranging from "misunderstandings" such as "failure" of one set of professionals to see what contribution the other can make to the patient's rehabilitation, to outright disagreement on how aftercare should be handled and what the helper's role in it should be. Discord seems most marked between workers trained in individual psychotherapeutic techniques and approaches—particularly psychiatrists, psychiatric nurses, and psychiatric social workers—and community helpers, such as public health nurses, vocational rehabilitation counselors, and group workers. Interestingly enough, it is the latter who most often explain the "misunderstandings" as differences in orientation; the former usually attribute them to inadequate communication, to be corrected by conferences or by training sessions to help the nonclinically trained gain "greater understanding of the problems and potentialities of the mentally and emotionally handicapped." (It is not reciprocally argued that the clinically trained professional can benefit from learning about practices and viewpoints of community workers!) However, conferences do not necessarily bring consensus between professionals guided by completely different conceptions.

Although there are marked differences in conceptions of how to give aftercare, no one has made a systematic study of differences in practices. Thus, it is not possible to specify the bases of disagreements, as Miller (1958) was able to do for organizations concerned with preventing juvenile delinquency. However, our interviews with participants in aftercare programs revealed two points of view: the first, that only individual psychotherapy will help ex-patients and, the second, that aftercare is a broad problem, requiring the integration of a variety of procedures, any one of which may turn out to be crucial for a given patient. Professionals adhering to the first theory believe that ex-patients can be helped only by someone, preferably a psychiatrist, trained in individual psychotherapeutic work with mentally disturbed persons, even going so far as to maintain that "ten minutes with such a professional can give the ex-patient more reassurance and support than hours spent with nonclinically trained workers." Rehabilitation services are secondary, useful in some instances, but only if the patient has the basic psychotherapeutic relationship.

Adherents of the other position share the assumption that ex-patients, like other members of the community, are a varied group needing a variety of services. They see ex-patients as persons to be helped in the same way as others, that is, by dealing not primarily with their pathology but with their strengths and by providing for both their social and psychological needs. Although they would agree that ex-patients need to be handled sympathetically, with an understanding of their particular difficulties in living in the community, they add that, for many, conventional psychiatric treatment or casework may not be of the first order of importance. Help can be that given by qualified community workers, such as, for example, the type of help social workers trained in general resocialization provide in rehabilitation centers (S. H. Fisher, *et al.,* 1960).

There is, however, a tendency to mask these differences in point of view by referring to them as problems of communication, as if they were merely questions of inadequate information. The community-service–oriented personnel's acceptance of the assumption that they can benefit from learning about the psychodynamic problems of mental hospital patients further obscures the real differences in philosophy of aftercare. Interorganizational conferences to "educate" personnel, to exchange information, and to reach joint decisions can fail to provide the common ground necessary for continuity of care by neglecting to come to grips with basic differences in orientation and philosophy.

Another complaint commonly made by workers involved in interorganizational aftercare is that it is difficult to make the arrangements necessary for effective work. For example, agency workers complain that they do not receive referrals from the hospital soon enough or with adequate case information. Sometimes the requested information is never given, the hospital regretfully acknowledging that institutional matters are so pressing that personnel can devote little time to the requests of outside workers.

The problem is not always merely one of time but rather of instituting inconvenient or even undesirable changes within the institution. For example, in an instance known to us, nurses giving post-hospital help to mental hospital patients wanted closer connection with the hospital's medical staff, more medical information, and more immediate notification of patients' impending release. For the hospital to grant these requests, the hospital record system would have had to be altered, and ward physicians would have had to spend more time writing notes and prescribing aftercare. Although this might have satisfied the nurses, it would have burdened already overloaded physicians. This would conflict with a major objective now being pursued in many state mental hospitals: to reduce psychiatrists' administrative work so that they can give more time to the individual patients and to ward programs. Furthermore, to involve the physicians more in giving information to agencies would change the role of the social worker, whose function it is to arrange for aftercare.

The same problem in reverse existed from the viewpoint of the hospital: social workers serving as liaison with the agency and as consultants to the nurses complained that the latter did not know how to use their services. The supervisory role assigned them by the hospital was not accepted by the nurses in the agency who maintained that only a member of their own profession or a psychiatrist should help them with their problems.

Underlying what appears to be merely different conceptions of how various professional groups prefer to work is the basic fact that each organization is committed first to solving its own problems of operation. Thus, maintaining a viable institution or avoiding the introduction of procedures that are inconsistent with the organization's present practices supersedes developing effective interagency cooperation.

CAREER NECESSITIES

The professionals' furtherance of his own career sometimes interferes with the practice of continuity of care, particularly in the continuity of a relationship with a patient. In the case of psychiatric residents or students in social work, the requirements of training can make the continuation of relationships with patients impossible. The personal advantages to the resident and the social work student of working on a variety of services, dealing with different types of cases, and, in the case of the psychiatrist, leaving hospital work to enter the more desirable world of private practice as soon as his training is completed, all work against continuity of care in the form of a continued relationship with patients.

These five barriers to continuity of care pose quite different problems, with varying possibilities of solution. Attempts to reduce these barriers have been made from a number of vantage points.

Whereas the increase in the number of psychiatric units in general hospitals will make it easier for the psychiatrist's private patients to get continuity of care, the problem of such care for most state mental hospital patients is not likely to be solved in a like manner. But they may ultimately receive it through training programs for general practitioners (Goshen, 1958; Matthews, 1958; Boag, 1957). For example, in one program, practitioners are invited to a seminar in a state mental hospital to discuss patients they referred for hospitalization and to help in their management after discharge. In another, the physicians are kept informed of their patients' hospital treatment and at the time of release are sent summaries of the patients' record. In yet another, the hospital sends the referring physicians weekly progress reports that are actually copies of the notes in the patients' record. And still another program operates an institute for general practitioners in which psychiatric specialists acquaint them with procedures for post-hospital care.

Continuity of service is provided in one community by a coordinating council of representatives of organizations giving services to the ex-patient. The public health nurse from the county health department visits him and forwards a report on his needs to a central committee; a social worker from another agency collates information about him from records of agencies and professionals having previous contact with him. The central committee of psychiatrist, psychologist, psychiatric social worker, public health nurse, and rehabilitation counselor then reviews the case and, if he is considered in need of continued help, he is referred to the most appropriate agency. Another scheme for reducing the barriers to continuity of service stems from a study of the rehabilitation of the mental hospital patient (Beach, *et al.* [n.d.]). It seeks to improve communication and coordination through committees at various levels of the hospital and the agency involved in the patient's care. Thus, the hospital part of the rehabilitation program is in the hands of "operating" groups composed of the various professional specialties; in the community, the working committees are composed of members of the various agencies. The whole operation is tied together by the project director who acts as a leader on procedural matters, a coordinator of decisions of the committees, a transmitter of information from one set of committees to the other, and an implementer of the research design.

Finally, in several communities, mental health workers, nursing consultants, and representatives of community welfare councils are attempting to coordinate the work of agencies involved in post-hospital care programs.

In the above we have focused on barriers that stand in the way of continuity in ex-patients' care rather than on the implications of practicing continuity of care. Believing as they do that continuity of care is highly desirable, most practitioners pay little attention to the problems it may entail. But the implementation of this now popular concept is probably not as free from disadvantages as some practitioners seem to believe.

We indicated that there are certain organizational requirements if continuity of care is to characterize the post-hospital help of any sizable number of ex-patients and that these requirements have been difficult to fulfill. We now suggest that *conflicts in values and in organizational aims and interests underlie the difficulties we outlined.*

A conflict in organizational goals makes it necessary to give one agency responsibility for providing continuity in care. Responsibility does not necessarily mean that the organization itself does aftercare, only that it should set up the machinery—administer funds, stimulate professional interest, provide consultation to community workers, bring together practitioners from various organizations, and so on. And some maintain that only a public agency can satisfactorily perform this coordinating function but there is no agreement on which agency it should be or how far it should go in exercising its powers. For example, how much and what kind of pressure should it exert on private practitioners and agencies to practice continuity of care? Faced with just this problem, the psychiatrist-director of a large public agency communicated to us that he felt there was a conflict between discharging his responsibility for the aftercare of state mental hospital patients and safeguarding the autonomy of private help agencies. Basically, of course, his is the problem of maintaining private welfare and medical services alongside their public counterparts, a dilemma not only of aftercare but of the entire field of the care and treatment of the mentally ill in our society.

There is no disagreement on the importance of basing helpers in communities, but controversy centers around whether these workers should be attached to the mental hospitals or to some other governmental bureau. Another controversy is whether control and administration of the program should be centralized or should be decentralized in local communities. And which professionals should do aftercare? Should workers who are not clinically trained play a major role in the programs? How may adequate supervision and consultation be assured for them? The shortage of mental health personnel in all communities means that most community workers will be inexperienced. If they are to be adequately supervised, clinically trained practitioners will have to reduce the amount of time spent in direct treatment in order to train others in aftercare. How can independent professionals or those in independent agencies be persuaded to do this?

To what extent should the authority responsible for aftercare interfere with the autonomy of professionals in agencies and in private practice in arranging continuity of care? Regardless of whether an outside agency urges it, the logic of a continuity of care program requires that both mental hospitals and community agencies change their practices. To some degree hospital personnel will have to give up the exclusive right to decide how their patients should be handled in the post-hospital period. In a similar fashion, agency personnel will probably have to forego complete independence when they participate in aftercare.

A patient does not move in a straight progression from outpatient to in-patient and thence to ex-patient status; frequently he moves back and forth between hospital and community. Therefore, plans for continuity in the care he is given must begin at the time he enters the system and must continue through the various phases of his difficulties. If this principle is to be put into practice, it means the reorganization or alteration of a number of treatment facilities, especially making their boundaries less impermeable. This would mean some change in the relations of physicians in private practice and those in public and private organizations (social agencies, mental health clinics, and mental hospitals) and in the relations between receiving hospitals and treatment hospitals.

Few practitioners have been concerned about the possible disadvantages of continuity of care for particular patients, probably because its advantages seem so attractive. And since its practice is limited, most practitioners advocating it have not had the opportunity to see what might happen when it is put into operation. It is important, therefore, to point out some of the problematic aspects of introducing continuity in a patient's care. For one thing, an unintended conservatism may be fostered. Continuity of care may be interpreted to mean that, above all else, a particular service must be continued for an ex-patient. New services may not be considered for him, and he may not be referred, for example, to a group work program because his hospital case worker focuses solely on getting him continued casework. In any philosophy of help there is always the possibility of a narrow construction and the danger in the case of the concept of continuity of care is that it will be taken to mean a particular service. Thus, it may become a mere mechanical repetition of the treatment given in the mental hospital whether appropriate or not. Often hospital care is focused exclusively on pathology, little attention being given to the patient's social needs and to the problems he will meet in relearning or adapting to the roles expected of him after hospitalization. And if, in the interest of providing continuity of care, his pathology is focused on exclusively, aftercare may become stereotyped and fixed in a mold not suited to his needs.

Emphasis on continuity of service also carries with it the possibility of its being used to extend the domain of a particular specialty. This, too, may be quite unintentional. But when a worker invests himself in the service he gives, he may see new ways in which it could operate to help patients and may quite honestly fail to appreciate the superior value of another specialty in the given situation. Such role imperialism, of course, arouses the hostility of professionals on whom it is exercised and interferes with collaboration with workers in other specialties. More serious, in the skirmish over who is to help the ex-patient, he may take second place.

Continuity of care promotes the possibility of stereotyped conceptions of the patient's needs and attributes. Though little attention has been given to it, the fact is continuity of care involves the communication of more than objective information about him. The better the continuity of care, the more likely are his past reputations and failures to follow him from setting to setting, robbing him, as it were, of the opportunity to develop new patterns of relationships and new modes of adaptation.

Finally, continuity of care, as it often is brought about administratively, seems to require keeping the ex-patient in the status of patient while he is receiving aftercare. For example, until a committed patient receives his discharge, he is unable to exercise ordinary civil rights and thus to transact the business of living as a normal adult. Frequently, the court appoints a guardian for the committed patient, an action that psychologically as well as legally places him in the status of a minor and only increases his difficulty in standing on his own feet. This is a most curious state of affairs, for, while he is being rehabilitated, he is deprived of the very rights on which his rehabilitation depends. This may reduce or even destroy the possibility that he will benefit from the services he receives.

Our observations should not be construed to mean that we urge the suspension of continuity of care until all the problems we have raised are solved. We suggest only that, despite the high place the idea of continuity of care occupies in the esteem of practitioners in aftercare, we do not yet have evidence that it significantly contributes to the patient's reintegration into community life. Several research projects designed to test assumptions about it are underway, and, eventually, we may have more detailed information. At present, however, there is a high level of faith and little dependable knowledge. Consideration of the advantages as well as possible disadvantages of the trend toward providing continuity in the care of mental hospital patients might lead to a greater refinement of the concept than now exists, to its application in more selective ways, and to the development of action research projects in which some of its assumptions may be tested.

Chapter 17

Problems and Issues of Aftercare*

"The goal of aftercare is to reintegrate the mental hospital patient in his community." Although this has become a cliché of practitioners, that should not obscure the fact that it represents a significant change in their thinking. Until recently even hospital social workers—to say nothing of other professionals—were too preoccupied with in-patient care to devote themselves to reintegration of patients into the community even though they saw it as one of their functions.

As psychiatric practitioners have become concerned with their patients' resettlement in a community, they become impressed with the difficulty ex-patients have in being accepted. To understand the response of the community to the ex-patient, one must ask what mental illness and hospitalization in a mental institution mean in our society.

The Devaluation of the Mentally Ill

Laymen, as distinct from psychiatric helpers, have regarded those who suffer serious mental disturbance and who are hospitalized in mental institutions as persons apart from themselves—individuals outside society. It is not only that the seriously mentally ill are unable to meet social responsibilities or are physically or verbally abusive. More important, the incomprehensibility of their behavior, their incapacity to respond in expected ways, and their uacceptable ways of behaving all are evidence of their disregard for societal norms. When someone violates our laws, refuses to abide by our conventions, and questions our values, he threatens

* We are indebted to Sheldon Messinger for his suggestions regarding the formulation presented here.

our social order and invites ostracism. In contrast to them, the
physically ill, although they, too, are incapable of fulfilling their
usual responsibilities, do at least accept their obligations as members of society, understand that they are sick, in general try to get
well, and cooperate with those trying to cure them. Furthermore,
they behave more or less predictably. Thus, the physically ill are
seen as "legitimate deviants." [1] But those defined as "insane" are
not considered *legitimately* sick. Once they are so defined, they are
expected not to get well, or to become sick again if they should
recover. With the freight of these attitudes directed toward them
and with the enduring stigma placed upon them, it is difficult for
even socially adequate ex-mental hospital patients to be reintegrated into society easily.

Patients' difficult behavior before admission to the hospital
creates an obstacle to their reintegration into the community. Hospitalization, itself, adds another obstacle. The conventional large
state mental institution traditionally separates patients from their
families and communities and takes away most of their adult rights
and responsibilities. Thus, they are started on the road to institutionalization that increases the difficulty of achieving full return
to community life. And perhaps the greatest obstacle to community
reintegration is created when an ex-patient manifests bizarre symptoms that reaffirm him as an illegitimate deviant.

Some practitioners, noting developments such as open hospitals,
patient government, "therapeutic communities," and other expressions of the new social psychiatry, conclude that community
reintegration can now be easily accomplished, given the personnel,
money, professional interest, and the like. Public attitudes are now
assumed to be relatively favorable. It is true that the public seems
more ready to accept this form of deviance.[2] But acceptance of
mental illness on the intellectual level is one thing; receiving the
ex-patient in one's everyday life is quite another.[3] As Smith (1959,
p. 26) points out, community reintegration is not solely the problem of helping the patient adjust or master the transition from
hospital to community; the helper must negotiate the bridge over
which the patient can return because important forces prevent his

assimilation. And, unfortunately, some of these forces find expression in resistance to aftercare programs.

Sources of Resistance to Aftercare Programs

EX-PATIENTS

Strangely enough, one important locus of resistance to aftercare is the ex-patient himself.[4] He may have had disheartening experiences with professionals in the past; he may believe that his hospital treatment was ineffective or that nothing is wrong with him. Whatever his reasons, in general he is trying to avoid two undesirable experiences: surveillance and stigma.

In its least acceptable form, surveillance is associated in the patient's mind with custodial care in a mental institution—with the physical and psychic deprivations of mass treatment, routinization of a daily regimen, enforced idleness, and extensive control. Even when the worst features of custodial care are absent, some degree of surveillance accompanies hospitalization. Although the patient may be given more opportunities for activities and for contacts with the outside world, an increased amount of responsibility for himself, and some voice in what happens to him, hospitalization generally brings denial of freedoms that an adult takes for granted. He is stripped not only of the right to move freely but also of the right to what and when he wants, to go to bed when he wishes, to have relationships with the opposite sex, to seek entertainment, and so forth—all these rights being limited by what is considered therapeutic or protective or by the exigencies of hospital administration. As he shows improvement, he may be allowed freedoms as privileges, the very term indicating that in the hospital these, the ordinary rights of the person on the outside, are special dispensations. Thus, to one who has experienced hospital surveillance, his release marks the end of it and the beginning of freedom to direct his life as he pleases. While a given patient, particularly if he has been hospitalized for a long time, may be reluctant to leave his dependent status, many are eager to do so. It is just be-

cause he is anxious to avoid the inevitable restriction and supervision in aftercare that the ex-patient in so many cases steers clear
of help.

An ex-patient may avoid aftercare for other reasons than that
he hates surveillance. He may be aware that former patients functioning at low levels of adequacy remain in the community because helpers have not detected their difficulties, and he therefore avoids aftercare in order to hide his failures and difficulties.
He does not want his improvement or lack thereof to be assessed
by the social agents who have the power to return him to the
hospital. Thus, although aftercare may be designed to help him
avoid rehospitalization, in some instances it may lead to the opposite. His avoidance of aftercare attests to his preference for remaining in the community, even at a low level of functioning,
rather than turning to the hospital for further help.

The ex-patient quite understandably wishes to avoid a stigmatized status. He knows that the community regards those hospitalized for mental illness with suspicion and distrust. Hospital release
gains him certain freedoms but not the fundamental freedom of
being regarded as an ordinary person. Usually he can secure it
only by concealing the fact of his hospitalization. By identifying
him as an ex-patient, the agents of aftercare threaten to expose
him. His avoidance of aftercare, then, may be partly motivated by
his desire to be reintegrated into society as quickly and easily as
possible. The most direct route is for him to play normal social
roles and act conventionally, regardless of aberrant intrapsychic
processes—in other words, to try to "pass" as never having been
mentally ill. His avoidance of aftercare is an expression of his desire
to negotiate the bridge between hospital and community himself,
rather than to have a helper do it for him.[5]

In general, one might say that the reason for an ex-patient's
resistance to aftercare is the fear that what he thought was temporary—the role of mental patient—may turn out to be permanent.
Once in the patient status (even in its ex-patient variant), he may
realize that it is both more inclusive and more enduring than he
visualized. When one becomes a patient in a general hospital,
one's other statuses—occupational, familial, and so on—are not

quite as inoperative as when one becomes a mental hospital patient. That the staff as well as the community should regard him as having only the one status while he is in the hospital he could bear, perhaps, for the sake of treatment, but, when he returns to the community, he finds himself in a status that entails a more or less permanent stigma. Thus, the more profound reason for his avoidance of aftercare is his desire to divest himself of a deviant status and to avoid possible permanent rejection and alienation from society.

EX-PATIENTS' FAMILIES

One might assume that the family would be eager to have its deviant member receive aftercare, that they would seek it for him and consultation for themselves as well. Although the evidence is still fragmentary,[6] this does not appear to be the case. Even further, some families actively avoid aftercare in their eagerness to prevent the ex-patient and themselves from being stigmatized. As a consequence, the family may begin concealing his hospitalization even before he is released (Yarrow, et al., 1955b.).

Many families are trying to reintegrate the patient into the community without professional help. As Sampson, Messinger, Towne, and others (1961) point out, reintegration may involve the suppression or repression of memories incompatible with the role the family is trying to reconstruct. Thus, both patient and family may tacitly agree not to discuss past disruptive behavior or the hospitalization, and this is made easier by the family's reluctance to define one of its members as mentally ill (Yarrow, et al., 1955a; C. G. Schwartz, 1957). As soon as the patient shows signs of "normality," many a family reverts to its original explanation of his behavior which excludes mental illness as the reason for his difficulties. But, of course, these strategies would be interfered with by aftercare, since it not only identifies the ex-patient as such, but it prolongs his status as a deviant member of society. Reintegration actually may be easier if he is not in the status of ex-patient. That denial or dissociation of his difficulties may not lead to the desired goal does not discourage the family from trying. Only when they fail may aftercare be considered as the alternative.

The opposite motivation, the desire to keep the ex-patient from being reincorporated into the family in adult roles, may also lead to rejection of aftercare. Aftercare may be viewed as a threat to the status quo of the family because it attempts to change the ex-patient and his role in the family.

Finally, the lack of common ground between the family's and the professional helpers' goals and values appears to play a significant role in the resistance of those of the lower class to professional help (Hollingshead and Redlich, 1958, pp. 172–79).

Whatever the family's specific reasons for resisting aftercare, such help has an intrinsic "flaw." The very attempt to help the ex-patient requires his identification as a deviant. As a consequence, community members are not eager to afford him the opportunities aftercare workers seek for him. Thus, his participation in aftercare is the very thing that stands in the way of community reintegration.

COMMUNITY MEMBERS

The general experience of aftercare practitioners is that employers, ministers, leaders of social clubs, general medical practitioners, and professionals in health or welfare agencies are opposed or ambivalent to accepting ex-patients as employees, members, patients, or clients. Their explanation is not that ex-patients are violent, unpredictable, or strange, but they say: "We are unable to handle that type of client," or "Ex-patients are difficult to help, and my agency must serve those with whom we are more likely to show results," or a given ex-patient "will not fit into our organization." What they are saying is that their enterprise is not designed for persons deviant in the way they conceive ex-patients to be. Realistically, aftercare helpers can maintain only that *some* ex-patients are no longer deviant and that many are not deviant in ways that matter for the business in hand. When this actually is shown to be the case, helpers find considerably less resistance and even a willingness to have contact with ex-patients. Their greater problem is to gain community members' cooperation in reestablishing in ordinary social roles those whose behavior is still abnormal.

In these efforts, helpers are addressing themselves to two separate problems: first, to establish a "normal" social role for no longer deviant ex-patients; second, to change the community's response to deviance, specifically to the deviance of ex-patients who have not recovered from their illness.

The first problem reflects the absence of a bridge back to society for the "recovered" mental hospital patient. Ordinarily he must live through the considerable discontinuity between patient and non-patient roles and avoid stigma as best he can. Because society nowadays is generally more hopeful about recovery and because hospitalization does not always completely cut off the patient from his social network, considerable progress has been made in easing his transition from hospital to community.

The second problem is more difficult because a solution to it involves changing the community's response to behavior that undermines the stability of societal norms and values. Ordinarily deviance is ignored, denied, or punished. When aftercare helpers ask the community to employ or otherwise help on therapeutic grounds those whose behavior is deviant, they ask it to alter basic organizational patterns and social values. Two questions face the community: What place *can* it make for such persons, that is, to what extent and under what circumstances can it behave therapeutically toward those who cannot perform adequately in normal social roles? What place *should* it make for them, that is, to what extent should it sacrifice other values so that the mentally ill are accepted and their rehabilitation in the community facilitated?

Many practitioners take the stand that they are only seeking for the ex-mental-hospital patient the same status as that accorded physically ill persons. But it is clear that they want more for ex-patients than the mere exemption from responsibilities that are allowed by the sick role.[7] What they are asking is that society develop another status for ex-patients, one that will help them *learn how to live* in society while at the same time *not penalize them for their failures* to perform adequately during the learning period. Thus, what the practitioner wants is not that the ex-patient be dealt with by society as a sick person but as a *trainee in living*.[8] This is a vastly different matter and involves not only the acceptance of an ex-patient's inability to function but also his right to experiment in society with finding more satisfactory ways of living. If and when such a role becomes established, it will symbolize a basic alteration in the way mental illness is conceived in our society and a profound change in the way it is handled by laymen and practitioners.

It is important, then, for practitioners to recognize that what they are after is a major change in how society deals with threatening behavior, actual and anticipated, of the mentally ill. And, further, that the resistance to their attempts to bring this change about is not mere prejudice but represents responses to the threat of alteration of basic, and in some ways, quite functional social patterns (Cumming and Cumming, 1957).

In any case, aftercare is at that stage of development in which the motivation of those who want to provide the service is stronger than of those who are candidates for it. Perhaps that will always be so. It may be that a different kind of aftercare, based less on surveillance and more on meeting individual needs, will meet with less opposition. Nonetheless, professionally trained helpers and others are assuming that aftercare is a necessary part of treatment even if it maintains the ex-patient in a deviant status for a while. At a time when in-patient care is moving from custodial to more therapeutic institutions and aftercare from simple surveillance to active rehabilitation, certain courses of action appear indicated. In general, these actions involve discovering various techniques for ensuring that aftercare becomes a viable social service for a population that will not choose it voluntarily and in a society that would prefer not to face the problems it implies.

Part V

Conclusion

Chapter 18

Recommendations

Our aim up to now has been to provide a frame of reference for understanding the consequences of certain ways of organizing help for mental patients. Our recommendations primarily concern a mode of thinking about improvements. We offer, therefore, an orientation rather than prescriptions for action. We suggest some major policies that need to be pursued, and we indicate ways these policies may be effected in each of the systems of help, separately as well as in all of them together. Detailed changes will be suggested primarily to make clear our frame of reference.

We have taken this approach for a number of reasons. First, there are serious limitations in knowledge about what processes and structures will help various kinds of mental patients; hence there is no secure ground for recommending specific changes in care and treatment. Secondly, communities vary greatly, in services, treatment modalities, availability of trained personnel, and other resources, as well as in the type of person seeking help. It is difficult, therefore, to recommend measures applicable to all parts of the country that go beyond those now widely accepted by leaders in the field. Finally, detailed recommendations would leave the impression that the answers to the problem of mental patient care are at hand. We believe that many are yet to be discovered by critical examination of practitioner experience, by demonstration research, and experimental research. Especially important will be an openness and receptivity to unusual perspectives and to pursuit of their implications.

Throughout our discussion we have emphasized the importance of the social system in permitting professionals to achieve the goals they set for themselves in caring for mental patients. The way care is organized and the patterned sequences that characterize this organization can serve as a barrier or facilitator to adequate and effective help. The system of care inevitably is interposed between the objectives practitioners have and the practices they can and do engage in. More effective management of this social system for therapeutic ends will depend in part upon their sensitivity to the impact of significant aspects of the help system upon patients within it. We come now to some dimensions of the total system of care for mental patients that need to be considered in projecting changes.

Policies

There are a number of general policies that can help practitioners to formulate changes for improved patient care: (1) a comprehensive orientation; (2) a planned approach; (3) diversification of services; (4) flexibility of organizational response; and (5) focus on the patients' needs.

A COMPREHENSIVE ORIENTATION

The goal of this policy is to counteract the prevailing fragmentation and lack of coordination of services and to permit the development of greater continuity and consistency in the care of patients.

In the first place, a comprehensive orientation is achieved by viewing a service or a helping institution in relation to its context, attention being given to the effect of the context on the service as well as the effect of the service on its context. Thus, for example, in addition to seeing the mental hospital as a self-contained social organization, it is seen in relation to its immediate local community, which includes the available social services, as well as in relation to the wider political and legal systems by which its budget and social fate are determined. This, then, involves an analysis of the relevant internal and external variables that affect its functioning.

Secondly, help for emotionally disturbed persons should be seen as a single or unitary undertaking with many ramifications and secondary problems. Thus out-patient, in-patient, and ex-patient care are not to be seen as separate but as interrelated aspects of the same enterprise; the subsystems, then, are considered part of an inclusive system of care. The central problem becomes: How can practitioners care for patients of various sociocultural backgrounds, with several types of psychosocial difficulties that may change with time, who are living in communities with varying amounts and kinds of personnel and other resources?

The practitioners approaching care in this way face a number of concrete problems. One is to discover the kinds of helping organizations that can maximize therapeutic situations for different kinds of patients being helped at the same time as well as for the same patient at different phases in his patient career. This may require utilization of his particular network of significant others, as well as specific treatments and methods of therapy. A second is to discover and develop the most effective linking of agencies in the system of patient care, connecting them with other community organizations and agents, as well as all of these with the patients' ordinary social situations.

A critical necessity, in a comprehensive orientation, is the openness of the practitioner to the possibility that processes within the immediate system as well as indirect or more remote processes affect or can be utilized to facilitate improvement in the patient. Thus, a comprehensive view of the system of help might generate conceptualization of new modes of intervention.

A PLANNED APPROACH

The social planning of innovations in care calls for the generalizing of past experiences, the developing of proximate and long-range goals and modes of procedure in advance of action, and systematic ways of thinking through courses of action. Planning, in the sense in which we use the term, therefore, involves a design for bringing about specific changes as well as a systematic effort to project future goals and needs, to think through alternative means, and to evaluate and determine priorities for the various objectives.

One of the current major difficulties is the haphazard development of most programs and services. Little attention is paid to the wider social field in which they are to fit, to the basic and more pressing of the needs of the community or group of patients, and to the most feasible next step. It may be that the integration of in-patient, out-patient, and ex-patient services which practitioners aim at can occur only in a patterned sequence. What is needed is a plan for their integration in which it is specified what steps can best be taken at the outset. It might be that at first each system must be modified individually, the *systematic* planning for which is often by-passed by practitioners. With a plan as a guide, they might become clearer about the necessary ingredients of institutional changes, more aware, for example, of the importance of support and supervision of personnel at each step of the change and of the fact that, if such support is to be effective, it, too, must be planned for. The more innovating the program, the more likely that planning in support of it will be necessary—a statement that seems to be as valid for ex-patient and out-patient as for in-patient programs.

It must not be thought that we wish to rule out spontaneous innovation and the emergence of new and unplanned practices. Rather, our view is that creative activity will be furthered if deliberately stimulated—that is, planned for. An important condition for the emergence and continuation of spontaneity and creativity is the organization of, and its expectation in, the social context. When a social context is shaped so as to encourage, reward, and use innovations, we believe it increases the likelihood that such spontaneous and creative behavior will occur.

DIVERSIFICATION OF SERVICES

By this we mean the availability of a variety of procedures, treatment modalities, and social contexts for simultaneous or consecutive use in carrying out a treatment program. Underlying the policy is the notion that it is important to counteract the limitations on help that are a result of exclusive reliance on standardized, conventionally accepted, or restricted and segmental modes. By paying attention to new and promising ideas as well as by supporting the growth of the older and more acceptable ones, and by using them in combination, greater leverage may be given to the help effort. Where knowledge is inadequate and where methods of treatment are chosen on the ground of ideological conviction or selective evidence, a policy of diversification might encourage the growth and development of promising but untried concepts and procedures. Such a policy now seems urgent because of the variety of psychological and social difficulties being treated as mental illness. Such multiplicity of conditions would appear to require constant examination of the nature of the fit between the help, the person, and the context and suggests that a variety of strategies may be needed for effective help.

FLEXIBILITY OF ORGANIZATIONAL RESPONSES

A challenging problem for practitioners is to recognize and to respond over time to differences between patients and to changes in them. Since institutions tend to become rigid, they need built-in mechanisms for constant individualized responsiveness to the patient, to the changing needs of patient and staff, and to new social conditions. Ultimately these mechanisms come to determine the effectiveness of a given program. Thus, continuing institutional flexibility is required as is a continuing search for more appropriate processes and structures.

A flexible organizational response promotes the optimum balance between the new and the old and increases the probability of maintaining the institution's stability without "locking in" the status quo, and of introducing changes without causing malfunctioning and disorganization.

FOCUS ON THE PATIENTS' NEEDS

Although every mental health system insists that meeting patients' needs and effecting improvement in the ill are its overriding purposes, we noted frequently a sizable gap between the profession of purpose and the pursuit of it. Often existing practices are rationalized as being developed for patients' benefit, and it is difficult for practitioners to realize that they may, in fact, work against this goal. Thus, if patients' needs are to assume a central place in the institution, the practitioners first must be willing to subject the whole system and its practices to continual scrutiny and to evaluate their actual, rather than their presumed or hoped for, effects.

If the institution's processes are to be dedicated to patients' welfare, there must be an intimate knowledge of each one's needs, and difficulties, and avenues of possible improvement. It must include information about the patients' sociocultural background, their network of social relations, and their somatic and psychological functioning. Individual patients, as well as groups, must be studied to develop an understanding of the fit between them and the system of help and of the ways in which their relations to their social world might be used therapeutically.

Also necessary and also based on an intimate knowledge of the institution's functioning is skill in providing for the needs of the institution as a social system as well as for the needs of patients as its individual beneficiaries. By careful study the practitioner must discover the most accessible and favorable points for intervention in the system of help and the most rewarding times to introduce changes.

The point is that an institution giving help must constantly evaluate itself to learn how well it meets patients' needs, how suitably it is organized to maximize therapeutic measures, and how successful it is in achieving therapeutic results.

Applications

Our hope is that practitioners will use these policies as guides in undertaking specific changes and that new programs will be based on them, at least in part.

Here, we first use these policies to suggest modifications, accepting the present division of care into out-patient, in-patient, and ex-patient systems. Second, with the policies as a basis, we offer a way of reconceptualizing and reorganizing systems of care.

There are certain important preconditions of improvement. Before any of the changes we suggest can be undertaken sufficient sums of money must be invested, first, to insure a considerable growth in the number, quality, and training of service and research personnel. Second, there must be continued basic and demonstration research, particularly research on the organizational forms and specific processes that bear on the patient's improvement. Third, the community must give support to the various programs and innovations. And, fourth, legislation must be enacted to prevent either legal or official stigmatizing of the mentally ill.

OUT-PATIENTS

If a larger proportion of seriously emotionally disturbed persons in the community are to have skilled help, the out-patient psychiatric services must be changed. Out-patient care suffers from extreme shortages of professional personnel, unequal geographic distribution of clinical facilities and helpers, and unequal opportunities for different kinds of emotionally disturbed persons to secure treatment, to say nothing of the difficulties in securing effective help for those who do enter treatment. These problems are not easily remedied. For example, only gradually will it be possible to improve our knowledge about mental disorders and their treatment, ignorance of which makes it difficult to give effective help. We suggest that a start be made by attacking some critical problems that must be dealt with to secure improved care or greater coverage in any kind of out-patient program.

Increased knowledge should have high priority. Before vast sums of money are expended, there clearly is a need to establish the validity of many of the new conceptions of help now rapidly being accepted in out-patient care. A research program aimed at testing key ideas, with emphasis on the conditions under which they are applicable, would provide a firmer basis as well as more specific direction for the development of out-patient services.

Research is basic to a sound mental health program, but communities cannot wait until all the evidence is in before beginning to improve their services. Many new programs offer enough promise of greater opportunities for treatment to justify their development and expansion while they are being carefully evaluated. Following the principles outlined above, some of the critical deficiencies in present psychiatric out-patient care can be attacked immediately.

Given the great shortage of professional personnel, more efficient use and greater integration of them and of services appears to be imperative. Careful planning of services would maximize their usefulness, but just how communities should go about it necessarily will vary from one place to another. A first step is for the community to solicit consultation with mental health experts from state or federal agencies and with persons in a variety of fields with different frames of reference. Expert outside help is important in program-planning because the assorted shortcomings in out-patient care are perpetuated by the tendency of local communities to confine themselves to conventional or restricted psychiatric services. Consultation is needed on how to deal with recurrent professional shortages, restrictions in treatment approaches, and limitations on those accepted for service. Outside experts in the field of community organization may help the community's leaders to clarify local needs, to see their problems in a broader framework, to ascertain and meet priorities, and to develop greater comprehensiveness of treatment.

The principles of flexibility of approach and of making patient needs central mean that programs of out-patient treatment should vary from community to community depending upon the local needs and that there should be greater experimentation with community programs. It seems particularly important to change the conventional out-patient facilities' unresponsiveness to the needs of persons facing crises of acute emotional disturbance. All new out-patient clinical services should in some way provide for greater flexibility in time and place of contact with the emotionally disturbed, perhaps through home treatment services, emergency clinics, immediate treatment groups, panels of physicians on call, or the like. Similarly, a wider variety of recruitment techniques should bring help to segments of the population now denied it. And all this must be carried out as part of a planned program if it is to yield maximum results.

Provision of opportunities for treatment that lie between hospitalization in a state mental institution and out-patient clinic treatment, though not extensive, is developing rapidly. The current belief is that many emotionally disturbed persons might avoid lengthy hospitalization with the resulting institutionalization and stigmatization if short-term treatment units or day treatment units were available. Again, if the *patient's needs* were the major rationale in developing services, some type of *community treatment* for the seriously emotionally disturbed person would be instituted. Since individual communities often cannot support such units, several communities or an entire region might unite in supporting a psychiatric unit in a general hospital or a day or night hospital.

The principle of a more comprehensive approach bears on the greater effectiveness that might be achieved by a broader purview than usually characterizes out-patient psychiatric treatment. For example, when a severely emotionally disturbed person is treated in his home community and when his family is asked to assume greater responsibility for his care (as contrasted with sending him to a state mental institution where the family's responsibility for him during treatment is much less), the treatment facility should consider not only his needs but those of his family as well. In this instance, the effectiveness of the service may depend on dealing with a larger unit of treatment than the patient. For example, the success of a day hospital program may be largely decided by the family's ability to cope with the patient when he is not at the day center. And the family's coping ability may be ensured only by extending help to it as well as to the patient.

Comprehensive out-patient psychiatric care also includes provision for the patient who needs hospitalization. Special attention needs to be given to developing links between out-patient services and hospital units for psychiatric care, to easy movement from one service to the other when necessary, and to continuity and consistency of care when such movement occurs.

IN-PATIENTS

A number of changes would be made in mental hospitals if these policies were to be used as guide lines for restructuring in-patient treatment.

If the patient is to become the center of institutional operation in practice as well as in theory, major structural changes will have to be made on both a comprehensive and segmental level. If institutional operations are genuinely to be focused on patient needs, the institution as a whole, as well as its parts, will have to be continually evaluated in light of this objective. Eventually, various types of institutions will have to be devised to meet the needs of the several types of patients. The institution's division of labor, definition and interrelation of roles, system of authority and decision making, modes of communication, and various institutional routines and procedures—all will have to be examined in terms of the goodness or badness of fit to patients' needs.

Two changes will have to be made. The first is the revision of the role of the patient. Genuine respect for the patient and for the dignity of his person, some privacy in living arrangements, and opportunities for the cultivation of self-esteem must be built into his role. In addition, his responsibility and share in decisions must be increased; opportunities must be provided for work and constructive activity that approximate normal living; and normal social performance, consistent with his sociocultural background, family context, and reference groups should be made possible. What is needed for the patient is a role that primarily serves his interests and is oriented toward his improvement and not toward the staff's convenience or the institution's conventions.

The second change calls for a restructuring to make all levels of staff agents of, and vehicles for, the patient's therapeutic resocialization. Staff members would support and facilitate the patient's role as described above. This means that, through participation with patients, they would encourage the optimum amount of responsibility and independence in decision making of which each is capable. Further, they would use their interpersonal relations with patients as instruments to teach them, directly and indirectly, how to live according to accepted norms and would advise them in their attempts to understand and successfully negotiate difficult and painful human experiences. Finally, they would bring about social situations and group contexts in which patients would have opportunities for learning new modes of human relations.

For the staff member to keep an operational focus on the patients' needs, more is required than a staff of high caliber and a desire to help. In addition, mechanisms must be created in the institution for motivating personnel to carry out their new roles and for maintaining high morale and enthusiasm. Through continuous supervision, training, and support, especially of nurses and attendants, the authorities should demonstrate their concern for staff as well as for patients. For it seems clear that the gratification staff can provide patients and the psychological and emotional growth they can encourage in them is directly related to their own satisfactions, stimulation, and psychological and emotional growth.

If flexibility of response to patients' changing needs is to be achieved in the mental hospital, there must be a change in the size of the hospital and of individual wards. Large mental hospitals are notoriously cumbersome, slow in responding to patients' needs, and difficult to free from their rigidities. But in smaller hospitals with fewer patients on a ward as well as increased staff-patient ratios, the staff can focus on patients as individuals, and at the same time the small numbers of patients can live together in ways that resemble life outside the institution.

Ease of movement within the hospital and between hospital and community is another characteristic of flexibility. This means that patients are not fixed in their ward locations because of past behavior but are moved freely on the basis of current functioning. Differences in ward milieus must be taken into account, in determining the most suitable ward for a given patient at a given time. Ease of movement also means easy admission and easy release. The goal is an institution giving short-term help, encouraging voluntary admissions, and acting as a transitional rather than a terminal point in a patient's career.

Application of the principle of diversification to a particular in-patient treatment institution might lead to the creation of a variety of relatively independent subunits within which its various patients are cared for and treated. Or a number of independent treatment units, each based on a different institutional model, might comprise the diversified facilities of a community or region. Thus, in addition to the conventional model of the mental hospital with its range of treatment modalities, other institutions might be introduced. One, modeled on the home, might be composed of a group of small cottages with from eight to twelve "patient-members," run by a male and female "staff member," in which the primary emphasis is on family living and on interpersonal processes of resocialization. Another model might copy Gheel in Belgium, in which the families of an entire community provide the resocialization experience by accepting patients into their homes to live with them as members of the family. Others might be modeled on the school, focusing on teaching social and other skills in a manner approximating, but not duplicating, that of an ordinary classroom. Finally, still others might be modeled on a factory or workshop where the patient learns work habits and skills and is remunerated for work performance. All models might profitably be experimented with and used in various combinations to establish diversity in help. This might lead to the development of a treatment setting better adapted to patients' needs than any we now have.

Diversity of service also can be effected through establishing units specializing in the treatment of children, alcoholics, psychopaths, and geriatric patients. Treating these persons separately might achieve a number of purposes simultaneously: it would relieve the mental hospital of a large population, rescue it from being a dumping ground for the undesirable or unwanted, and lead to a more appropriate milieu for those who remain, as well as for those sent to the specialized facilities.

The principle of a planned approach might be implemented by planning for continuous training of all levels of staff in the discovery and practice of therapeutic attitudes and procedures, particularly in how to facilitate meaningful experiences and create therapeutic social contexts. There might also be planning for continuous observation and evaluation of institutional processes and structures by qualified observers, and the feedback of their findings to those in authority should bring about enlightened changes. The work of the observers might lead to the interruption of untherapeutic processes and the reorganization of illness-maintaining social structures and to the instituting of more therapeutic processes and structures. Throughout, continuous evaluation might lead to further change and modification of the institution.

In this way, a planned approach becomes a continuing process of discovery and utilization of knowledge and experience.

With a more comprehensive orientation toward the mental hospital, practitioners would grow more interested in its relations with the wider community and its place in it. One of their problems would then be to discover how the hospital could serve the community as well as how to use the community more effectively for its own purposes. Practitioners would have to identify the common interests of hospital and community and promote effective liaisons, particularly with other systems that care for mental patients and with community agencies providing health, psychological, or social services. Thus, they would undertake to link together the hospital and the out-patient and aftercare systems to ensure continuity and consistency; and they would seek ways in which the local community agencies could help their patients with problems of work, recreation, and so on. Finally, practitioners in the mental hospital would maintain relationships with patients' families and others in patients' social networks, using their significant associates in effecting their improvement and in ensuring a place for them after they leave the hospital.

EX-PATIENTS

As our analysis suggests, ex-patients suffer from the lack of active and continuing aftercare by the state agency charged with it. Though a mental health authority exists in every state, few states have allotted sufficient power and resources for programs dealing with the ex-patients' range of problems. Placing them on convalescent leave and keeping in touch with them through brief monthly interviews may be adequate for some but falls short of the diversified services that many apparently need. Despite the progress of the past decade there still are extraordinarily few ex-patient services, considering the numbers of former patients unable to maintain themselves in communities. Where aftercare services do exist, they are piecemeal answers to ex-patients' problems, unrelated to each other and the other services. If readmissions are to be decreased and released mental hospital patients to manage outside hospitals, a set of interrelated services geared to specific disabilities will have to be planned and activated in communities with sizable ex-patient populations.

We believe that the precondition of effective aftercare is a state agency with sufficient power and financial support to stimulate a varied program of ex-patient services. It can no longer be assumed that the hospitals automatically will engage in the assorted activities of diversified aftercare or that individual community agencies can or will do so. More is required than establishing a clinic or even several specialized facilities. A sound aftercare program is based on the specification and location of the ex-patients' needs, recognition of gaps in health and welfare services available to ex-patients now in communities, formulation of the types of specialized help needed but lacking at present, and direct assistance in coordinating the efforts of community agencies that could or do give ex-patient services.

Even though aftercare may be provided by various organizations, the responsibility for stimulating planning and coordinating services should lie with a single state agency. It may well be that mental hospitals can perform all these functions if their scope and resources are enlarged. The point is not so much which agency should be charged with the responsibilities as that some agency must undertake them.

We wish to emphasize one point: before a specialized aftercare facility is set up, practitioners must ascertain the need for it and the specific characteristics it ought to possess. For example, if study of an ex-patient population in a given community indicates that suitable homes for lower-class men of marginal social adjustment are not available, a halfway house then might be especially designed for them. Not only would this utilize resources more effectively but would maximize care by tailoring it to individual patients.

Practitioners with a comprehensive orientation are aware that ex-patients' attitudes toward help and willingness to participate in aftercare are shaped in part by their hospital experiences. Thus, a custodial experience may discourage them from entering and remaining in aftercare, other than in a *pro forma* sense. In addition, aftercare programs are likely to be effective only when patients have reached a certain level upon release. Furthermore, there is reason to believe it crucial to enlist their participation in aftercare before they leave the hospital. In short, in-patient and ex-patient care must be coordinated. Not only must their programs be developed in relation to each other, so that the patients' transition from one to the other is meaningful and orderly, but it is clear that patients must establish relationships with helpers in aftercare before officially entering it. Cooperation between hospital and aftercare agencies is essential for developing bridges out of the hospital, and back into it if rehospitalization becomes necessary. If aftercare agencies were able to maintain contact with rehospitalized patients, their stay might be shorter than it now is, and the hospital itself would come to view rehospitalization as a temporary short-term therapeutic measure rather than as the disposal of community failures.

A comprehensive view of aftercare also might lead to the elimination of gaps that decrease the effectiveness of services. The period immediately following release from the hospital seems particularly critical in its effect on whether patients stay in the community or return to the hospital, a fact that has not been sufficiently appreciated in planning aftercare. Intensive help at this time may do more to decrease readmission than less intensive help spread over a longer period.

Often, detailed attention is given to one problem with no provision for helping with other equally important problems. Providing a sheltered work experience but ignoring living arrangements or recreation may decrease the effectiveness of the service and may even make it entirely useless. It may well be that no one organization can provide for all the former patient's needs—if so, there must be interorganizational planning and cooperation.

The policies of diversification and operational focus on patients' needs do not mean merely providing help in various areas of life such as work, recreation, and family living. Nor do they refer only to various arrangements for housing ex-patients, helping them work productively, and finding them suitable recreation. They also mean giving them help during different stages of their ex-patient career.

Thus, the transitional phase would not be only or even the major focus. It would be seen as one stage requiring help, and there would be a readiness to give help in crises occurring at later periods. Further, an attempt would be made to provide for different types of ex-patients, taking the needs of "chronic" ex-patients at marginal levels of social adjustment as seriously as the needs of the more integrated ex-patients. Adequate coverage of the needs of the ex-patient population would require short-term as well as long-term help, temporary as well as continued service, assistance to voluntary as well as to committed patients, aid for the elderly as well as the young, and so forth.

Finally, flexibility of organizational approach suggests not only that a given aftercare facility may need to use different approaches with different kinds of persons but that many community agencies might participate more effectively in aftercare, provided they adopt greater elasticity in rendering their services. We believe that efforts to use as many of the normal community resources as possible should be made. The rationalization that nothing can be done for ex-patients because specialized treatment facilities are not available should be guarded against. Many ex-patients may profitably use ordinary community facilities, particularly as specialized ones tend to prolong their deviant status and make transition to normal social roles more difficult.

One specific point regarding a flexible approach in planning an ex-patient's care might be mentioned. Legislation and agency rules need to be revised to allow for adjustment in the length of treatment and convalescent care to suit the ex-patient's requirements. As long as the rules remain more or less standardized, it may be impossible to individualize care.

Finally, we cannot overemphasize the importance of evaluating when to refer a patient for aftercare and when to discharge him directly to the community. The deviant status of the ex-patient and the stigma of his hospitalization mean that aftercare may have adverse as well as favorable repercussions that must be assessed realistically before the decision is made. In short, sometimes the best aftercare is no aftercare.

RECONCEPTUALIZATION AND REORGANIZATION

Up to this point our discussion was premised upon the current separation of in-patient, out-patient, and ex-patient services. But a new way of organizing these services may be imperative for successful dealing with some of the basic problems. Thus, for example, instead of coordination and integration of the separate systems, perhaps there should be an inclusive system integrating all care into one administrative structure. It might be a mental health center providing a diversified set of services, including an emergency care unit, a day and night hospital and out-patient clinic, a sheltered workshop and so forth. This would provide for the various needs of disturbed persons at any stage in their difficulties, coordinate services to a given patient at any one time, and arrange for the continuity of the care given him through time. If all mental patient services for a territory were concentrated in one center, response to patient needs might be more flexible and help might be more appropriate and better informed.

It should be pointed out that to reorganize in the form of a mental health center is to perpetuate the conventional medical model which conceptualizes disturbance as "illness," labels persons as "patients," and helps them by "treatment" directed and controlled by professionals who are physicians. A more radical reconceptualization and departure from this model might be entertained and experimented with. Some of the phenomena now labeled "mental illness" might be viewed as psychosocial disabilities, help for which might mean placing the disabled person in the role of "student" or "trainee." Help might be given by persons skilled in psychodynamic and sociodynamic processes, consisting of attempts to reeducate and resocialize persons by way of interpersonal and group interactions in specified milieus. A *resocialization center* thus might be one type of social system for helping certain kinds of psychologically or socially disturbed or inadequate persons. The assumption would be that experiences in the center could contribute significantly to improving and expanding the trainees' psychic-emotional-social life. The center's focus would be on the "emotionally disturbed" person as a social being whose difficulties require various kinds of social contexts, interpersonal experiences, and role demands, all developed with his needs in mind. A further assumption is that such participation might counteract and correct previous socialization (or lack thereof) and change the nature of the trainees' motivations, affective life, self-conceptions, attitudes toward others, and social skills.

Although it is difficult to specify the precise form such an institution might take, some of its general characteristics might be as follows. The institutional model might be a combination of home, school, and community center, oriented toward the resocialization of its trainees through relationships in peer groups, through the student role in relationship with a teacher, and through participation in "family" relationships. The therapeutic value of "ordinary" human relationships would be emphasized. Participation in task-oriented groups, such as workshops, classes and study groups, and recreational programs would occupy a central place in the program. In sum, the institution would try to provide the social context in which trainees could experiment with new roles, learn new values and norms, and participate in meaningful and satisfying relations so that a change would be wrought in their patterns of living.

Considerable research is needed to evaluate the usefulness and effectiveness of different institutional models and specific modalities of help for the various types of the emotionally disturbed. Demonstration projects might be developed to experiment with combining and extending the medical-psychological approaches. Similarly, projects that radically reconceptualize help in psychosocial terms, such as the resocialization center, should be supported, for from such research may issue the needed knowledge for effectively combining psychological and social procedures in the treatment of emotional disturbance.

In conclusion, we hope that mental health workers will consider other courses of action on the basis of the policies we have delineated. Finally, we wish to state again our belief that the analysis of facilities for patient care as social systems is a necessary stage in providing effective help to the emotionally disturbed and the mentally ill.

Notes

CHAPTER 1. THE CONTEXT OF THE STUDY

1. U.S. Congress (1955), *Mental Health Study Act,* P. L. 182. For a description of the Joint Commission on Mental Illness and Health, see its *First Annual Report* (1956), Sections A–E.

2. Joint Commission on Mental Illness and Health (1956), Section E, pp. 1–2.

3. We use the term "system" to refer to those interdependent organizations that function together in a patterned way to provide care for mental patients.

4. A Model Reporting Area for Mental Hospital Statistics was established in 1951 under the impetus and guidance of the Biometrics Branch of the National Institute of Mental Health (NIMH). The Branch's functions are "to encourage studies of statistical reporting and uniform application and standardization thereof throughout the nation," and it has been concerned primarily with the statistical problems of the public mental hospitals. Yet, while this has been an influence in sensitizing persons to problems in the collection and interpretation of such data, the quality and quantity of data available on a nationwide basis is largely unaffected. The Model Reporting Area grew from 11 to 19 in the numbers of member states during the first seven years of its existence. For the original resolution and outline of the Branch's functions, see NIMH (1951). The lack of a standardized system of reporting out-patients and ex-patients is even more glaring. Some systematic but partial efforts are underway to correct this in the case of the former. See Bahn and Norman (1957). Nothing is as yet being done or planned with regard to nationwide information about ex-patients and aftercare services.

5. We estimated that in 1959, for instance, between two and two and one-half million persons during a one-year period received some form of psychiatric treatment for a mental or emotional disorder, exclusive of the mentally retarded but including those who began treatment during the period as well as those left over from the previous year. We arrived at this figure by adding the 1,250,000 patients treated in mental hospitals each year to the 389,000 patients treated in out-patient clinics, and by adding to this between 400,000 and 800,000 patients that we estimate are seen annually by private practitioners of psychiatry. But no figure is good for long and for later statistics the reader is referred to the Biometrics Branch of the NIMH, Washington, D.C.

6. Early studies are summarized in Lemkau, *et al.* (1943). The American studies of the 1930s and 1940s are described in Felix and Kramer (1952

and 1953). An extensive bibliography is in Gruenberg (1950). Important studies are described in Milbank Memorial Fund (1953).

7. See Group for the Advancement of Psychiatry (1949); Lemkau, *et al.* (1943); Rountree, *et al.* (1945); W. C. Menninger (1948).

8. Leighton (1956). The Midtown figure was reported by Leo Srole at a Conference on Methodology of Mental Health Studies sponsored by the World Federation for Mental Health, April 17–22, 1958, at Princeton, New Jersey.

9. Attitudes, beliefs, and values regarding mental illness and mental patients are very complex, and this brief summary is far from adequate. A number of the relevant issues are discussed in Star (n.d.), which reports a nationwide study of opinion on metal illness and psychiatry. See also Cumming and Cumming (1957) and Nunnally (1957).

10. Many illustrations of sociocultural factors in illness and treatment are in Paul (1955) and in Jaco (1958).

11. "The Relationship of City Size, Geographical Location and Proximity to Mental Hospitals with Hospitalized Incidence of Psychoses of the Aged," in New York State Department of Mental Hygiene, Mental Research Unit (1955).

12. The following is a partial list of sources used in preparing this section: Benjamin (1952); Bleuler (1955); Gregory (1953); Hare (1952); Hastings (1955); Hoch (1955); Hoch and Zubin (1953); Johnson (1955); Kohn and Clausen (1955); Kruse (1957); Kubie (1954); Lowrey (1955); National Advisory Mental Health Council (1955); Opler (1955 and 1956); Osmond and Smythies (1952); Pollak (1956); Rado and Daniels (1956); Redlich (1952); Scott (1958); Szasz (1957); *Theory and Treatment of the Psychoses* (1956); Tulchin (1955); Wikler (1952).

CHAPTER 2. DEVELOPMENT OF THE STUDY

1. There were two other persons on the staff for less than the full period of the project. Anton Wiener, a lawyer, gathered material on the relations between psychiatry and the law. Henry Wechsler, a social psychologist, studied ex-patient clubs and half-way houses. A number of persons who worked for us on a part-time basis provided synopses of various aspects of the literature.

2. We use the term "practitioner" for personnel directly engaged in providing help to mental patients (for example, psychotherapists) and for those who provide indirect help (for example, administrators in mental hospitals and in departments of mental health).

CHAPTER 3. CHARACTERISTICS OF THE OUT-PATIENT SYSTEM

1. The following sources were particularly helpful in preparing this section: Hollingshead and Redlich (1958); Milbank Memorial Fund (1956); Milbank Memorial Fund (1957).

2. The following sources were especially useful in providing the information on which this section is based: Deutsch (1944); Hall (1944); Lowrey (1948); Witmer (1946); Zilboorg (1941).

3. For data about the number and auspices of clinics, the number and kinds of professional personnel and their geographic distribution, the number and kinds of patients served and the services rendered, see the reports issued by the Biometric Branch of the National Institute of Mental Health and the Central Office of the American Psychiatric Association. Early data on the out-patient clinic can be found in Bahn and Norman (1957 and 1959).

4. Some of the reports that give a glimpse of the private practice situation are the following: Blain (1953); Muncie and Billings (1951); Davidson (1956); Hollingshead and Redlich (1958); Vaughan (1952); and Ginsburg (1955).

CHAPTER 4. PROVIDING IMMEDIATE HELP

1. In advocating immediate help for emotional disturbance, some professionals maintain that candidates should be those whose difficulties are severe enough to be diagnosed as a psychiatric disorder. But others maintain that candidates should be normal persons undergoing emotional crises. For a distinction between emotional upsets connected with life crises and those diagnosed as psychiatric disturbances, see Caplan (1959) pp. 172–73, 240–41. For a discussion of emergencies in a psychiatric clinic, see Shirley Cooper (1960).

2. For an analysis of this self-help organization, see Wechsler (1960).

3. Dr. Querido's motto is *"Cito, tuto et jucundo."* He intends *"cito"* to convey the idea that the service must be ready to meet any personal emergency at any time, without delay or bureaucratic red tape; *"tuto"* to signify that the service must see the person as a whole, i.e., together with those around him, his family, work background, and attitudes toward society; and *"jucundo"* to indicate that the service "must show a warm understanding of human needs and matter-of-fact equanimity towards any of the multitude of incredible situations which the warpedness of misdirected human activities may throw up" (Querido, 1956, p. 163–64).

CHAPTER 5. EXTENDING OUT-PATIENT SERVICES
IN THE COMMUNITY

1. See for example, Hollingshead and Redlich (1958); Myers and Schaffer (1954); and Rosenthal and Frank (1958).

2. J. V. Coleman and Switzer (1951). See also U.S. Public Health Service (1959).

3. Also referred to as the "life-space" interview. See Redl (1959) and Wineman (1959).

4. Some therapists who conduct group psychotherapy have come to similar

conclusions. For an example of the ways in which therapists' roles in group treatment were altered from passive to active participation, see Wheat, *et al.* (n.d.).

CHAPTER 6. BROADENING THE CONCEPTIONS OF HELP

1. For a consideration of psychiatric illness in a multicausal frame of reference, see *Symposium on Preventive and Social Psychiatry* (1958), p. 529; also Karl Menninger (1948); Seguin (1946); Bellak (1949).
2. For examples of this point of view, see Ackerman (1958); Spiegel (1957); Wynne, *et al.* (1958); Rhona Rapoport (1960); Lidz, *et al.* (1957a and 1957b); and Jackson (1958).
3. For a discussion of this, see Hollister (1959) and Caplan (1955).
4. For a review of efforts in community mental health consultation see Milbank Memorial Fund (1956); Hallock and Vaughan (1956); Caplan (1959); and Hutcheson (1959).

CHAPTER 8. CHARACTERISTICS OF THE IN-PATIENT SYSTEM

1. For the latest figures on the persons resident in mental hospitals, see the reports of the Biometrics Branch of the National Institute of Mental Health.
2. For an early account of the attendant culture, see Rowland (1938 and 1939). For more recent reports see Belknap (1956) and Weinberg (1952), Part IV.
3. See Stanton and Schwartz (1954); Greenblatt, *et al.* (1957), Part III, "The Ward"; and Caudill (1958).
4. See the comparison between the staffs in a state hospital and a private hospital in Hollingshead and Redlich (1958), pp. 148–52.
5. Estimates of the numbers of general hospitals accepting psychiatric patients are highly variable. Reporting is voluntary and definitions change with time. Surveys have been reported by the American Psychiatric Association, and the National Institute of Mental Health publishes figures based on hospitals that report to them.

CHAPTER 9. INDIVIDUALIZING CARE AND TREATMENT

1. See for example Belknap (1956), Goffman (1958), and Greenblatt, *et al.* (1957).
2. These ideas are associated most strongly with the concept of ego identity, first introduced by E. H. Erikson some years ago and elaborated by him later in a series of papers and monographs. For an example of its meaning and use see his *Childhood and Society* (1950). Alan Wheelis (1958), in exploring im-

plications of the concept, raises a number of important questions about the place of psychotherapy in a world that has lost clear social and personal identities. The early and original work of Louisa P. Holt (1948) is a particularly important contribution to our theoretical understanding of the relationships between the individual and the group.

3. Examples of this process may be found in William Caudill, *et al.* (1952); and Stanton and Schwartz (1949), pp. 243–49.

CHAPTER 10. BREAKING DOWN THE BARRIERS BETWEEN HOSPITAL AND COMMUNITY

1. *Mental Hospitals,* 9, No. 5 (May, 1958), p. 14.
2. This tendency to generalize views of psychosis to all emotional disturbances is discussed along with other complex features of attitudes toward mental illness in Star (n.d.). Cumming and Cumming (1957) describes an unsuccessful attempt at changing attitudes.
3. That this view may be closer to the truth for some social groups than we generally like to acknowledge is suggested in the Hollingshead and Redlich study, *Social Class and Mental Illness* (1958). Their data point to a much higher rate of accumulation in state mental hospitals of patients from the lowest social class than of patients from other strata.
4. See Hoch (1957). With the impetus largely from the British experience, there has been much attention to this development; for example, see O'Neill (1958) and Snow (1958).
5. There has been a general push in this state on all of these items. It is not possible to separate out the effects of this over-all state policy from one hospital's open door policy. However, the open hospital in each instance has a better record than other hospitals in the state.
6. For example, see Belknap (1956) and Greenblatt, *et al.* (1955 and 1957).
7. For a description of a program directed toward training physicians in these combined skills, see Engel, *et al.* (1957).
8. Some exponents of the psychiatric section have argued that it can be truly effective only when it is open to all types of patients, and that new forms of treatment now make this possible. For example, see Cameron (1957). However, more usually patients are highly selected, with preference given to those who, it is believed, will receive the maximum benefit from short-term intensive treatment and whose disruptive effect on the unit and the hospital will be minimal.
9. The phrase is Erving Goffman's, who explores some of the features of the patient's role in "The Characteristics of Total Institutions" (Goffman, 1958).
10. Our description is taken in large part from Pfeffer, *et al.* (n.d.).
11. See, for example, Conference on Volunteer Services to Psychiatric Patients (1959).
12. For a description of such a program using college student volunteers, see Dohan (1957), Kantor (1957), and Spencer (1957).

CHAPTER 11. DEVELOPING A THERAPEUTIC MILIEU

1. See the description of the Belmont Social Rehabilitation Unit in Jones (1953). See also R. N. Rapoport, *et al.* (1960).
2. Aichorn (1936); Redl and Wineman (1951 and 1952); Bettelheim (1951); and Freud and Burlingham (1944).
3. See, for example, Scher (1957).
4. For examples of patients' participation in such meetings, see Wilmer (1958), particularly Chap. 7.

CHAPTER 12. PROBLEMS AND ISSUES OF THE IN-PATIENT SYSTEM

1. For a critical discussion of this point of view, see Szasz (1960).
2. For a discussion of the custody-control orientation and the operation of attendant culture, see Belknap (1956) and Dunham and Weinberg (1960).
3. K. T. Erikson (1957) discusses some other aspects of the patient's role that make for its perpetuation.
4. For a discussion of the bureaucratic features of the mental hospital, see Goffman (1958).

CHAPTER 13. THE DEVELOPMENT OF AFTERCARE

1. For a major proponent of this thesis, see Hunt (1958).
2. For a discussion of the various ways in which the term "rehabilitation" has been used, see C. G. Schwartz (1953). For two conceptions of the distinction between treatment and rehabilitation, see R. N. Rapoport, *et al.* (1960), Chap. I, and Williams (1953).
3. This hypothesis has been tested both in this country and in England. For an analysis of the relationship between family setting and performance level see Freeman and Simmons (1958). For a study conducted in Great Britain, see G. W. Brown, *et al.*, (1959).
4. It is generally believed that there has been some growth in tolerant attitudes toward mental illness, but a recent study suggests that stigma is still a problem for ex-patients. Whatley (1959) concludes that attitudes of social acceptance of discharged patients are greatest in relatively impersonal situations and least in more intimate relations.

CHAPTER 14. TAILORING AFTERCARE

1. These services are described in detail by Williams (1960).
2. We should note though that the reverse is not true. Patients with the best prognoses are not necessarily the ones who receive the most post-hospital

help. Freeman and Simmons (1961) note that in their sample of ex-patients those with good prognoses tend to exclude themselves from post-hospital help. In general, these are voluntary patients who are not obligated to continue post-hospital supervision, the major form of ex-patient care in the area studied.

CHAPTER 15. GRADING STRESS

1. The concept of graded stress is not unique to psychiatric practice and has several points of resemblance to Gesell's developmental psychology and Havighurst's concept of developmental tasks (Gesell and Ilg, 1943; Havighurst, 1953). Both emphasize sequences in growth based on norms of development in relationship to individual differences and cultural demands. Timing and availability of opportunities to develop one's unique potentiality are of great importance. Finally, both make the growing person an active participant rather than just an interested observer in the developmental process.

2. Personal communication to the authors.

3. For the criteria for high and low performance, see Freeman and Simmons (1958).

CHAPTER 16. PROVIDING CONTINUITY OF CARE

1. Practitioners sometimes refer to convalescent care as evidence of continuity of care. In many instances, convalescent leave is an arbitrary period, six months or a year, in which the patient is expected to report back to the hospital or aftercare clinic periodically and during which the hospital has legal responsibility for him and he is retained on the hospital books. In itself, arrangements for convalescent leave cannot qualify as continuity of care. Often the patient is not seen during convalescence and is simply discharged at the prescribed time if no "incidents" have occurred; no concrete help has been given him nor is the lack of it based on an evaluation of his need. As it now commonly exists, convalescent leave serves as a framework within which continuity of care might be practiced, though, in itself, it amounts to little more than legal and administrative control over patients released to the community.

CHAPTER 17. PROBLEMS AND ISSUES OF AFTERCARE

1. See Smith (1959) for an elaboration of the concepts of illegitimate and legitimate deviance in regard to the problem of reintegrating the mental hospital patient in the community. For a discussion of the role of the mental hospital in perpetuating the patient's role as an illegitimate deviant, see Goffman (1959).

2. See Woodward (1951); Ramsey and Seipp (1948); Cumming and Cumming (1957), pp. 91–108; Star (n.d.).

3. In a study of public attitudes toward mental illness and actions toward persons considered mentally ill, Whatley (1959) specifies two levels of attitude: that of the general public and that which influences action at the primary group (ego-involved) level. Though public attitudes are more liberal than formerly, where contact and personal interests are involved, the mentally ill are still rejected. Crawford, *et al.* (1960) found that, though the ex-patient appears to have a different and more acceptable status in his community than the mental hospital patient, reintegration does not appear to be any easier than it used to be. The work of Davis, *et al.* (1957) and Adler (1955) tend to support this view.

4. For studies reporting ex-patients' avoidance of aftercare, see Chapter 15.

5. Many are forced to continue contact by hospital regulations. Freeman and Simmons (1961) report that, of the 649 ex-patients they studied, approximately two-thirds maintain contact with hospital personnel. "Rather than being initiated by the patients, however, virtually all out-patient treatment is requested by the hospital, primarily to comply with laws regarding trial visit supervision and discharge" (p. 1268). They conclude: "Except when their continued tenure in the community is placed in possible jeopardy as a consequence of failure to participate in treatment programs, it seems that former patients seek to cope with their adjustment problems without the benefits of professional assistance" (p. 1269).

6. Freeman and Simmons (1961). In regard to families of patients who received professional help they report "there were only a few cases in which consultation was both regular and sustained from the hospital to the post-hospital period; less than 10 per cent of the relatives who visited a professional person during the hospital period continued this relationship subsequent to the patient's return to the community. Similarly, there does not appear to be sustained consultation during the post-hospital period. Over one-fourth of the relatives who consulted a professional person did so only during the first week after the patient returned home. By the end of the first month, three-fourths of the contacts were terminated" (p. 1270).

7. For an analysis of the sick role, see Parsons and Fox (1952).

8. We are indebted to Yonina Talmon for this concept.

Abbreviations Used in Bibliography

Amer. J. Orthopsychiat.	American Journal of Orthopsychiatry
Amer. J. Psychiat.	American Journal of Psychiatry
Amer. J. Psychother.	American Journal of Psychotherapy
Amer. J. Public Health	American Journal of Public Health
Amer. J. Sociol.	American Journal of Sociology
Amer. Psychologist	American Psychologist
Amer. Sociol. Rev.	American Sociological Review
Ann. Amer. Acad. Pol. Soc. Sci.	Annals of the American Academy of Political and Social Science
Ann. Intern. Med.	Annals of Internal Medicine
Arch. Neurol.	Archives of Neurology
Arch. Gen. Psychiat.	Archives of General Psychiatry
Behav. Sci.	Behavioral Science
Berkeley J. Sociol.	Berkeley Journal of Sociology
Bull. Isaac Ray Med. Library	Bulletin of Isaac Ray Medical Library
Bull. Menninger Clin.	Bulletin of the Menninger Clinic
Dis. Nerv. Syst.	Diseases of the Nervous System
Harv. Bus. Rev.	Harvard Business Review
Hum. Organization	Human Organization
Hum. Relations	Human Relations
Int. J. Group Psychother.	International Journal of Group Psychotherapy
Int. J. Psychoanal.	International Journal of Psychoanalysis
Int. J. Soc. Psychiat.	International Journal of Social Psychiatry
J.A.M.A.	Journal of the American Medical Association
J. Clin. Psychol.	Journal of Clinical Psychology
J. Health Hum. Behav.	Journal of Health and Human Behavior
J. Med. Educ.	Journal of Medical Education
J. Ment. Sci.	Journal of Mental Science
J. Nerv. Ment. Dis.	Journal of Nervous and Mental Disease
J. Soc. Issues	Journal of Social Issues
Med. Ann. D.C.	Medical Annals of District of Columbia

Ment. Hosp.	Mental Hospitals
Ment. Hyg.	Mental Hygiene
Nat. Prob. Parole Ass. J.	National Probation and Parole Association Journal
Nurs. Outlook	Nursing Outlook
Pacific Sociol. Rev.	Pacific Sociological Review
Personnel Guid. J.	Personnel and Guidance Journal
Psychiat. Quart.	Psychiatric Quarterly
Psychoanal. Quart.	Psychoanalytic Quarterly
Psychol. Bull.	Psychological Bulletin
Psychosom. Med.	Psychosomatic Medicine
Public Health Rep.	Public Health Reports
Sat. Eve. Post	The Saturday Evening Post
Soc. Casework	Social Casework
Soc. Probl.	Social Problems
Soc. Work	Social Work

Bibliography

Ackerman, N. W. 1958. *The Psychodynamics of Family Life*. New York, Basic Books.

Adler, L. M. 1955. "Patients of a State Mental Hospital: The Outcome of Their Hospitalization," in A. M. Rose, ed., *Mental Health and Mental Disorder*. New York, Norton.

Aichorn, August. 1936. *Wayward Youth*. New York, Putnam.

Albee, George. 1959. *Mental Health Manpower Trends*. New York, Basic Books.

Allinsmith, Wesley, and G. W. Goethals. 1962. *The Role of the Schools in Mental Health*. New York, Basic Books.

American Occupational Therapy Association. 1958. *The Objectives and Functions of Occupational Therapy*. Dubuque, Iowa, Brown Book Co.

Aronson, Jay, and S. Polgar. 1960. "Pathogenic Relationships in Schizophrenia." Paper presented at the Annual Meeting of American Psychiatric Association, May, 1960.

Bahn, A. K., and V. B. Norman. 1957. *Outpatient Psychiatric Clinics in the United States, 1954–1955: Characteristics and Professional Staff*. Washington, D.C., U.S. Public Health Service. Public Health Monograph No. 49.

—— 1959. "First National Report on Patients of Mental Health Clinics." *Public Health Rep.* 74: 943–56.

Baltimore Council of Social Agencies. 1957. The Management of Psychiatric Emergencies. Mimeographed.

Barhash, A. Z., *et al.* 1952. *The Organization and Function of the Community Psychiatric Clinic*. New York, Association for Mental Health.

Baumrind, Diana. 1959. "Conceptual Issues Involved in Evaluating Improvement Due to Psychotherapy." *Psychiatry* 22: 341–48.

Beach, G., *et al.* [n.d.] The Oregon Study of Rehabilitation of Mental Hospital Patients: An Outline of Theory, Design and Organization. Mimeographed.

Beers, Clifford. 1908. *A Mind That Found Itself*. New York, Longmans, Green.

Belknap, Ivan. 1956. *Human Problems of a State Mental Hospital*. New York, McGraw-Hill.

Bellak, Leopold. 1949. "The Multiple Factors Psychosomatic Theory of Schizophrenia." *Psychiat. Quart.* 23: 738–44.

Bellak, Leopold, and B. J. Black. 1960. "The Rehabilitation of Psychotics in the Community." *Amer. J. Orthopsychiat.* 30: 346–55.

Bellak, Leopold, *et al.* 1956. "Rehabilitation of the Mentally Ill through

Controlled Transitional Employment." *Amer. J. Orthopsychiat.* 26: 285–96.

Benjamin, J. D. 1952. "Directions and Problems in Psychiatric Research." *Psychosom. Med.* 14: 1–9.

Bettelheim, Bruno. 1951. *Love Is Not Enough.* Glencoe, Ill., Free Press.

—— 1955. *Truants from Life.* Glencoe, Ill., Free Press.

Black, B. J. 1957. "The Workaday World: Some Problems in Return of Mental Patients to the Community," in Milton Greenblatt, *et al.,* eds., *The Patient and the Mental Hospital.* Glencoe, Ill., Free Press.

Blain, Daniel. 1953. "The Private Practice of Psychiatry." *Ann. Amer. Acad. Pol. Soc. Sci.* 286: 136–49.

Bleuler, Manfred. 1955. "Research and Changes in Concepts in the Study of Schizophrenia, 1941–1950." *Bull. Isaac Ray Med. Library* (Butler Hospital, Providence, R.I.) 3: 1–32.

Boag, T. J. 1957. "Treatment after Discharge." Paper presented at meeting on Coordinating Community Resources in Psychiatric Aftercare, April, 1957. Philadelphia, Fountain House, Inc., and Pennsylvania Mental Health, Inc. Mimeographed.

Bockoven, J. S. 1957. "Some Relationships between Cultural Attitudes toward Individuality and Care of the Mentally Ill: An Historical Study," in Milton Greenblatt, *et al.,* eds., *The Patient and the Mental Hospital.* Glencoe, Ill., Free Press.

Brown, G. W., *et al.* 1959. "The Post-hospital Adjustment of Chronic Mental Patients." *Lancet* 2: 685–89.

Brown, W. H., *et al.* 1957. "Using Community Agencies in the Treatment Program of a Traveling Child Guidance Clinic." *Ment. Hyg.* 41: 373–77.

Buell, Bradley, *et al.* 1952. *Community Planning for Human Services.* New York, Columbia University Press.

Cameron, D. E. 1957. "The Psychiatric Unit of the General Hospital." *Ment. Hosp.* 8: 2–7.

Caplan, Gerald. 1954. "The Mental Hygiene Role of the Nurse in Maternal and Child Care." *Nurs. Outlook* 2: 14–19.

—— 1955. "Mental Health Consultation in Schools," in Milbank Memorial Fund, *Elements of a Community Mental Health Program.* New York.

—— 1959. *Concepts of Mental Health and Consultation: Their Application in Public Health Social Work.* Washington, D.C., U.S. Children's Bureau. Publication No. 373.

Carse, Joshua, *et al.* 1958. "A District Mental Health Service: The Worthing Experiment." *Lancet* 1: 39–41.

Caudill, William. 1958. *The Psychiatric Hospital as a Small Society.* Cambridge, Mass., Harvard University Press.

Caudill, William, *et al.* 1952. "Social Structure and Interaction Processes on a Psychiatric Ward." *Amer. J. Orthopsychiat.* 22: 314–34.

Cheney, C. O. 1923. "New York State Hospital Mental Clinics." *Amer. J. Psychiat.* 80: 234–42.

Clausen, J. A., and M. R. Yarrow. 1955. "Paths to the Mental Hospital." *J. Soc. Issues* 11: 25–32.

Cohen, Leon. 1955. "Vocational Planning and Mental Illness." *Personnel Guid. J.* 34: 28–32.

Coleman J. V. 1949, "Distinguishing between Psychotherapy and Casework." *Soc. Casework* 30: 244–57.

Coleman, J. V., and R. E. Switzer. 1951. "Dynamic Factors in Psychosocial Treatment in Traveling Child-Guidance Clinics." *Ment. Hyg.* 35: 386–409.

Coleman, M. D. 1958. "Remarks" at Roundtable on Emergency Psychiatric Services, American Psychiatric Association Annual Meeting, San Francisco, May 13. Mimeographed.

Coleman, M. D., and Israel Zwerling. 1959. "The Psychiatric Emergency Clinic: A Flexible Way of Meeting Community Mental Health Needs." *Amer. J. Psychiat.* 115: 980–84.

Conference Group on Correctional Organization. 1960. *Theoretical Studies in the Social Organization of the Prison.* New York, Social Science Research Council.

Conference on Volunteer Services to Psychiatric Patients. 1959. *The Volunteer and the Psychiatric Patient.* Washington, D.C., American Psychiatric Association.

Cooper, J. V. 1957. "New Program of Aftercare Services for Convalescent Psychiatric Patients in New York City." Paper presented at meeting on Coordinating Community Resources in Psychiatric Aftercare, April, 1957. Philadelphia, Fountain House, Inc., and Pennsylvania Mental Health, Inc. Mimeographed.

Cooper, Shirley. 1960. "Emergencies in a Psychiatric Clinic." *Soc. Casework* 41: 134–39.

Crawford, F. H., *et al.* 1960. "Variations in the Evaluation of the Mentally Ill." *J. Health Hum. Behav.* 1: 211–19.

Cressey, D. R. 1960. "Limitations on Organization of Treatment in the Modern Prison," in Conference Group on Correctional Organization, *Theoretical Studies in the Social Organization of the Prison.* New York, Social Science Research Council.

Cumming, Elaine, and John Cumming. 1957. *Closed Ranks.* Cambridge, Mass., Harvard University Press.

Curle, Adam. 1947. "Transitional Communities and Social Re-connection: A Follow-up Study of the Civil Resettlement of British Prisoners of War. Part I." *Hum. Relations* 1: 42–68.

Curle, Adam, and E. L. Trist. 1947. "Transitional Communities and Social Re-connection: A Follow-up Study of the Civil Resettlement of British Prisoners of War. Part II." *Hum. Relations* 1: 240–88.

Davidson, H. A. 1956. "The Structure of Private Practice in Psychiatry." *Amer. J. Psychiat.* 113: 41–44.

Davis, J. A., *et al.* 1957. "Rehospitalization and Performance Level among Former Patients." *Soc. Probl.* 5: 37–44.

Davis, Keith, and W. G. Scott, eds. 1959. *Readings in Human Relations.* New York, McGraw-Hill.

Deutsch, Albert. 1944. "The History of Mental Hygiene," in J. K. Hall, ed., *One Hundred Years of American Psychiatry.* New York, Columbia University Press.

—— 1949. *The Mentally Ill in America.* 2d ed. New York, Columbia University Press.

Dohan, J. L. 1957. "Development of a Student Volunteer Program in a State Mental Hospital," in Milton Greenblatt, *et al.*, eds., *The Patient and the Mental Hospital*. Glencoe, Ill., Free Press.

Dunham, H. W., and S. K. Weinberg. 1960. *The Culture of the State Mental Hospital*. Detroit, Wayne State University Press.

Ellenberger, Henri. 1955. "A Comparison of European and American Psychiatry." *Bull. Menninger Clin.* 19: 43–52.

Engel, George, *et al.* 1957. "A Graduate and Undergraduate Teaching Program on the Psychological Aspects of Medicine." *J. Med. Educ.* 32: 859–70.

Erikson, E. H. 1950. *Childhood and Society*. New York, Norton.

Erikson, K. T. 1957. "Patient Role and Social Uncertainty—A Dilemma of the Mentally Ill." *Psychiatry* 20: 263–74.

Etzioni, Amitai. 1958. "Human Relations and the Foreman." *Pacific Sociol. Rev.* 1: 33–38.

Felix, R. H. 1956. "The Strategy of Community Mental Health Work," in Milbank Memorial Fund, *Elements of a Community Mental Health Program*. New York.

Felix, R. H., and Morton Kramer. 1952. "Research in Epidemiology of Mental Illness." *Public Health Rep.* 67: 152–60.

—— 1953. "Extent of the Problem of Mental Disorders." *Ann. Amer. Acad. Pol. Soc. Sci.* 286: 5–14.

Fernald, W. E. 1920. "An Outpatient Clinic in Connection with a State Institution for the Feebleminded." *Ment. Hyg.* 4: 848–56.

Fisher, C. E., and S. I. Hirsch. 1957. "Trial Visit: A Case Study of Placement of a Psychiatric Patient in the V.A. Foster Home Program." *Ment. Hyg.* 41: 34–43.

Fisher, S. H., *et al.* 1960. "Rehabilitation of the Mental Hospital Patient: The Fountain House Program." *Int. J. Soc. Psychiat.* 5: 295–98.

Frank, J. D. 1959. "The Dynamics of the Psychotherapeutic Relationship." *Psychiatry* 22: 17–39.

Freeman, H. E., and O. G. Simmons. 1958. "Mental Patients in the Community: Family Settings and Performance Levels." *Amer. Sociol. Rev.* 23: 147–54.

—— 1961. "Treatment Experiences of Mental Patients and Their Families." *Amer. J. Public Health* 51: 1266–73.

Freud, Anna, and Dorothy Burlingham. 1944. *Infants without Families*. New York, International Universities Press.

Friedman, T. T., *et al.* 1960. "Home Treatment of Psychiatric Patients." *Amer. J. Psychiat.* 116: 807–9.

Gayle, R. F. 1956. "Some Thoughts on Psychiatric Units in General Hospitals." *Ment. Hosp.* 7: 5–8.

Gesell, Arnold, and F. L. Ilg. 1943. *Infant and Child in the Culture of Today*. New York, Harper.

Gibson, R. W. 1954. "The Psychiatric Consultant and the Juvenile Court." *Ment. Hyg.* 38: 462–67.

Gilbert, D. C., and D. J. Levinson. 1957. " 'Custodialism' and 'Humanism' in Mental Hospital Structure and in Staff Ideology," in Milton Greenblatt, *et al.*, eds., *The Patient and the Mental Hospital*. Glencoe, Ill., Free Press.

Ginott, H. G. 1956. "Group Screening of Parents in a Child Guidance Setting." *Int. J. Group Psychother.* 6: 405–9.

Ginsburg, S. W. 1955. "The Private Practice of Psychiatry." *Bull. Menninger Clin.* 19: 33–42.

Goffman, Erving. 1958. "The Characteristics of Total Institutions," in *Symposium on Preventive and Social Psychiatry*. Washington, D.C., U.S. Government Printing Office.

—— 1959. "The Moral Career of the Mental Patient." *Psychiatry* 22: 123–42.

Goshen, C. E. 1958. "Expanding Hospital Services with the Aid of Community Physicians." *Ment. Hosp.* 9: 10–11.

—— 1959. "A Mental Health Plan for General Practitioners." *Med. Ann. D.C.* 28: 312–15.

Granger, L. B. 1954. "The Changing Functions of Voluntary Agencies," in Cora Kasius, ed., *New Directions in Social Work*. New York, Harper.

Greenblatt, Milton, 1959. "The Rehabilitation Spectrum," in Milton Greenblatt and Benjamin Simon, *Rehabilitation of the Mentally Ill*. Washington, D.C., American Association for the Advancement of Science.

Greenblatt, Milton, and Benjamin Simon. 1959. *Rehabilitation of the Mentally Ill*. Washington, D.C., American Association for the Advancement of Science. Publication No. 58.

Greenblatt, Milton, *et al.* 1955. *From Custodial to Therapeutic Patient Care in Mental Hospitals*. New York, Russell Sage Foundation.

Greenblatt, Milton, *et al.*, eds. 1957. *The Patient and the Mental Hospital*. Glencoe, Ill., Free Press.

Gregory, W. E. 1953. "Life Is Therapeutic." *Ment. Hyg.* 37: 259–64.

Group for the Advancement of Psychiatry. 1949. *Statistics Pertinent to Psychiatry in the United States*. Topeka, Kansas. Report No. 7.

Gruenberg, E. M. 1950. "Review of Available Material on Patterns of Occurrence of Mental Disorders," in Milbank Memorial Fund, *Epidemiology of Mental Disorder*. New York.

—— 1957. "Application of Control Methods to Mental Illness." *Amer. J. Public Health* 47: 944–52.

Gurin, Gerald, *et al.* 1960. *Americans View Their Mental Health: A Nationwide Interview Survey*. New York, Basic Books.

Hall, J. K. ed. 1944. *One Hundred Years of American Psychiatry*. New York, Columbia University Press.

Hallock, A. C., and W. T. Vaughan, Jr. 1956. "Community Organization—A Dynamic Component of Community Mental Health Practice." *Amer. J. Orthopsychiat.* 26: 691–706.

Hallowitz, David, and A. W. Cutter. 1954. "Intake and the Waiting List: A Differential Approach." *Soc. Casework* 35: 439–45.

Hamburg, D. A. 1958. "Therapeutic Hospital Environment: Experience in a General Hospital for Research," in *Symposium on Preventive and Social Psychiatry*. Washington, D.C., U.S. Government Printing Office.

Hammond, W. A. 1879. *Non-asylum Treatment of the Insane*. New York, Putnam.

Hare, E. H. 1952. "The Ecology of Mental Disease." *J. Ment. Sci.* 98: 579–94.

Hastings, D. W. 1955. "The Contribution of Orthopsychiatry to Psychiatry." *Amer. J. Orthopsychiat.* 25: 458–64.

Havighurst, R. J. 1953. *Human Development and Education.* New York, Longmans, Green.

Henry, Jules. 1957. "Types of Institutional Structure," in Milton Greenblatt, *et al.,* eds., *The Patient and the Mental Hospital.* Glencoe, Ill., Free Press.

Hoch, P. H. 1955. "Progress in Psychiatric Therapies." *Amer. J. Psychiat.* 112: 241–47.

—— 1957. "Observations on the British 'Open' Hospitals: Introduction." *Ment. Hosp.* 8(7): 5–6.

Hoch, P. H., and Joseph Zubin, eds. 1953. *Current Problems in Psychiatric Diagnosis.* New York, Grune and Stratton.

Hollier, N. W., and R. M. Harrison. 1956. "A Home-Care Program in the Community." *Ment. Hyg.* 40: 574–82.

Hollingshead, A. B., and F. C. Redlich. 1958. *Social Class and Mental Illness: A Community Study.* New York, Wiley.

Hollister, W. G. 1959. "Current Trends in Mental Health Programming in the Classroom." *J. Soc. Issues* 15: 50–58.

Holt, L. P. 1948. Psychoanalysis and the Social Process: An Examination of Freudian Theory with Reference to Some of the Sociological Implications and Counterparts. Unpublished PH.D. dissertation, Radcliffe College.

Hopple, L. M., and H. R. Huessy. 1954. "Traveling Community—Mental Health Clinics: Their Extra-Therapeutic Aspects and Functions." *Ment. Hyg.* 38: 49–59.

Hubbard, Oscar E. 1956. "Alaska's Flying Mental Hygiene Clinics." *Ment. Hosp.* 7(8): 7–8.

Hunt, R. C. 1958. "Ingredients of a Rehabilitation Program," in Milbank Memorial Fund, *An Approach to the Prevention of Disability from Chronic Psychosis.* New York.

Hurd, H. M., *et al.* 1916. *The Institutional Care of the Insane in the United States and in Canada.* 4 vols. Baltimore, Johns Hopkins Press.

Hutcheson, B. R. 1959. "Quincy, Massachusetts," in Milbank Memorial Fund, *Progress and Problems of Community Mental Health Services.* New York.

Isaacson, John. 1958. "From Sitter to Citizen—A Project of Vocational and Social Rehabilitation." *Ment. Hyg.* 42: 538–43.

Jackson, Don. 1958. Family Interaction, Family Homeostasis and Some Implications for Conjoint Family Psychotherapy. Paper presented at the Academy of Psychoanalysis, San Francisco, May, 1958.

Jaco, E. G., ed. 1958. *Patients, Physicians, and Illness.* Glencoe, Ill., Free Press.

Jacobs, D. F. 1957. Round Table on "Coordinating Community Resources in Psychiatric After-care." Paper presented at meeting on Coordinating Community Resources in Psychiatric Aftercare, Philadelphia, April, 1957. Philadelphia, Fountain House, Inc., and Pennsylvania Mental Health, Inc. Mimeographed.

Johnson, K. D. 1955. "The Contribution of Orthopsychiatry to Social Work." *Amer. J. Orthopsychiat.* 25: 465–71.

Joint Commission on Mental Illness and Health. 1956. First Annual Report. Cambridge, Mass. Lithographed.

Jones, Maxwell. 1953. *The Therapeutic Community*. New York, Basic Books.

Kahn, A. J. 1953. *A Court for Children*. New York, Columbia University Press.

Kantor, David. 1957. "The Use of College Students as 'Case Aides' in a Social Service Department of a State Hospital: An Experiment in Undergraduate Work Education," in Milton Greenblatt, *et al.*, eds., *The Patient and the Mental Hospital*. Glencoe, Ill., Free Press.

Kasius, Cora, ed. 1954. *New Directions in Social Work*. New York, Harper.

Kohn, Melvin, and J. A. Clausen. 1955. "Social Isolation and Schizophrenia." *Amer. Sociol. Rev.* 20: 265–73.

Korkes, Lenore. 1957. "Physicians' Attitudes toward the Mental Health Problem." *Ment. Hyg.* 41: 467–86.

Kramer, Morton, *et al.* 1955. *A Historical Study of the Disposition of First Admissions to a State Mental Hospital: Experience of Warren State Hospital during the period 1916–1950*. Washington, D.C., U.S. Public Health Service. Public Health Monograph No. 32.

Kris, Else. 1957. "Social Implications of the New Drugs." *Soc. Work* 2: 57–60.

Kruse, H. D., ed. 1957. *Integrating the Approaches to Mental Disease*. New York, Hoeber-Harper.

Kubie, L. S. 1954. "The Fundamental Nature of the Distinction between Normality and Neurosis." *Psychoanal. Quart.* 23: 167–204.

Leighton, D. C. 1956. "The Distribution of Psychiatric Symptoms in a Small Town." *Amer. J. Psychiat.* 112: 716–23.

Lemere, Frederick, and A. B. Kraabel. 1959. "The General Practitioner and the Psychiatrist." *Amer. J. Psychiat.* 116: 518–21.

Lemkau, P. V. 1957. "Planning a Mental Health Program for New York City," in Milbank Memorial Fund, *Programs for Community Mental Health*. New York.

Lemkau, P. V., *et al.* 1943. "A Survey of Statistical Studies on the Prevalence and Incidence of Mental Disorder in Sample Populations." *Public Health Rep.* 58: 1909–27.

Lesser, Walter. 1960. "The Developing Role of Social Work in a Neuro-Psychiatric Day Center." *Soc. Casework* 41: 413–18.

LeVan, E. K. 1958. Rehabilitation of the Mental Patient in a Day Care Treatment Center and the Part Played by the Nurse. Unpublished.

Levinson, Harry. 1959. "A National Perspective on Industrial Human Relations," in Keith Davis and W. G. Scott, eds., *Readings in Human Relations*. New York, McGraw-Hill.

Lidz, Theodore, *et al.* 1957a. "The Intrafamilial Environment of the Schizophrenic Patient: I. The Father." *Psychiatry* 20: 329–42.

—— 1957b. "The Intrafamilial Environment of Schizophrenic Patients: II. Marital Schism and Marital Skew." *Amer. J. Psychiat.* 114: 24–48.

Low, A. A. 1959. "Recovery, Inc., a Project for Rehabilitating Postpsychotic and Long Term Psychoneurotic Patients," in W. H. Soden, ed., *Rehabilitation of the Handicapped*. New York, Ronald Press.

Lowrey, L. G. 1955. "The Contribution of Orthopsychiatry to Psychiatry: Brief Historical Note." *Amer. J. Orthopsychiat.* 25: 475–78.

Lowrey, L. G., ed. 1948. *Orthopsychiatry, 1923–1948: Retrospect and Prospect.* New York, American Orthopsychiatric Association.

McCann, R. V. 1962. *The Churches and Mental Health.* New York, Basic Books.

MacMillan, Duncan. 1956. "Rehabilitation Programs in England," in Milbank Memorial Fund, *Elements of a Community Mental Health Program.* New York.

—— 1958. "Hospital-Community Relationships," in Milbank Memorial Fund, *An Approach to the Prevention of Disability from Chronic Psychosis.* New York.

McMurray, R. N. 1959. "Mental Illness in Industry." *Harv. Bus. Rev.* 37: 79–86.

Maisel, A. W., ed. 1960. *The Health of the People Who Work.* New York, National Health Council.

Marcus, E. S., and M. N. Gilchrist. 1959. "A Pilot Study in the Selection of Psychiatric Hospital Patients for Treatment in a Family Agency." *Soc. Casework* 40: 551–58.

Markey, O. B., and C. L. Langsam. 1957. "What Happens to Psychiatrists' Contributions in the Juvenile Court Setting." *Amer. J. Orthopsychiat.* 27: 789–99.

Matthews, R. A. 1958. "Involving Community Physicians in Psychiatric Facilities." *Ment. Hosp.* 9: 28–30.

Meerloo, J. A. 1956. "Emergency Methods in Psychotherapy." *Amer. J. Psychother.* 10: 117–40.

Menninger, Karl. 1948. "Changing Concepts of Disease." *Ann. Intern. Med.* 29: 318–25.

Menninger, W. C. 1948. "Facts and Statistics of Significance for Psychiatry." *Bull. Menninger Clin.* 12: 1–25.

Meyer, H. J., and E. F. Borgatta. 1959a. *An Experiment in Mental Patient Rehabilitation: Evaluating a Social Agency Program.* New York, Russell Sage Foundation.

—— 1959b. "Paradoxes in Evaluating Mental Health Programs." *Int. J. Soc. Psychiat.* 5: 136–41.

Milbank Memorial Fund. 1950. *Epidemiology of Mental Disorder.* New York.

—— 1953. *Interrelations between the Social Environment and Psychiatric Disorders.* New York.

—— 1956. *Elements of a Community Mental Health Program.* New York.

—— 1957. *Programs for Community Mental Health.* New York.

—— 1958. *An Approach to the Prevention of Disability from Chronic Psychosis: The Open Mental Hospital within the Community.* New York.

—— 1959. *Progress and Problems of Community Mental Health Services.* New York.

Millar, W. H., and J. G. Henderson. 1956. "The Health Service in Amsterdam." *Int. J. Soc. Psychiat.* 2: 141–50.

Miller, W. B. 1958. "Inter-institutional Conflict as a Major Impediment to Delinquency Prevention." *Hum. Organization.* 17(3): 20–23.

Moore, R. F., and R. S. Albert. 1959. "Prevention of Hospitalization of Psychotic Patients." Working Paper for the Research Conference on Rehabilitation and the Management of Mental Disorders, June, 1959.

Morris, D. P., and E. P. Soroker. 1953. "The Follow-up Study on a Guidance Clinic Waiting List." *Ment. Hyg.* 37: 84–8.

Muncie, Wendell, and E. C. Billings. 1951. "A Survey of Conditions of Private Psychiatric Practice throughout the United States and Canada." *Amer. J. Psychiat.* 108: 171–72.

Myers, J. K., and B. H. Roberts. 1959. *Family and Class Dynamics in Mental Illness.* New York, Wiley.

Myers, J. K., and L. Schaffer. 1954. "Social Stratification and Psychiatric Practice: A Study of an Outpatient Clinic." *Amer. Sociol. Rev.* 19: 307–10.

National Advisory Mental Health Council. 1955. *Evaluation in Mental Health: A Review of the Problem of Evaluating Mental Health Activities.* Washington, D.C. Public Health Service Publication No. 413.

National Institute of Mental Health. 1951. *Proceedings of the First Conference of Mental Hospital Administrators and Statisticians.* Washington, D.C. Public Health Service Publication No. 295.

New York State Department of Mental Hygiene, Mental Research Unit. 1959. *Technical Report.* Albany, N.Y.

Nunnally, J. C. 1957. "The Communication of Mental Health Information: A Comparison of the Opinions of Experts and the Public with Mass Media Presentations." *Behav. Sci.* 2: 222–31.

Ohlin, L. E., *et al.* 1956. "Major Dilemmas of the Social Worker in Probation and Parole." *Nat. Prob. Parole Ass. J.* 3: 211–25.

Oliver, J. R. 1959. "Treatment Goes to Jail," in National Conference on Social Welfare, *Casework Papers, 1959.* New York, Family Service Association of America.

Olshansky, S. S., *et al.* 1960. "Survey of Employment Experiences of Patients Discharged from Three State Mental Hospitals during Period 1951–1953." *Ment. Hyg.* 44: 510–21.

O'Neill, F. J. 1958. "Laying the Foundation for the Open Hospital." *Ment. Hosp.* 9(2): 10–12.

Opler, M. K. 1955. "Cultural Perspective in Mental Health Research." *Amer. J. Orthopsychiat.* 25: 51–9.

—— 1956. *Culture, Psychiatry and Human Values: The Methods and Values of a Social Psychiatry.* Springfield, Ill., C. C. Thomas.

Orlund, Frank. 1959. "Use and Overuse of Tranquilizers." *J.A.M.A.* 171: 633–36.

Osmond, Humphrey. 1958. "Rehabilitation Services within the Hospital." *Ment. Hosp.* 9(5): 45–47.

Osmond, Humphrey, and John Smythies. 1952. "Schizophrenia: A New Approach." *J. Ment. Sci.* 98: 309–15.

Parsons, Talcott. 1951. *The Social System.* Glencoe, Ill., Free Press.

Parsons, Talcott, and Renee Fox. 1952. "Illness, Therapy, and the Modern Urban American Family." *J. Soc. Issues* 8: 31–44.

Paul, B. D., ed. 1955. *Health, Culture and Community.* New York, Russell Sage Foundation.

Peck, H. B. 1953. "An Application of Group Therapy to the Intake Process." *Amer. J. Orthopsychiat.* 23: 338–49.

Peeples, William. 1959. Community Follow-up Program for Mental Hospital Patients. Mimeographed.

Perry, S. E. 1959. "Research and Demonstration Problems in a Psychiatric Home Treatment Service." Working Paper for the Research Conference on Rehabilitation and the Management of Mental Disorders, June, 1959. Mimeographed.

Pfeffer, P. A., *et al.*, eds. [n.d.] Member-Employee Program: A New Approach to the Rehabilitation of the Chronic Mental Patient. Lithographed.

Pollak, Otto, 1956. *Integrating Sociological and Psychoanalytical Concepts.* New York, Russell Sage Foundation.

Querido, Arie. 1955. Discussion with Dr. A. Querido, Director of Mental Health Service of Amsterdam, Holland, before the New York City Community Mental Health Board, December 6, 1955. Mimeographed.

—— 1956. "Early Diagnosis and Treatment Services," in Milbank Memorial Fund, *Elements of a Community Mental Health Program.* New York.

Rado, Sandor, and G. E. Daniels, eds. 1956. *Changing Concepts of Psychoanalytic Medicine.* New York, Grune and Stratton.

Ramsey, G. V., and Melita Seipp. 1948. "Public Opinions and Information concerning Mental Health." *J. Clin. Psychol.* 4: 397–406.

Rapoport, Rhona. 1960. "The Family and Psychiatric Treatment." *Psychiatry* 23: 53–62.

Rapoport, R. N., *et al.* 1960. *Community as Doctor: New Perspectives on a Therapeutic Community.* Springfield, Ill., C. C. Thomas.

Redl, Fritz. 1959. "Strategy and Techniques of the Life Space Interview." *Amer. J. Orthopsychiat.* 29: 1–18.

Redl, Fritz, and David Wineman. 1951. *Children Who Hate.* Glencoe, Ill., Free Press.

—— 1952. *Controls from Within.* Glencoe, Ill., Free Press.

Redlich, F. C. 1952. "The Concept of Normality." *Amer. J. Psychother.* 6: 551–76.

Reid, John. 1957. "Logical Analysis." *Amer. J. Psychiat.* 114: 397–404.

Rioch, D. M., and A. H. Stanton. 1953. "Milieu Therapy." *Psychiatry* 16: 65–72.

Rolfe, Phyllis. 1959. Psychiatric Home Treatment Service. Paper presented at meeting of the Massachusetts Public Health Association, February, 1959.

Rose, A. M., ed. 1955. *Mental Health and Mental Disorder.* New York, Norton.

Rosenthal, David, and J. D. Frank. 1958. "The Fate of Psychiatric Clinic Outpatients Assigned to Psychotherapy." *J. Nerv. Ment. Dis.* 127: 330–43.

Rountree, L. G., *et al.* 1945. "Mental and Personality Disorders in Selective Service Registrants." *J.A.M.A.* 128: 1084–87.

Rowland, Howard. 1938. "Interaction Processes in the State Mental Hospital." *Psychiatry* 1: 323–37.

—— 1939. "Friendship Patterns in the State Mental Hospital." *Psychiatry* 2: 363–73.

Ruilman, C. J. 1960. "Post Graduate Training in Psychiatry for General Practitioners." *Dis. Nerv. Syst.* 21: 570–72.
Sampson, Harold, *et al.* 1961. "The Mental Hospital and Marital Family Ties." *Soc. Probl.* 9: 141–55.
Scher, J. M. 1957. "Schizophrenia and Task Orientation." *Arch. Neurol.* 78: 531–38.
Schwartz, C. G. 1953. *Rehabilitation of Mental Hospital Patients: Review of the Literature.* Washington, D.C., U.S. Public Health Service. Public Health Monograph No. 17.
—— 1957. "Perspectives on Deviance—Wives' Definition of Their Husbands' Mental Illness." *Psychiatry* 20: 275–91.
Schwartz, M. S. 1957. "What Is a Therapeutic Milieu?", in Milton Greenblatt, *et al.*, eds., *The Patient and the Mental Hospital.* Glencoe, Ill., Free Press.
Scott, W. A. 1958. "Research Definitions of Mental Health and Mental Illness." *Psychol. Bull.* 55: 29–45.
Seguin, C. A. 1946. "The Concept of Disease." *Psychosom. Med.* 8: 252–57.
Silver, J. R. 1959. "Treatment Goes to Jail," in National Conference on Social Welfare, *Casework Papers.* New York, Family Service Association of America.
Silverman, Milton, and Margaret Silverman. 1958. "Asylums without Bars." *Sat. Eve. Post* 231: 28–9, 110–14.
Simmel, Ernst. 1929. "Psychoanalytic Treatment in a Clinic." *Int. J. Psychoanal.* 10: 70–89.
—— 1937. "The Psychoanalytic Sanatorium and the Psychoanalytic Movement." *Bull. Menninger Clin.* 1: 133–43.
Simmons, O. G., and H. E. Freeman. 1959. "Familial Expectations and Post-hospital Performance of Mental Patients." *Hum. Relations* 12: 233–41.
Sivadon, Paul. 1956. "Adaptation Factors in the Work of Mental Patients." *Int. J. Soc. Psychiat.* 2: 112–17.
—— 1958. "Technics of Socio-therapy," in *Symposium on Preventive and Social Psychiatry.* Washington, D.C., U.S. Government Printing Office.
Smith, D. E. 1959. "Legitimate and Illegitimate Deviance: The Case of the State Mental Hospital." *Berkeley J. Sociol.* 5: 15–39.
Snow, H. B. 1958. "The Open Door Concept." *Ment. Hosp.* 9(5): 33–35.
Soden, W. H., ed. 1959. *Rehabilitation of the Handicapped.* New York, Ronald Press.
Spencer, S. M. 1957. "They Befriend the Mentally Ill." *Sat. Eve. Post* 230: 19–21, 90–92.
Spiegel, J. P. 1957. "The Resolution of Role Conflict within the Family." *Psychiatry* 20: 1–16.
Stanton, A. H., and M. S. Schwartz. 1949. "Medical Opinion and the Social Context in the Mental Hospital." *Psychiatry* 12: 243–49.
—— 1954. *The Mental Hospital.* New York, Basic Books.
Star, Shirley. [n.d.] The Dilemmas of Mental Illness. Chicago, National Opinion Research Center. Mimeographed.
Stevenson, Ian, and T. M. Fisher. 1954. "Techniques in the Vocational Rehabilitation of Chronically Unemployed Psychiatric Patients." *Amer. J. Psychiat.* 111: 289–300.

Symposium on Preventive and Social Psychiatry. 1958. At Walter Reed Army Institute of Research, 15–17 April, 1957. Washington, D.C., U.S. Government Printing Office.

Szasz, T. S. 1957. "The Problem of Psychiatric Nosology." *Amer. J. Psychiat.* 114: 405–13.

—— 1960. "The Myth of Mental Illness." *Amer. Psychologist* 15: 113–18.

Theory and Treatment of the Psychosis: Some Newer Aspects. 1956. Paper presented at Dedication of Renard Hospital, St. Louis, October, 1955. St. Louis, Mo., Washington University.

Trussell, R. E. 1956. *Hunterdon Medical Center: The Study of One Approach to Rural Medical Care.* Cambridge, Mass., Harvard University Press.

Tulchin, S. H. 1955. "The Contribution of Orthopsychiatry to Clinical Psychology." *Amer. J. Orthopsychiat.* 25: 445–57.

Tyhurst, J. S. 1956. Minutes of the Meeting of the Committee on Mental Health Services, Scientific Planning Council, Canadian Mental Health Association, Montreal, May 11–12, 1956. Mimeographed.

Ullmann, L. P., and V. C. Berkman. 1959. "Efficacy of Placement of Neuropsychiatric Patients in Family Care." *Arch. Gen. Psychiat.* 1: 273–74.

U.S. Congress. 1955. *Mental Health Study Act.* P.L. 182.

U.S. Public Health Service. 1959. *Proceedings of the Conference of the Surgeon General, Public Health Service, with State and Territorial Mental Health Authorities.* Washington, D.C. Public Health Service Publication No. 705.

Vaughan, W. T., Jr., *et al.* 1952. *Survey of Community Psychiatric Resources in Massachusetts.* East Gardner, Mass., Massachusetts Department of Mental Health.

Vermont Project for Rehabilitation of Chronic Schizophrenic Patients. 1959. Progress Report, February, 1959. Mimeographed.

Wechsler, Henry. 1960. "The Self-Help Organization in the Mental Health Field: Recovery, Inc., a Case Study." *J. Nerv. Ment. Dis.* 130: 297–314.

Weinberg, S. K. 1952. *Society and Personality Disorders.* New York, Prentice-Hall.

Whatley, C. D. 1959. "Social Attitudes toward Discharged Mental Patients." *Soc. Probl.* 6: 313–20.

Wheat, W. D., *et al.* [n.d.] Rehabilitation of Chronically Ill Psychiatric Patients. Mimeographed.

Wheelis, Alan. 1958. *Quest for Identity.* New York, Norton.

Whitmer, C. A., and C. G. Conover. 1959. "A Study of Critical Incidents in the Hospitalization of the Mentally Ill." *Soc. Work* 4: 89–94.

Wikler, Abraham. 1952. "A Critical Analysis of Some Current Concepts in Psychiatry." *Psychosom. Med.* 14: 10–17.

Wilensky, J. E., and H. L. Wilensky. 1951. "Personnel Counseling: The Hawthorne Case." *Amer. J. Sociol.* 57: 265–80.

Williams, R. H. 1953. "Psychiatric Rehabilitation in the Hospital." *Public Health Rep.* 68: 1043–51.

—— 1957. Social Research and the Therapeutic Community. Washington, D.C., National Institute of Mental Health. Mimeographed.

Williams, R. H., ed. 1960. Report of the Subcommittee on Tertiary Prevention [of the National Institute of Mental Health]. Mimeographed.

Wilmer, H. A. 1958. *Social Psychiatry in Action.* Springfield, Ill., C. C. Thomas.

Wilson, D. H. 1960. "The Function of a Psychiatrist in a Municipal Law Enforcement Agency." *Amer. J. Psychiat.* 116: 870–72.

Wineman, David. 1959. "The Life-Space Interview." *Soc. Work* 4: 3–17.

Winston, Ellen. 1958. "Reducing the Number of Patients in Mental Hospitals by Providing Non-institutional Care for the Aged." *Ment. Hyg.* 42: 544–49.

Witmer, Helen. 1946. *Psychiatric Clinics for Children.* New York, Commonwealth Fund.

Woodward, J. A. 1951. "Changing Ideas on Mental Illness and Its Treatment." *Amer. Sociol. Rev.* 16: 443–54.

World Health Organization. 1953. *The Community Mental Hospital: Expert Committee on Mental Health, Third Report.* Geneva, Switzerland.

"The Worthing Version." 1959. *Lancet* 1: 668–69.

Wynne, L. C., et al. 1958. "Pseudo-mutuality in the Family Relations of Schizophrenics." *Psychiatry* 21: 205–20.

Yarrow, M. R., et al. 1955a. "The Psychological Meaning of Mental Illness in the Family." *J. Soc. Issues* 11(4): 12–24.

—— 1955b. "The Social Meaning of Mental Illness." *J. Soc. Issues* 11(4): 33–48.

Zilboorg, Gregory. 1941. *History of Medical Psychology.* New York, Norton.

Zwerling, Israel. 1958. "Remarks" at Roundtable on Emergency Psychiatric Services. Paper presented at American Psychiatric Association Annual Meeting, San Francisco, May 13, 1958. Mimeographed.

Index

Ackerman, N. W., 312

Adler, L. M., 316

Aftercare: background of, 207-8; factors in development of, 208-10; types of programs, 211; disadvantages of, 212; goals of 212-13; types of, 213; limitations of, 213-14; individualization of, 216-20; organizational framework for, 217-18; increasing resources for, 218-19; and mental health out-patient clinic, 221; conflict of individualization and coverage, 222-23; opposing positions on best means of, 223-24; social class and, 224-25; selection for, 232, 283-85; helpers in, 234; settings for, 238-46; reeducational orientation, 243; relationship of individualization to grading stress, 251-52; integration with in-patient care, 253-54; primarily a social problem, 263, 272-73; mental hospital participation in, 265; professional disinterest in, 269-70; hindrances to, 269-75; differing philosophies of, 272-73; family resistance to, 285-86; opposition of community to, 286-88; state agency necessary for, 304; evaluation of need for, 306; *see also* Continuity of care; Ex-patients; Individualization of care

Aichhorn, A., 164, 314

Albany (New York) Hospital, 144

Albee, G., 95

Albert, R. S., 42

Alcoholics Anonymous, 43

Allan Memorial Institute of Psychiatry, Follow-up Clinic (Montreal, Canada), 268

Allinsmith, W., 69

Altro Health and Rehabilitation Center (New York), 232, 246, 264

Altro Workshop (New York), 232, 246, 264

American Psychiatric Association, 70, 75, 311, 312

Amsterdam emergency psychiatric service, *see* Immediate help programs

Aronson, J., 248, 251

Attendants (aides), 104, 127-28, 141-42, 151-52, 154, 198-99

Bahn, A. K., 33, 309, 311

Baltimore Council of Social Agencies, 50

Barhash, A. Z., 31

Barriers between hospital and community, 136-39, 147, 157-62, 169, 190-91; implications of breaking down, 152-57, 161-62

Baumrind, D., 94

Beach, G., 276

Beers, Clifford, 32

Belknap, I., 312, 313, 314

Bellak, L., 232, 264, 312

Belmont Social Rehabilitation Unit, 314

Benjamin, J. D., 310

Berkman, V. C., 246

Bettelheim, Bruno, 111, 164, 314

Billings, E. C., 311

Black, B. J., 264

Blain, D., 311

Bleuler, M., 310

Boag, T. J., 268, 275

Borgatta, E. F., 246, 253, 254

Boston City Hospital, 44

Boston Psychopathic Hospital, 31

Boston State Hospital, 44, 65-66

Brown, G. W., 247, 248, 314

Brown, W. H., 62

Buell, B., 35

Burlingham, Dorothy, 164, 314

Cameron, D. E., 144, 313

Snow, H. B., 313
Social structure, *see* Social system
Social system: need to deal with, 17, 22-23, 36, 56, 61, 81-83, 91, 92, 163-64, 183-84, 204, 231, 246, 291-92; mental hospital as a, 140, 191-92, 195
Social worker(s), 28, 54: participation in psychotherapy, 72-73; training, 72-73, 272; and grading stress, 235, 237-38; continuity of care, 258; and continuity of relationship, 262-63; differing goals in aftercare, 272-73
Sociological frame of reference, 16, 17, 22-23, 54, 84-86, 196-97, 213, 307-8
Soroker, E. P., 40
Spencer, S. M., 313
Spiegel, J. P., 312
Spring Grove State Hospital (Maryland), 239
Srole, L., 310
Stanton, A. H., 163, 167, 168, 312, 313
Star, S., 310, 313, 315
State Hospital for the Insane, Warren, Pennsylvania, 31
State Pathological Institute, 31
Stevenson, I., 237
Stigma, *see* Mental illness
Stirling County Study, 6
Stress: and mental illness, 13; *see also* Grading stress
Switzer, R. E., 62, 311
Symposium on Preventive and Social Psychiatry, 312
Szasz, T. S., 310, 314

Talmon, Yonina, 316
Theory and Treatment of the Psychoses, 310
Therapeutic milieu, 87; definitions, 163; historical background, 164; orientations of, 164-65; therapeutic atmosphere, 166-70; broadening the base of therapeutic relevance, 170-71; questions arising from introduction of, 171-75; ecological-organizational aspect of hospital, 180-81; in relation to leadership, 182; staff roles in programs of, 184-85; relation to psychotherapy, 185-86; example of a comprehensive, 185-89; relation to individualization of care, 190; obstacles to, 198; and aftercare, 210
Therapy, 18, 28; organizations of facilities for, 11; group, 41-42, 105, 106, 123,

129, 172, 174, 175, 221; brief, 55-56, 95; psychoanalytic or intensive, 95; ancillary, 122-23; defined, 128; unstructured, for ex-patients, 221-22; *see also* Psychotherapy
Towne, R., 285
Training: community caretakers, 68-74; general practitioners, 69-72, 275-76; social workers, 72-73, 272; psychiatrists, 110, 194-96, 222; attendants, 198-99; workers for aftercare, 218; nurses, 272
Tranquilizers, 71, 105, 143, 259
Transitional setting: natural, 238-39; use in grading stress, 238-46; constructed, 239; conceptions of, 240-41; attributes of, 241-42; segregating functions, 241-42; attitude toward deviance in, 242-43; sheltered workshop as example, 244-45
Treatment: determining unit of, 17, 194-95; conceptions of, 17-19; success of, 18-19; unresolved problems of, 19; by nonmedical therapists, 28; historical survey, 29-31; somatic out-patient, 29, 70; psychosocial, 62-63; in home, 64-65, 66-68; given by general practitioner, 70-71; defined, 84; moral, 101, 164; in state mental hospitals, 104-5; in VA mental hospitals, 106; in small private hospitals, 107-8; connection with individualization of care, 112; Remotivation Group Therapy, 123; simple individualized care, 131; tranquilizers and open door policy, 143; in general hospital, 145; transference phenomena in, 164; expansion of concept, 176; patient participation in, 177-78, 178-79; and custody-control, 198-99; voluntary, 253-54; community, 299; specialization of units for, 302; *see also* Psychotherapy; Therapy
Treatment system: entry into, 9-10; professional groups involved in, 10; *see also* Aftercare; Clinics, out-patient mental health; Mental hospital
Trist, E. L., 209, 255
Trussell, R. E., 63
Tulchin, S. H., 310

Ullmann, L. P., 246
U.S. Public Health Service, 71, 311

Values and norms, in relation to mental illness, 7-8

56875

Date Due